JOSIAH WILLARD GIBBS

Josiah Willard Gibbs

Lynde Phelps Wheeler

Josiah Willard Gibbs
THE HISTORY OF A GREAT MIND

"...whose name not only in America but in the whole world will ever be reckoned among the most renowned theoretical physicists of all times..." – MAX PLANK

WITH A FOREWORD BY
A. WHITNEY GRISWOLD
PRESIDENT, YALE UNIVERSITY

OX BOW PRESS • WOODBRIDGE, CONNECTICUT

1998 reprint by:

OX BOW PRESS
P.O. Box 4045
Woodbridge, CT 06525

203-387-5900
Fax 203-387-0035

First published by Yale University Press 1951
Copyright © 1951, Renewed 1979

Library of Congress Cataloging-in-Publication Data

Wheeler, Lynde Phelps.
　　Josiah Willard Gibbs: the history of a great mind /
Lynde Phelps Wheeler ; with a foreword by A. Whitney Griswold.
　　　p.　　cm.
Previously published: Hamden, Conn. : Archon Books, 1970.
Includes bibliographical references and index.
ISBN 1-881987-11-6 (pbk. : alk. paper)
　　1. Gibbs, J. Willard (Josiah Willard), 1839-1903. 2. Math-
ematical physics--United States--History. 3. Physicists--United
States--Biography. I. Title.
QC16.G5W45　　1998
503' .092--dc21
[B]

　　　　　　　　　　　　　　　　　　　　　　　　　　97-46920
　　　　　　　　　　　　　　　　　　　　　　　　　　　CIP

The paper used in this book meets the guidelines for performance
and durability of the Committee on Production Guidelines for
Book Longevity of the Council on Library Resources

Printed in the United States of America

Foreword

by A. Whitney Griswold

When we mention the word scientist today, the image that springs to mind is one of power and authority—of Prometheus having wrested his secret from the gods but with heads of governments plucking at his sleeve instead of vultures pecking at his liver. Through our mind's eye we see the scientist against a background of wondrous machinery in laboratories of infinite complexity and infinite cost, supported by billion dollar federal appropriations, foundation grants, and industrial grants and contracts. We see him waging the cold war and preparing for the hot, holding the survival of the human race in balance. Action rather than contemplation seems to be his daily fare—action stimulated by crisis and fraught with tension.

What a contrast to this impression the life of Willard Gibbs presents. He was born in 1839, the son of a philologist and professor of sacred literature in the Yale Divinity School. He grew up in a small college town with neighborly ways, oil lamps, and muddy streets. While the passions that boiled over into civil war were mounting, he was winning prizes in Latin and mathematics as an undergraduate at Yale. The next five years were devoted to graduate work in applied science and engineering at Yale; and in 1863, the year of the Battle of Gettysburg, Gibbs took his Ph.D., the second in science and the first in engineering to be awarded in the United States. Deterred from war service by a suspected tendency to tuberculosis, whose symptoms interrupted and prolonged his graduate studies, Gibbs now accepted a three-year appointment as tutor in Yale College, teaching Latin for the first two years and natural philosophy, as physics was then called, in the third. Along the way he invented a hydraulic turbine and an improved railway car brake which was patented in 1866.

Already, at age 27, his genius had begun to reach for greater opportunities than Yale or any other American university could offer. Science in these institutions was in its infancy, its followers little appreciated, their equipment primitive, and their labors, like their thoughts, concerned more with practical than with theoretical matters. In virtually every field of learning the United States was still a province of Europe, and in none more decidedly than in the field of pure science. In these circumstances Gibbs, whose talent for practical inventions might have tempted him to stay home and cash in on it, decided instead to resume his studies under the most competent masters he could find abroad. In 1866 he departed with his sisters for three years of intensive study in the universities of Paris, Berlin, and Heidelberg under some of the most outstanding mathematicians and physicists of his day. Thus he proved himself a true child of his age, moving from the classics, via mathematics, practical mechanics, and inventions, into theoretical physics.

He returned to New Haven in 1869, and after two more years of independent study and research, at age 32 was appointed Professor of Mathematical Physics at Yale. There, in this decade following his return from Europe, he accomplished the great work on thermodynamics which made him the foremost authority on that subject of his age and on which his fame as a scientist largely rests. It is difficult for a layman to comprehend the scope of this work and of its influence, a scope which embraced mathematics, physics, and chemistry; in which was laid down the theoretical basis for physical chemistry; and in which were propounded theoretical rules and principles of vital consequence to such varied fields and enterprises as the energetics of biological processes, metallurgy, mineralogy, petrology, the production of alloys and of portland cement, and the manufacturing processes of numerous heavy industries. It was a remarkable accomplishment, springing, as Wheeler says, as much from Gibbs' character as from his intellectual genius, from "intellectual independence communing with the inner essence of things," from "scientific achievement conditioned by personality."

Instead of advertising or attempting to exploit his work on thermodynamics, Gibbs allowed it to speak for itself and went on to other things. From 1880 to 1884 he concentrated on a system of vector analysis for use in mathematical physics; and from 1882 to 1889 on theoretical optics. He then turned to statistical mechanics, which occupied his thoughts and energies until his death. The results of this final labor were not published until 1902 and not fully appreciated until the subsequent development of wave mechanics and the quantum theory. These showed that again, as in his work on thermodynamics, he had broken new ground—that the creative phase of his career as a theoretical physicist had concluded with a work as far ahead of its age as that with which it had begun.

Recognition did come to Willard Gibbs in his lifetime, first from his colleagues at Yale, then from fellow scientists in Europe, chiefly in Germany. If the former first saw the greatness in the man, the latter first saw and proclaimed the greatness of the scientist. Neither brought him fame. Williams and Princeton gave him honorary degrees, as did the universities of Erlangen in Germany and Christiania in Norway; the American Academy of Arts and Sciences awarded him its Rumford Medal and the Royal Society of London the Copley Medal—the highest honor open to a scientist until the founding of the Nobel Prize. The learned scientific societies of the United States, England, Holland, Germany, and France sought his membership. He did not, however, receive the Nobel Prize in 1901 or 1902, the first two years in which it was awarded and the last two in which he could have received it, because he was not, even then, well enough known to be nominated. Even now, with all our new-found interest in science and respect for scientific learning, his is a relatively obscure figure in the American pantheon. But fame did not matter to him. In the only currency he valued he had been amply rewarded, namely, in the judgment of his peers and the esteem of his nearer friends.

"No qualities of Professor Gibbs impressed his sympathetic colleagues and his pupils more," recalls Charles S. Hastings, who was both pupil and colleague, "than his serenity and apparent unconsciousness of his intellectual eminence." He was so modest about his honors that they did not become fully known to his friends until they appeared in his obituary notices. He lived a quiet and happy bachelor's life in the home of his sister, Mrs. Addison Van Name, and her husband, the Librarian of Yale.

Until 1883 he worked in a study in one of the dormitories of the old Brick Row, moving in that year to more commodious, but by modern standards extremely simple, quarters described by Wheeler as "plainly, not to say severely, furnished with tables, chairs, bookshelves, and a large movable blackboard." Such was one part of the laboratory of the greatest physicist of his age and one of the greatest of any age. The other part was the long walks he took for recreation and reflection, on the outskirts of New Haven during the academic year and in the mountains of Vermont and New Hampshire, where he spent his summers.

The transition from the surroundings whence his mind made its voyages of discovery to those in which he encountered his fellow men was an effortless one, perhaps because, as both his friends and his relatives testify, he was blessed with a sense of humor. His counsel in family matters was as much respected as it was in professional matters. Though he shunned social affairs, he was good company. But he was elevating company. His students came to him rather than he to them. Yet once they were in his presence, he got them to the heart of the matter so quickly and unerringly that they knew they were sitting at the feet of a master.

All who are concerned with the progress of American science can be grateful to Willard Gibbs for exemplifying true scientific genius in his own or any age. All who have at heart the furtherance of higher learning in the United States can be grateful to him for revealing in classic form and purity the main purpose of a university—the purpose of providing in the feverish circumstances of the hour the same opportunity Gibbs found in calmer circumstances and simpler surroundings for "intellectual independence communing with the inner essence of things."

New Haven, Conn.
December 15, 1961

Preface

IN THE spring of 1944 I was approached from three separate directions with requests to undertake the gathering of biographical material concerning my old teacher, Josiah Willard Gibbs. The first two of these came from Gibbs' surviving family represented by his nephew, Professor Ralph Gibbs Van Name, and from Professor Edwin Bidwell Wilson, then of the Harvard School of Public Health. Both of them were concerned about the scarcity of available biographical material of a personal nature, and about the use which had been made in recently published biographies of such as did exist. They were confident that more such material could be discovered and seemed to think I was competent to unearth it and so situated as to have the leisure to do so.

Almost at the same time came a proposal from the late Mr. F. W. Willard, president of the Nassau Smelting and Refining Company and editor of the scientific and technological monographs of the American Chemical Society, that I "prepare an authoritative biography which would contain not only the story of Professor Gibbs' life, but particularly illustrate the applications of his theory to the subsequent development of the physical sciences." This proposal was of a much greater magnitude than anything I had contemplated and, frankly, rather appalled me. It had been some twenty-five years since I had given any thought to thermodynamic questions; I was preoccupied with problems in an entirely different domain of physics, and burdened with official duties, since my retirement from government service had been postponed owing to the war situation. I did not feel competent or free to undertake such an ambitious task. I indicated that I was willing to prepare an account of my own recollections and to solicit similar recollections from other surviving students of Gibbs'; but I suggested that some such competent physical chemist as Dean R. C. Tolman * of the California Institute of Technology be asked to undertake the critical evaluation of Gibbs' scientific work and its influence on later developments.

To this suggestion Mr. Willard assented, and it was agreed that I should write a personal biography while he would endeavor to find someone to do the technical critique. As time went on, however, and Mr. Willard was unsuccessful in finding anyone who would commit himself definitely to the project, it became tacitly understood that I should attempt the whole program.

Meanwhile I had gone over with some care all of the lecture notes I had taken on Gibbs' courses in the nineties (and which fortunately I had preserved); examined the volume of the scientific correspondence assembled by Addison Van Name, Gibbs' brother-in-law and late librarian of Yale University, which was made available to me by his son, Professor Ralph Gibbs Van Name; and reread all of Gibbs' published work. Thus I began to get back some of the old "feel" for the subjects of Gibbs' researches and for the times when I knew him. So although I did not then (and do not now) feel that I was as competent to handle the task as others would be— notably Professor Wilson—the prospect of undertaking it did not overwhelm me as it had at first. Gradually I came to feel that it was perhaps my duty to undertake it and do the best I could.

During 1945 and 1946 I tried to trace some of Gibbs' replies to certain letters in his scientific correspondence which might have yielded some knowledge of his thought on various matters for which there was no other source of information. These quests were unsuccessful. Replies from those of Gibbs' former students to whom I had written for their recollections were slowly coming in; and the Van Names were preparing their reminiscences. An allied project also took up much of my time during this period. This was the publishing, at the time of the Centennial of the Sheffield Scientific School, of a volume containing Gibbs' thesis and other previously unpublished work of his early years. Hence it was not until the spring of 1947 that I really got down to the preparation of the manuscript. That same spring the Yale University Press was planning the publication of a series of biographies of eminent Yale

* Since deceased.

graduates in connection with the celebration in 1951 of the 250th anniversary of the founding of Yale College; and after consultation with Professor Van Name they proposed that I do the life of Gibbs.

In October of 1947 *The Early Work of Willard Gibbs in Applied Mechanics,* which I had assisted in assembling, was published. At the same time there was deposited in the Sterling Memorial Library a bound typescript volume entitled "Personal Recollections and Impressions of J. Willard Gibbs," by his niece, nephews and certain of his pupils, containing the material which I had collected. I was therefore free to devote such leisure as I could command to the biography. Fortunately or unfortunately, according to one's viewpoint, I seem to be one of those who are not permitted to retire; and on severing my government connection in 1946 I was drawn into consulting work which has made it impossible for me to find more than two or three days consecutively at any one time for writing. Handicapped also by inability to spend any considerable time in New Haven, I have been dependent on others for gathering, sorting, and verifying the material I have used. Indeed without the generous aid I have received from the Van Names, from Professor Wilson (who has made many constructive criticisms of the manuscript), from Professor Hollon A. Farr, Curator of memorabilia at the Yale library, and from others of the library staff, the task could not have been accomplished.

Especial credit must go to Professor Van Name. To his zeal, his ingenuity in seeking out new sources of information, his accuracy in the verification of references, and his devotion to the memory of his uncle this book owes more than can be told. He has read the manuscript with meticulous care, made many helpful suggestions as to the form of presentation, and corrected several slips that I had made. It was only because I knew that I could count on his wholehearted cooperation that I undertook the task in the beginning, and the event has more than justified my anticipation.

Others whose help has been most valuable are Dr. Samuel Herrick of the University of California at Los Angeles who through the good offices of Professor Wilson undertook the evaluation of the notes left by Gibbs on the computation of orbits; and my colleague Dr. Greenleaf Whittier Pickard, to whose advice as a photographer in getting the most out of old and faded prints is due the excellence of certain of the photographs. My thanks also go to the Library Committee of Yale University for permission to use the Gibbs material deposited in the library; and to Yale University Press for the care taken in the making of the book, in particular to the editor, Mr. Eugene Davidson, for his helpful advice and his aid in running down information.

And now that the work is completed I only wish that I had possessed the ability to make it more worthy of its subject. My life has been spent in trying to do things and not to describe them, and the writing of this biography has not been an easy task for me to perform. At first I intended to follow the dual plan suggested to Mr. Willard, with the more technical matters in a separate part. But as the subject grew on me I came to realize that to an unusual degree Gibbs' scientific work *was* Gibbs, and that really to understand him one must to a certain extent at least understand his work; as his life and his work were so largely one, so must the story be. This will make parts of the book hard reading for those not trained in physics, but it seemed to me the only way in which I could bring to life my picture of the man. The book has largely grown of itself. Several outlines that I made originally have all been discarded, and one thing has led to another more by force of the circumstances related than by overt planning. It has truly been a labor of love, and the satisfactions reached in writing it have been the greatest that have been vouchsafed to me in a long life.

Since the appearance of the first edition of this biography I have become acquainted with a considerable volume of material previously unknown to me which contains valuable information about the life and activities of Willard Gibbs. Although nothing in this new material alters significantly the portrait of Gibbs presented in the biography, nevertheless it supplies a sufficient number of new facts, fills in enough gaps in the existing record, or amplifies the previous picture so pertinently that a brief description of it seems to be justified. This will be found in the new Appendix VII at the end of the volume. Aside from the correction of a few minor errors and misprints, this appendix constitutes the only change from the first edition.

For the greater part of this new material I am indebted to Mr. Alfred V. Dasburg of Rochester, N. Y., a grandson of a cousin of Willard Gibbs, who has placed at my disposal nearly five hundred letters which had been preserved in his branch of the family, and which were either written by members of Gibbs' immediate family or contain references to him.

In addition Fräulein Grete Ostwald, daughter of the physical chemist Wilhelm Ostwald, has been kind enough to send me copies of six letters to her father written by Willard Gibbs. And finally, through the initiative of Mr. Murray Murphey, a Yale graduate student pursuing his dissertation research at the Library of the Johns Hopkins University, and through the cordial cooperation of Miss Frieda C. Thies, Chief Reference Librarian of that institution, there have been found there some fourteen letters either written by Gibbs or containing references to him.

To all of these who have so kindly placed this new material at my disposal my grateful thanks are due.

L. P. W.

1952

Contents

Illustrations

I

Backgrounds—Family and Civic

THE outward life of Josiah Willard Gibbs was singularly uneventful. He experienced no adventures different from those common to thousands of Americans of his time. He was a participant in no events of historical importance. He took no leading part in any of the movements of the age. He traveled less and lived at home more than the great majority of people of similar means. He neither sought nor occupied positions of influence even in his own scientific world. He was never in the public eye.

And yet his life was one of high adventure such as few anywhere or at any time have achieved. He explored the far horizons of the hitherto unknown and traveled farther in certain directions than any of his contemporaries. He mapped a major scientific continent. He rebuilt and completed one of the great edifices of nineteenth-century science so solidly that it has withstood one of the greatest intellectual earthquakes in history.

The story of the development of this genius—one of the last of the giants of the classical age in physical science—is illuminating and fascinating. It exhibits a rarely found continuity of method from his earliest to his latest work. It reveals a mind which proceeded from ascertained facts to their utmost implications by such rigorous logic that not one of his conclusions has ever been found in error. It shows great feats of the imagination founded on reason rather than speculation. Moreover the contrast between the relatively circumscribed surroundings of his physical existence and the great sweep of his intellectual vision is dramatic in itself.

Gibbs was a man of engaging characteristics. He had no aggressive pride of achievement, no desire to advertise himself, no assumption that his opinions were of value for anything but the logic supporting them. He possessed none of the mannerisms or eccentricities sometimes thought to be marks of genius. When you first met him all that you saw was a simple, unaffected gentleman, possessed of a quiet sense of humor, friendly and approachable. He was a man whose conduct in the affairs of everyday life was governed by the same imagination and the same logic that pervaded his scientific writings. He was sure of himself and had confidence in his judgments, whether they were of scientific matters or lay in the realm of social relationships. A man happy and absorbed in his work, happy and content in his home environment, with little inclination for the outside distractions that make up so much of the lives of most of us.

It is of course impossible to account fully for the occurrence of genius in terms of heredity and environment, separately or together. Hereditary factors such as scholarly tendencies, administrative ability, or physical prowess may make it more than an even chance that a man may become a professor, an executive, or an athlete. But they do not determine his profession with any certainty, and still less do they account for any spark of genius that may develop. Similarly, environmental factors such as the home atmosphere, educational facilities, and the existing state of civic rest or unrest do not make it certain that an individual will or will not make the most of his inherited qualities, that he will turn out to be a conformist or a nonconformist to the standards of his contemporary civilization, that he will be a success or a failure. The interactions of hereditary tendencies can be so numerous and so complex and reactions to environment may be so sensitive or insensitive that the resulting variety of possible personalities, even where the ancestry may be known for many generations, is too great to permit prediction of what a given man will do or become in any given circumstances. And it is even less possible to predict when or where, at what period or in what family, a genius may be expected. It is true that there are instances of abilities passed on from father to son for several generations, as there are of undesirable qualities persisting in a given strain. But the sporadic appearance of genius with no evidence of its elements discernible either in the ancestry or among the descendants is equally well known.

Nevertheless the ancestry and the environment which have produced great men will always be of importance as matters of history, and those of Willard Gibbs are of exceptional interest. His ancestry is notable for the long-continued service to scholarship, to church, and to state which it exhibits, while his formative years were passed in the stormy civic atmosphere of the days before the Civil War, and his education was obtained at one of the institutions which was first in this country to challenge the domination of the classical tradition in which so many of his forebears had been trained.

Gibbs' ancestry on both his father's and his mother's side is known fairly completely for some six or seven generations back and, with many gaps, for a much greater length of time. It reveals a great variety of interests and talents. From the genealogical chart for six generations, shown in Appendix I, it will be seen that thirteen of Gibbs' direct ancestors were college graduates, eight of Harvard, three of Yale, and two of the College of New Jersey (Princeton). This is probably a higher percentage of college graduates than most of his contemporaries could show. Of these graduates two became college presidents. Jonathan Dickinson on the maternal side was the first president of the College of New Jersey and in addition a physician of repute; Samuel Willard on the paternal side, pastor of the Old South Church in Boston, was acting president of Harvard College. He was really president in fact though only vice-president in title because he refused to reside in Cambridge as the college regulations required. Many of the other of the college graduates, as the chart shows, continued in the academic or the then closely allied clerical tradition. Among Gibbs' progenitors in England may also be found graduates of the universities.

However there is also to be seen on both sides of the family a considerable admixture of the military, administrative, mercantile, and agricultural traditions. One who would seem to have united all of these traditions in one person was Major Simon Willard in the paternal line. According to the inscription on a plaque erected in 1902 in Canterbury Cathedral by one of his English descendants, he came to New England in 1634 as a pioneer settler, was made commander-in-chief of the British forces against the hostile Indian tribes, and was distinguished in the military, legislative and judicial services of the colony. The plaque also records that "Of Simon Willard's ancestors one was Provost of Canterbury 1218 and another was Baron of Cinque Ports 1377," so that both the military and the clerical traditions at least would seem to be of respectable antiquity in the family! This same Simon Willard, "that doughty old Indian fighter, fur trader and settler" was father of the Reverend Samuel who served at Harvard in the place of Increase Mather while the latter was absent in England on an embassy to secure a new charter for the colony, and who later became vice president in his own right. He was one of the few in high places at that time who opposed the acceptance of "spectral evidence" in the examinations of the accused during the Salem witchcraft delusion. This resulted in his own denunciation as a witch by the psychopathic children of Salem and served to bring home the absurdity of the situation and hasten the end of the delusion.

Samuel's son, Josiah Willard, would seem to have been a man of most engaging characteristics. He had such a passion for the sea that, undiscouraged by two narrow boyhood escapes from drowning while sailing in Boston harbor, he resigned a tutorship at Harvard in 1706 to become a sailor. He rose to the command of his own ship "sailing the triangular route between Boston, Europe and the West Indies," and after many seafaring adventures (including two captures by privateers) returned to settle in Boston. He was later appointed by King George I secretary of the province of Massachusetts, and further demonstrated his versatility in this third of his walks in life, becoming known as the "good secretary." He continued in this office until his death in 1756, and his memory has been honored in the family by the bestowal of the name Josiah Willard upon no less than six of his descendants.

On the maternal side we also find a versatile and picturesque character in the person of Col. William Henry Smith. He was a favorite at the court of King Charles II, was appointed governor of Morocco in 1675, and resided in Tangier for some ten years. Here he apparently amassed quite a competence—in which respect he would not seem to have been singular among British colonial governors of the era. At any rate, after returning to England in 1685 he came to New York the following year and purchased a considerable estate at Brookhaven on Long Island, which he styled "St. George's Manor." "Tangier" Smith, as he is known in the family history, served his new country well. At one time he was president of the provincial council and later occupied several judicial positions, eventually becoming chief justice of the colony of New York. Of his direct descendants a grandson, Caleb Smith, was graduated at Yale College in 1743 and married Martha, daughter of Jonathan Dickinson, thus uniting those two lines of descent.

The Gibbs line in the seventeenth and eighteenth centuries, though of solid worth, would seem to have been of less versatility. They were for the most part theologians and merchants residing in Watertown and Salem, Massachusetts, graduates and fellows of Harvard College. The English progenitor of this line was Sir Henry Gibbs of Honington, Warwickshire, whose fourth son, Robert, came to Boston about 1658. Robert's son, the Reverend Henry Gibbs, was pastor of the church in Watertown. In the troubled times of the witchcraft delusion he would seem to have been one of those who "sat on the fence," if we can judge from a passage in his diary recording impressions of an "examination" at Salem village which he attended: "Remarkable and prodigious passages. Wonders I saw, but how to judge and conclude I am at a loss." It was a son of this clergyman, another Henry, who in 1747 married Katherine, daughter of the versatile Josiah Willard, and united the Gibbs and the Willard strains.

The removal from Massachusetts of the branch of the Gibbs family in which we are interested occurred in the next generation. A son of Henry and Katherine Gibbs, a third Henry, married Mercy Greenough Prescott and died while their only child, Josiah Willard Gibbs, was still in his boyhood. The widow, in order to be near her sister Rebecca and at the same time to secure good educational advantages for the boy, moved to New Haven, Connecticut. Rebecca had married Roger Sherman of that town, distinguished lawyer and statesman, signer of the Declaration of Independence and of the Constitution of the United States, and they lived in close proximity to the buildings of Yale College. The boy Josiah was educated at Yale and later became the father of the subject of this biography.

In neither the Willard nor the Gibbs lines have I been able to find, except in the case of his own father, any notable anticipation of the mathematical or scientific traits of the younger Gibbs. On his mother's side, however, there are to be found several individuals with such predilections. Thus we find that Jonathan Dickinson published in 1740 a description of and a treatment for a "throat distemper"—quite probably diphtheria—which was the earliest account of this disease to be printed in this country. Another instance is to be found in Gibbs' grandfather, Dr. John Van Cleve, who in addition to being a physician of note in New Jersey also served for some years as professor of chemistry at Princeton. But the most noteworthy anticipation of the scientific traits of Gibbs is found in a great grandfather, William Churchill Houston. This scholar and scientist was professor of mathematics and natural philosophy at the College of New Jersey from 1770 to 1783. While he was not known for any original contributions to these fields, his broad interest in applied science (then the only branch of science recognized in this country) is evidenced by the support he gave to John Fitch, the steamboat inventor, in the latter's struggle for recognition. Houston was also distinguished as a lawyer, a jurist, and a captain of infantry during the Revolution, and was prominent in various offices of the New Jersey legislature and in committees of the Continental Congress. He was a delegate to the Constitutional Convention of 1787 and took part in its deliberations although he did not (possibly because of illness) sign the Constitution. He also served during the later years of his professorship as treasurer of the College of New Jersey. His career furnishes an example, all too rare in our history, of scholarship successful in public service.

It is not surprising, in view of the necessity for male predominance in the early struggles to settle the country, to find that not so much record remains of the women in the Gibbs ancestry as of the men. But one learns from such accounts as are available that a number of these women were notable for their intellectual qualities. Martha Tunstall, wife of "Tangier" Smith; Katherine Willard, daughter of Josiah Willard and wife of Henry Gibbs; Martha Dickinson, daughter of Jonathan Dickinson and wife of Caleb Smith; and Louisa Anna Houston, daughter of William Churchill Houston and wife of Dr. John Van Cleve, are all mentioned as

Samuel Willard

Jonathan Dickinson

GIBBS' MOTHER

GIBBS' FATHER

women of exceptional intellectual gifts. In the quaint language of the time it is said of the last named, "She was a lady of superior talents and cultivated mind. She was well read in medical and scientific subjects, and possessed high colloquial talents." It is of particular interest to note that with the women as well as the men, it is on his mother's side that the anticipation of Gibbs' scientific traits is to be found.

As a whole, the personalities of these ancestors cannot be better described than in the words of Gibbs' niece [1] (from whom I have taken most of the above facts):

Though but a few of them, perhaps, could be termed of exceptional distinction, yet we find that for generations back they were, without exception, men notable for their intellect, education and integrity, who held positions of public responsibility; while their wives, as far as the more limited records show, were often women of an intellectual character.

Josiah Willard Gibbs the younger was born on February 11, 1839, the fourth child and only son of Josiah Willard Gibbs the elder and of Mary Anna Van Cleve Gibbs. Of his three older sisters, Anna, Eliza, and Julia, only the first and third were a continuing influence in the family life, as Eliza died in 1849. His younger sister Emily was also destined to wield a smaller influence than the two older; she died in 1864 when only twenty-three years old. As his mother died in 1855 while he was still in college and his father in 1861 while he was a graduate student, Gibbs was called upon to face the responsibilities of adult life earlier than most. Thus the influence of the character of his parents on the formative years of his youth takes on a special interest.

The father, born in 1790, was graduated from Yale College in the class of 1809 at the early age of nineteen, which was incidentally the same age at which his son was graduated. Of the elder's undergraduate career it is told that he was proficient in all of his studies and that his aptitude for mathematics was such that at one time he considered taking that subject for his life work in place of

1. "Personal Recollections and Impressions of J. Willard Gibbs," by his niece, nephews, and certain of his pupils; a bound typescript volume (Sterling Memorial Library, Yale University, 1947). As occasion will arise to refer frequently to this volume, it will be cited hereafter as "P.R.I."

theology, to which both his heritage and his education predisposed him.[2] We may perhaps be permitted to be thankful that the same dilemma was not presented to the son. At any rate, after two years of teaching school at Salem, Massachusetts, and four spent as a tutor at Yale the elder Gibbs compromised with his heritage and decided on the philology of the sacred languages as his life work. He retired from teaching at Yale and spent the next nine years prosecuting his studies in his chosen field, mostly at Andover, Massachusetts. He received the honorary degree of Master of Arts from Harvard College in 1818, and in 1824, shortly after the organization of the Divinity School in New Haven, he was appointed lecturer in sacred literature and college librarian. Two years later he was made professor of sacred literature, a position which he held for the rest of his life.

He brought to this chair great distinction as a philologist and an authority on comparative grammar. Although he was licensed to preach, it is of record that he appeared but once in the college pulpit. His studies were not confined exclusively to the sacred languages but ranged over archaeology and the comparative grammar of the Indo-European languages. He contributed twelve articles on philological matters to the *American Journal of Science,* in addition to many more in religious journals. The honorary degree of doctor of laws was conferred upon him by Princeton in 1853. The letter from the board of trustees of that institution notifying him of the award [3] stated that the granting of this award to a "biblical student and critic, not a minister of the Gospel," was an innovation, but that in view of their belief that "philology is by itself a science of the highest order and importance" the recognition of his achievements in that field was amply justified. The granting of this degree is interesting not only as attesting the eminence of the recipient but also as an indication of the broadening of scholarship standards and the weakening of the hold of the theological tradition then beginning to be felt in American education even in such an ultraconservative atmosphere as then prevailed at Princeton.

2. George P. Fisher, "A Discourse Commemorative of the Life and Services of Josiah Willard Gibbs, L.L.D., Professor of Sacred Literature in Yale College," *The New Englander* (July, 1861).

3. This letter is preserved in Sterling Memorial Library.

The elder Gibbs seems to have been a man of gentle manners, reticent in social intercourse except with intimate friends. In these respects he must have resembled his more distinguished son. In other personal and mental traits father and son would seem to have been rather closely alike. Thus Professor Fisher [4] says of the elder's teaching:

But the amount of benefit they received, depended largely upon themselves. He required the stimulus of an active and inquisitive class, to call him out. When such a company of young men was gathered round him, who knew how to ply him with inquiries, and to bring forward topics of interest, he gave them, from his treasures of knowledge, enough amply to reward their zeal.

And of his scholarship:

His judgment was sober and sound. . . . To speak of the thoroughness of Mr. Gibbs in his researches, would be to repeat what has been said before, and to dwell on a trait with which all who knew him are familiar. He was, in truth, a genuine scholar, who put forth no pretentions that were not, in the judgment of others, far below his merits.

On his abhorrence of dogmatic opinions he remarks:

I come now to a striking peculiarity of Mr. Gibbs, namely, his hesitancy in forming and avowing opinions. This sprung from no fear of consequences to himself. He was not wanting in moral courage. It was partly due to the uncommon candor which led him, contrary to the usual practice, to open his ear to both sides of every question.

And with regard to his writing: "Mr. Gibbs loved system, and was never satisfied until he had cast his material into the proper form. His essays on special topics are marked by the nicest logical arrangement."

Every one of these words can be said with equal truth of the son, as will appear in all that follows. The father, however, would seem to have been less genial and not to have possessed as lively a sense of humor, although of somewhat more robust, or at least more openly exhibited, moral convictions. That he was a man who would contribute to the family life a respect for duty, honesty, and a conception of the beauty of truth is indisputable. A man who

4. See "A Discourse" for a more detailed account of the elder Gibbs' character.

would be to his children a guide, counselor, and friend rather than a companion in their juvenile interests.

Gibbs' mother was a woman of unusual character and attainments. These are well portrayed in her granddaughter's account,[5] which also gives a glimpse of the happy family life.

We have Mary Anna's portrait, and a charming picture it is, dignified yet kindly; the smiling face with clear blue eyes and an intellectual forehead is crowned by massive coils of dark brown hair. To judge from her likeness, she was an unusual as well as a lovely person, and this judgment is corroborated in every respect by what we know about her, though she died many years before the present generation was born. She was the centre of an unusually happy family life, and her children adored her. She entered with enthusiasm into their games and pastimes. She it was who helped them to build the quaint little four-roomed doll house, which was afterward the delight of my own childhood. That the house was of home manufacture made it all the more interesting, because it portrayed a manner of living so much like that of the Gibbs family at that period. The built-in kitchen range was identical in type with that in the Gibbs kitchen; it was made of black tar paper, and its little round stove-lids could be lifted up to show the red hot coals (made of crimson tinfoil) underneath. And on the bookshelves the tiny volumes, scarce an inch in height, were covered with bright paper, with real titles neatly lettered on their backs.

In our library today, is a copy of Nuttall's "Ornithology" in two volumes, 1832 and 1834, which belonged to Mary Anna Gibbs; on the flyleaf her name is written in her clear delicate handwriting. The ownership of this work shows a scientific interest in birds most unusual in a woman of the 1830's. A mild acquaintance with botany was, to be sure, a not unusual accomplishment, but the study of ornithology was certainly not often pursued by women of her day. We have been told that she taught her children to recognize the different species, arousing in them an interest which has continued down to the present generation.

This charming picture of a mother who combined serious intellectual interests with a sympathetic and active share in those of the children is one entirely in accord with the simpler spirit of a less hurried day than ours of a century later. There were then few organized activities—aside from those connected with the church —to take up the time and energies of the household heads, as is the

5. "P.R.I."

case today. Their world was the world of ideas, and their recreations were relaxations and not stimulants. The ideas, and not the pleasures, were the business of life.

The part of the sisters in the family life and their influence on their brother were apparently quite the normal and wholesome ones to be expected in the circumstances. Both Anna and Julia were of gentle, self-sacrificing, unaggressive dispositions, Anna having an especially retiring personality, accentuated by poor health. Judging from their relations with their brother in later years as they appeared to the younger generation,[6] it would seem that the atmosphere of affection and trust then existing must have grown naturally from childhood relationships in which no one dominated the others and in which the right of individual self-development received considerate recognition from all. Although little record remains of the character of the other sisters, Eliza and Emily, it is reasonable to suppose that they too shared the harmonious family disposition. Indeed, the family atmosphere as we know it to have been, is the only one consistent with the character and attitudes of the parents.

Until 1846 the Gibbs' home in New Haven was in a house on Crown Street owned by President Day of Yale College, who then resided in the president's house on the college campus.[7] In that year, which marked the retirement of President Day from office and his return to occupy his Crown Street house, Professor Gibbs built a house on High Street at first numbered 71 and in later years becoming 121, which continued to be the Gibbs' home for some three quarters of a century. The site of this house, in which the younger Gibbs lived for the rest of his life, is now marked by a plaque on the wall of the garden of the master's house of Berkeley College on High Street. The location of the house, not half a city block from the school of Gibbs' boyhood, just about one block from the haunts of his college days, some two blocks from the office where he spent most of his working days, and less than two blocks from the cemetery where his body now lies, is symbolic of the com-

6. *Ibid.*, especially the contributions of the nephews.

7. This occupied a portion of the site of the present Farnam Hall on the old campus. After President Day's retirement it was used for some years as the laboratory of the Yale School of Applied Chemistry.

pact academic nature of the physical environment in which he
grew up and which he so loved.

A picture of the pleasant unhurried life in faculty circles in the
New Haven of the 1840's and fifties, when the town boasted some
twenty thousand inhabitants and the Grecian State House still
adorned the Green, is given in Miss Van Name's recollections,[8]
which I cannot do better than quote:

We have had from the older generation many accounts of the pleasantly
informal parties, picnics and other festivities which my uncle and his
sisters enjoyed during their childhood and early youth. Thus we obtain
a fairly definite picture of the rather close-knit faculty group in New
Haven, and of life in the Gibbs household, and in the homes of their
intimate friends and companions.

A series of letters, written in 1856 and 1857, by Laura Woolsey, youthful daughter of President Woolsey of Yale, to an older sister travelling in
Europe, contains in almost every letter mention of one or more members
of the Gibbs family, or of social activities in which they participated.
Through the kindness of Miss Laura Heermance, niece of their writer,
I was permitted to examine and quote from these letters. Many of the
incidents mentioned had been described to us by our parents or other
relatives, in some cases by our uncle himself.

The so-called "Faculty Parties" were held at frequent intervals, and
usually featured a "lecture" by some member of the faculty on such a
topic as, to cite one instance, "New Haven Fifty Years Ago." The re-
freshments which followed were naturally important in the eyes of the
young people; and indeed they sound attractive today, whether oysters
and calfsfoot jellies were served, ice cream with "a great many kinds of
cake," or coffee and sandwiches with "grapes and sweetmeats."

There were Christmas Tree gatherings, "Beehives," concerts, skating
parties (often on Lake Saltonstall), a "Nutting picnic of fifty persons to
West Rock Waterfall," an occasional formal evening party, a dance, or
a fancy dress "Carnival," and of course the regular College functions
such as the "Junior Ex.," and the "Wooden Spoon" celebration. Little
fourteen-year-old Laura Woolsey was thrilled to be "respectfully invited"
to attend the Junior Exhibition in April, 1857, and her childish comments (and spelling!) are amusing. "Willie Gibbs spoke first, a Latin
oration 'De Veri Amore.' He did not seem much frightened, and spoke
trés bien and jestured very well aussi. . . . Some of them spoke well, and
others did not. Some were much terrified and frightened half out of

8. "P.R.I."

their wits, while others were as bold and composed as possible." She writes of a "Wooden Spoon" Ceremony in June 1857 to which "a party of nine" was going from the Gibbs household, including several of Julia and Willard's young friends. And of an agreeable supper party at the Gibbs house in High Street, "where we had a delightful time, as we always do when we go there."

A simple life, whose simple gaieties were not such as the youth of today would relish, but which were undoubtedly enjoyed by the young people of that generation, who never even dreamed that their pleasant little diversions would be regarded with contempt by those writing about them a century later.

A similar impression of the leisurely social life of the times is obtained from the recollections of stories of those times told by members of the older generation to others of the family.[9]

But if the intimate family and faculty life of the time was marked by a peaceful routine and quiet pleasures, the same cannot be said of the world of affairs outside. And these also exerted an influence on the growing boy. Nationally, the years between the establishment of the federal government and the Civil War, and particularly those following the second war with England (1812–14), were characterized by the expansion and settlement of the country toward the west. This westward movement was much accelerated during the twenty years or so before the Civil War by the perfecting of the steam engine and its application to transportation both by land and water. The availability of steam power was also a major factor in the growth of the manufacture of machine-made goods, which made great strides in this period. Accompanying these developments there was extensive exploration of the mineral resources of the country and improvement in agricultural methods and their adaptation to the larger scale of farming appropriate to the plains and prairies of the new land.

That these developments were not always peaceful and orderly and led ultimately to political dissension and Civil War was due primarily to that economic schism which confined the major part of this industrial expansion to one section of the country. The South, with its presumed dependence on a single crop and the slave

9. *Ibid.*, especially the contribution of Willard Gibbs Van Name.

labor which seemed to be necessary for its exploitation, felt less of the urge to explore or to seek new ways of livelihood. The North on the other hand, on which from the beginning natural conditions had imposed a more diversified way of life and which had a more rapidly growing population due both to smaller individual land holdings and to the greater immigration increase which it received, retained more of the pioneering spirit; a restless seeking for the improvement of old things, the discovery of new things, and the impetus to search out new sources of wealth. Thus the South, tenaciously clinging to its old and gracious way of life, and the North, forced to find subsistence for its rapidly growing population, traditionally more adventurous, inventive, and commercial, and with a deepening conviction of the moral iniquity of the institution of slavery, were inevitably in conflict; a conflict that left an ineradicable impress on the national life and on that of every individual citizen of the time.

In the industrial, mechanical, and exploratory developments of this era as well as in the political turmoil of the time, New England was one of the principal storm centers of the North. Its inventors and industrialists were largely responsible for the material leadership of that section of the country; its emigrants dominated the settlement of the "Western Reserve"; its puritan tradition sponsored the antislavery agitation. And in all of these phases New Haven and Yale took no small part. It is one of the major historic ironies that it was a New Haven inventor, Eli Whitney, who with the cotton gin contributed so much to the foundation of the South's economic prosperity, and who at the same time by his pioneering in the manufacturing method of quantity production by means of interchangeable parts was largely responsible for the material supremacy of the North which was ultimately the cause of the downfall of the Confederacy. It was another New Haven inventor and architect, Ithiel Town, who devised a simple and effective form of bridge structure which was widely used both here and abroad and which contributed materially to the rapid settlement and expansion of the western country. It was a Yale graduate of 1810, Samuel Finley Breese Morse, who in 1844 demonstrated the practicability of the electric telegraph. It was a Yale professor,

Benjamin Silliman, Jr., who laid the foundations of the petroleum industry by his analyses of the "rock" oil of Pennsylvania and by his comprehensive survey of the methods for refining it. A New Haven inventor, Charles Goodyear, pioneered the vast rubber industry by his discovery of the method of "vulcanization" of the crude gum with sulphur and heat. New Haven engineers and capitalists were prominent in the canal and railway construction projects of the time, and Yale professors were pioneers in the mineral and geographical exploration of the West.

New Haven and Yale were also prominent in the antislavery agitation of New England and the North. In the days of the controversy over the admission of Kansas as a territory a contingent of Connecticut emigrant settlers bound for that region was financed and armed by the voluntary contributions of New Haven citizens, among whom were many from the Yale faculty led by Benjamin Silliman, Sr. And the celebrated memorial of protest to President Buchanan on his proposal to use troops of the U.S. Army to aid the proslavery Kansas settlers was drafted and signed by a group of Yale professors including President Woolsey, the Sillimans, and the elder Gibbs. President Buchanan's reply and the rejoinder of the memorialists created considerable furor not only locally but in the press of the nation and in the halls of Congress.[10]

It was with this turbulent background of adventurous development, new discoveries, and expanding applications of science, together with the political rancor, the moral issues, and the mounting tensions of the prewar period, that Gibbs' boyhood was spent. That the engineering elements of the background—the discoveries, inventions, and the new uses for science—rather than the political and moral drama of the time were the more potent factors in the development of a studious, self-reliant boy such as we shall see him to have been is not strange. That this was in truth the fact is indicated by the choice of engineering as his principal subject of study at the very first opportunity permitted in the educational

10. For an account of the work of the New Haven inventors and engineers see Richard Kirby, ed., *Inventors and Engineers of Old New Haven* (New Haven Colony Historical Society, 1939). For accounts of the work of the younger Silliman on petroleum and of the exploratory work of the elder Silliman and of Brewer, together with a narrative of the antislavery memorial, see John F. Fulton and Elizabeth Thomson, *Benjamin Silliman, Pathfinder in American Science* (New York, H. Schuman, 1947).

system under which he grew up. It is further shown by the evidence of an intimate familiarity with mechanical details and requirements exhibited in his later inventions,[11] which may fairly be assumed to presuppose an interest in such matters extending well back into his boyhood. Also, he is known to have possessed in later life considerable skill in the use of simple carpenter's tools,[12] not acquired or pursued as an adult hobby but such as would be learned naturally by a boy interested in mechanical things.

But although it may have been the more peaceful elements in the civic background that exerted the greater influence on Gibbs' intellectual growth, it is not to be assumed that he was indifferent to the political and moral issues then dividing the country. It is true that we have no documentary evidence, as we have in the case of his father,[13] of an interest in these things. But the assumption that he did not keep himself informed on the national scene or was lacking in appreciation of the moral issues involved would be contrary to all the evidence of the habits and practices of his later life.[14] Throughout his adult life he was always reticent about expressing any views on political or religious matters, at least outside of the family circle; but no one who knew him well could doubt that he held convictions on such matters. It has always seemed to me that this reticence was due neither to lack of appreciation of their importance nor to want of thought about them but rather to an inherited deep-seated aversion to the expression of opinions about anything on which he did not have first-hand and reasonably complete knowledge. This aversion was personal to himself and in no sense critical of the practices of others. It was simply an integral part of his philosophy. That he had achieved such a philosophy in the days before the Civil War is of course problematical but not impossible.

The fact that the stress of the times outside of the sheltered home, school, and social life in which he moved had so little outwardly

11. Wheeler, Waters, and Dudley, eds., *The Early Work of Willard Gibbs in Applied Mechanics* (New York, H. Schuman, 1947).

12. "P.R.I.," contributions of his nephews.

13. Professor Fisher in "A Discourse" notes that the elder Gibbs' antislavery sentiments were outspoken and formed a marked exception to his general avoidance of public expression of dogmatic opinions.

14. That he was a regular newspaper and magazine reader as well as a consistent attendant at church services is attested by W. G. Van Name in "P.R.I."

visible effect on a boy who had already developed such a strong bent for science and invention is perhaps only evidence of the strength of that bias. It is probable, though, that the controversies of that time did have an effect in developing, in defense of his inner aspirations, that reticent self-sufficiency so marked in his later life.

II

Backgrounds—Educational

GIBBS' formal education outside the family circle began in a small private school in the year 1848, when he was nine years old. We learn of this from some letters among the "Baldwin Papers" preserved in the Yale library. One of these, written by the young Simeon Baldwin [1] to his father, is dated only "Dec. 10," but since it was written on a Sunday it must have been in 1848. It runs as follows:

Dear Father

Last Monday a week from tomorrow I began a boys school. I now like it pretty well. Willie Gibbs entered with me and I believe has formed pretty much the same opinion I have.

S. Baldwin

From others of the letters we learn that it was known as "Mr. Farren's School." Where it was located or how long it survived I have been unable to ascertain.

The following year, 1849, Gibbs entered the Hopkins Grammar School, then located on a large lot on the northwest corner of High and Wall streets, a scant half block from the Gibbs' home at 71 High Street. This old site is now occupied by a portion of the Yale Law School quadrangle. "Hopkins" was the fourth institution offering instruction in Latin and Greek to be established in this country.[2] It had had many ups and downs in the then nearly two hundred years of its history, but had recently profited by the services of an able and beloved rector, Hawley Olmstead, who in

1. Willard Gibbs and Simeon Baldwin were second cousins, as the former was a grandson of Mercy Gibbs and the latter a grandson of her sister Rebecca Sherman. Simeon Baldwin became a well-known authority on international law and chief justice of the Supreme Court of the state of Connecticut. After retiring from the bench he was three times elected governor of the state.

2. The Boston Latin School, 1635, Harvard College, 1636, and the Roxbury Latin School, 1645, are the three which antedate the Hopkins Grammar School, which was founded in 1660.

THE GIBBS' HOUSE ON HIGH STREET

Photographed after alterations by Yale University for use as
an office building

PRESIDENT DAY'S HOUSE, BIRTHPLACE OF GIBBS

GIBBS AS A STUDENT

HOPKINS GRAMMAR SCHOOL IN THE 1860's

the ten years of his tenure had markedly increased the school's prestige and numbers. He was a devotee of the classical tradition in education, although he did yield to the growing demand for liberalization of the traditional curriculum by the addition in 1846 of instruction in English and English composition. The "Old Dominie," as he was affectionately called by his boys, retired in 1849 and was succeeded by the "Young Dominie," his son Edward.

That the "Young Dominie" was not of the caliber of his father would seem to be obvious, as during his regime the number of pupils fell off rapidly. The deterioration of the school had proceeded so far that at the time of Olmstead's resignation in March, 1854, there were but twenty boys enrolled, and in the fall of that year when Mr. James M. Whiton assumed the rectorship there were only six. The recovery of the school under the new leadership and its later vicissitudes do not concern us here, and Gibbs' part in its subsequent history will be recounted in its appropriate place in a later chapter. It is only necessary now to note that in Willard's student days the fortunes of the school were at a low ebb and that his preparation for college—which judging from the prizes he took in his freshman year was entirely adequate—must be attributed more to his innate scholarship and studiousness than to the quality of the instruction he received.

An amusing glimpse of the boy and of some of his classmates is given in schoolboy doggerel which we quote from the *Chronicles of the Hopkins Grammar School* [3] and which is dated 1850:

The Grammar School
A poem by
Gregory Grinwigg

First at his seat close by our Rector's throne
Sits Tomlinson, without companion—all alone
Whose task it is each morn with key in hand
To turn the lock at Dominie's command.

---

3. Thomas B. Davis, Jr., ed., *Chronicles of the Hopkins Grammar School, 1660–1935* (New Haven, Quinnipiack Press, 1938). Mr. Davis surmises that this may have been the composition of Simeon Baldwin. Of the boys mentioned, Charles Tomlinson and Edward Foster Blake were classmates of Gibbs in college and among his companions on picnics, parties, and trips in both his school and college days. The former received a medical degree

Next to him Gibbs with visage grave
Sits in the seat our Rector to him gave.
A student he—and one who seldom looks
With playful countenance from off his books.

Dutton comes next, a splendid scholar he
As any good phrenologist might see.
Upon examination you will find
That though he's small in size he's great in mind.

Next to this one comes Winchester, but don't
Expect of him such excellent account.
In scholarship the worst of all the school
Though not by Nature's he at all the fool.

The neighbor now of Winchester comes on
Our dear friend Blake by name; moreover one
Who though afflicted sore by a lame foot
Of ingenuity is not destitute.

From some passages in the "Baldwin Papers," preserved in the Yale library, which give a picture of the lighter side of the school-boy social life of the time, we gain the impression that Gibbs was a rather shy, self-contained boy whose "visage grave" was probably a defense mechanism for his inner spirit. Although he participated in many of the current "doings" he was not apparently a leader in them, and then, as later in life, he got a quiet enjoyment from social intercourse without the slightest desire to appropriate any credit for its success. Then as always his deepest satisfactions came from study and the contemplation of the things of the mind.

These same letters also record that in his last year at Hopkins, when he was fifteen years old, Gibbs was at least mildly interested in one of the girls of the group which made up the picnics and parties of that time. She was a Fanny Storer, and according to a rather ill-natured letter of one who was possibly a rival for her

at Yale in 1862. The latter served as a major in the 5th Connecticut U.S. Volunteers in the Civil War and was killed in action at Cedar Mountain. Henry Melzar Dutton was graduated from Yale in 1857, was also one of the same social coterie of school and college days, took a law degree at Yale in 1859, served as a lieutenant in the same regiment, and was killed in the same action as Blake. William Wirt Winchester was a son of Oliver F. Winchester, founder of the Winchester Arms Company.

favors, she did not reciprocate the interest. The letter relates that on one occasion Willy brought her "a most beautiful bunch of pond lilies . . . but Fanny does not like him at all, and we teaze her about him, but she likes his flowers much better than she likes him." At any rate this interest never developed seriously, and it is the only instance I have been able to find of Gibbs having more than a friendly interest in anyone of the other sex, outside of his family.

The course of study pursued by the boys of that time in the Hopkins Grammar School can be inferred quite accurately from the entrance requirements published in the Yale College catalogues of the period, since the chief function of the school was to prepare boys for Yale. These requirements provided for examinations in Latin covering certain of Cicero's orations, Sallust, and the whole of Vergil, together with tests on grammar, prosody, and prose composition; in Greek covering certain specified Greek readers and three books of the *Anabasis*, together with a test on grammar; in mathematics covering Thomson's *Higher Arithmetic* and Day's *Algebra* up to quadratic equations; in English grammar; and in geography. Thus it can be seen that the school curriculum was almost purely the traditional classical one which had persisted from the earliest Colonial days, with but small concessions to the growing demands for an education more adapted to fit the student to meet the requirements of contemporary living, demands that were leading to considerable modifications of the curriculum of publicly supported schools and the establishment of public high schools.[4]

The entrance examinations for Yale College in the 1850's were still held orally, the candidates appearing individually before one of the professors. Miss Margaret D. Whitney in a paper called "One of the prophets"[5] tells of Gibbs' entrance examination:

Edith Woolsey has a story that she thinks came from her father,[6] that being very shy he [Gibbs] dreaded the entrance examinations and went to his good friend Prof. Thacher to consult him about it. Prof. Thacher questioned him on a variety of subjects and at the end said that he had

4. The New Haven High School was organized in 1859.
5. Read before the Saturday Morning Club of New Haven by Miss Whitney, daughter of Professor William D. Whitney.
6. Theodore Dwight Woolsey, president of Yale College, 1846–72.

passed the equivalent of an entrance examination and was admitted to college.

This may be substantially correct, although as Miss Whitney states the story was not known in Gibbs' family. But that it may be apocryphal is suggested by the similar story related by Professor G. P. Fisher about Gibbs' father. He says:

President Day, who was then Professor of Mathematics in College, remembers a little incident, illustrative, perhaps, of the character of Mr. Gibbs, even when a youth. Presenting himself to Professor Day, to apply for admission, he expressed the utmost anxiety lest he should prove unable to stand the examination. The Professor kindly offered, if he would open his books, to put him some questions, and then to advise him whether to undergo the ordeal, or to defer it to a future day, when he might come with a greater prospect of success. In this the diffident lad acquiesced, and his answers were such that the Professor, on closing the book, informed him, no doubt much to his surprise, that he was a member of College.[7]

As this version of the story comes to us at only second hand instead of at the third hand of the previous version, it would seem possible that Miss Whitney's story may be another case of the sins of the father being visited upon the children!

But whatever may be the truth of the matter, the success of the younger Gibbs' probationary period in college was a brilliant one, for in his freshman year (1854–55) he was awarded a Berkeley Premium[8] for excellence in Latin composition and shared the first prize for the solution of mathematical problems with his future brother-in-law Addison Van Name. He continued to take prizes in each year of the college course. In sophomore year he shared the first prize for the solution of mathematical problems with two others. In junior year he received another Berkeley Premium for Latin composition, took the Clark Premium third prize for excellence in Latin, and delivered the Latin oration at the junior exhibition at the close of the year. In senior year he was awarded two scholarships, the Clark and the Bristed (the former carrying the obligation to continue with graduate work), took the first of the

7. "A Discourse."
8. Established from a bequest of Bishop Berkeley of Cloyne.

senior mathematical prizes, and gave the Latin oration at commencement.

This record not only is evidence of unusual mental powers but
could have been attained only by sustained and systematic industry.
Thus it is not surprising to find little record of participation in extra-
curricular activities on his part. He was a member of Brothers in
Unity, one of the two societies which at that time included all of the
undergraduate body, but there is no evidence that he took part in
any of the debates or other activities of the society. Organized athletics, later such a prominent feature of undergraduate Yale life,
were virtually unknown in the 1850's, and the recreations enjoyed
by the students, judging by accounts in the "Baldwin Papers," were
quite similar in nature to those described in Miss Van Name's account of the parties, quoted in the last chapter. It seems probable
that the habit of taking long country walks, the form of exercise
most favored by Gibbs throughout his life, was formed in his
college days.

Thus the picture we form of the youth in his school and college
days is that of a boy of brilliant mental endowment, industrious
and more interested in the facts and ideas to be obtained in the
classroom than in social campus pursuits. He lived at home from
choice, or in accordance with the then usual custom for sons of
faculty members, rather than from necessity, and if he thereby
missed some of the advantages of dormitory life he also avoided
its distractions. One can hardly escape the conclusion that here
was a boy who knew already that his life work was to lie in the
world of ideas and who was steadfastly preparing himself for its
efficient exploitation.

Hence it is of interest to examine the extent and character of the
mathematical and scientific training afforded at Yale in Gibbs' time.
The courses at Yale may be taken as typical of the best available at
the period in this country, for the prestige of Yale in science was
then very high due to the reputation of the Sillimans, father and
son, and of James Dwight Dana in the natural sciences and chemistry, as well as to the widespread use of the textbooks of former
President Day in mathematics and Professor Dennison Olmsted in
natural philosophy. While of these men it is probable that only
Dana can be considered to have been of world-wide significance as

a creative scientist, the others were certainly well in the forefront of the national scientific picture. From 1854–58 the younger Silliman, Dana, and Olmsted were active teachers in the college; and the appointment of Hubert Anson Newton as professor of mathematics in 1855 added materially to the strength of that department. These four men together with some half-dozen tutors (who served under three-year appointments) made up the faculty in science and mathematics under which Gibbs studied. It would seem probable that the one who exercised the most influence on his development was Newton, who continued through all the after years to be his close friend and adviser. Just who were the actual instructors in the various courses pursued by Gibbs it is impossible to determine precisely, for the college catalogues of the times are in general rather vague on this point. But as they usually do list the textbooks used, it is possible to form some idea of the nature and extent of the ground covered. Another means of estimating the quality of the instruction is furnished by Gibbs' solutions of the prize mathematical problems—freshman, sophomore, and senior—which are preserved in a bound manuscript volume entitled "Varia" in the Rare Book Room of the Yale library.

From the catalogues it appears that the work in pure mathematics (which extended through differential and integral calculus) was equally thorough although less extensive than that open to a good college student today. On the other hand, the work in applied mathematics (mensuration, navigation, and surveying) was more extensive than that now generally offered in academic institutions, and approximated that given in modern scientific and engineering schools. This emphasis on applications was in all probability one of the chief factors leading to Gibbs' choice of engineering for his graduate work. The work in natural philosophy (physics) was confined to a year's elementary course without laboratory practice and with relatively more time devoted to mechanics than is customary at present. There was a comparatively brief course in astronomy (theoretical), while chemistry, metallurgy, and geology were covered together in a course of somewhat less than a year's duration. Thus as compared with the work in mathematics, that in physics, chemistry, and the other sciences was meager and by modern standards quite elementary.

One gains the impression that the mathematical prize problems were of sufficient difficulty to discourage the average student and to furnish means for discovering those possessing mathematical ability. The freshman problems were in the domain of elementary algebra and plane geometry; the sophomore ones covered more advanced algebra, solid geometry, and plane trigonometry; and those of the senior year included problems in solid trigonometry, analytics, and calculus. In all of them, reflecting the trend of the courses of instruction, a considerable number of problems were concerned with practical applications. While on the whole the difficulty of these problems may not have been as great as those encountered, for instance, in the contemporary mathematical tripos examinations at the University of Cambridge in England, yet their difficulty was such that to have solved all of them and to have taken the first prize in all three tests, as Gibbs did, was a certain indication of unusual mathematical powers and intuition.

Thus it can be said that although the Yale undergraduate training in science of that time was somewhat overweighted with practical applications to the exclusion of the higher theoretical developments, it was nevertheless sound and thorough as far as it went, and yielded an entirely adequate foundation for the graduate work then offered at Yale or any other American institution. The undergraduate work provided in physics and chemistry was hardly of the same caliber as that in mathematics, although probably adequate as preparation for the graduate study then available. It furnished less of the higher theoretical developments in those subjects, was even more dominated by the practical, and outside of the domain of mechanics was almost wholly descriptive in nature. The preparation afforded can only be regarded from the standpoint of the present day as woefully inadequate.

It is difficult to compare this preparation for a career in science with that available at the same time in England and on the continent of Europe. There was no unit of the educational systems abroad which corresponded closely with the American college, so that it is not easy to find a fair basis of comparison. It can, however, be said that the instruction in mathematics and science in Europe was, on the whole, for boys of comparable age, less concerned than was ours with the applications of science, that it was somewhat

more advanced, and that there existed an appreciation of the value
of science for science's sake alone which was almost wholly wanting on this side of the Atlantic. This situation is not surprising in
view of the youth of our country and the necessary preoccupation
of our best minds with the practical problems of the exploration
and settlement of a vast new territory; and also in consideration of
the fact that our main educational heritage was from an age when
there was but scant scientific knowledge and less appreciation of
its value. But the fact remains that if even so brilliant a student as
Gibbs had proceeded directly from the Yale of that time to his
European studies he would have found the deficiencies of his pre-
liminary training a serious handicap.

But Gibbs did not go abroad to study immediately. Indeed it can
be doubted if the idea of foreign study had yet been born in his
mind. His predilections, the materialistic trend of the times, and
his training with its emphasis on practical applications all were
tending to incline him to a career in mechanical invention. So he
did what might have been expected in the circumstances, and
entered the Department of Philosophy and the Arts of Yale in the
fall of 1858 as a student of engineering.

This department had been set up in 1847, mainly through the
initiative and influence of the Sillimans, to furnish advanced instruction not otherwise provided for in Yale College or in the Medical, the Divinity, or the Law schools. Its organization marked the
birth of three important developments in the Yale educational system which were soon followed in other institutions. In the first place
it recognized and implemented the demand for a more advanced
training than was afforded in the traditional college curriculum
and was the first real expansion of that tradition to be made in
this country. Secondly, there was introduced in the work in chemistry the then novel method of instruction by means of laboratory
experiments performed by the students themselves. And in the
third place it led (a little later) to the establishment of a largely
independent undergraduate college with a curriculum—representing a complete break with the older tradition—made up of the
sciences, modern languages, English, economics, etc. At first called
the Yale Scientific School, it was in 1861 renamed the Sheffield

Scientific School [9] in honor of Joseph Earl Sheffield who provided its first building, equipment, and a teaching endowment.

These three developments were of great significance in the history of higher education in the United States, but organized graduate work and the laboratory method are now such commonplaces that it is scarcely necessary to dwell on them further here, while with regard to the eary history of "Sheff" we need only note that the members of the faculty of the new school formed an important part of the faculty of the Department of Philosophy and the Arts, and that its graduate students together with those of the college were enrolled in that department.

Thus during the period when Gibbs was pursuing his graduate studies we find from the catalogues of the time that his principal teachers must have been William A. Norton and Chester S. Lyman in engineering, Hubert A. Newton and Elias Loomis in mathematics, and Benjamin Silliman, Jr. in chemistry; the first two from the scientific school and the last three from the college faculty. It is even more difficult than in the case of his undergraduate courses to find any definite information about the nature of the courses pursued by Gibbs as a graduate student. Almost no records were kept at the time, and the catalogues, in lieu of any description of the work covered, usually state that professor so and so will give instruction to suit the needs of the student in topics chosen from such and such subjects. Nevertheless, from the obvious adequacy of his mathematical preparation when he finally went abroad, it is reasonable to infer that under Newton and Loomis he must have made good much if not all of the undergraduate deficiency in the higher theoretical developments in mathematics; and we can judge from the scholarly reputations of both Professors Norton and Lyman that his engineering training, on the theoretical side at any rate, was both extensive and thorough.

As evidence of one direction taken by his studies, which in those days of informality must have been largely determined by his own predilections, we have the thesis that he submitted for

9. For a more detailed account of these early years and the personalities involved see Russell H. Chittenden, *History of the Sheffield Scientific School* (New Haven, Yale University Press, 1928), 2 vols.

his doctor's degree.[10] It is interesting to note, as Professor Waters in his comments on this thesis has pointed out, that the method of attack used by Gibbs on the problem of this paper was geometrical rather than analytical, although an approach by the latter method was possible and attractive. Here in Gibbs' first work is revealed his predilection for and skill in the use of the geometrical approach, which was later so prominent in his thermodynamic studies and which he used extensively in his lectures. The value of the thesis as a contribution to knowledge is naturally less today than it might have been at the time it was written. Much water has gone over the dam since 1863 in the art of gear design and manufacture; the gap then existing between the theorist and the practical designer has been largely closed; and if this work has not exerted the influence on the progress of the art which it might have done if it had been published when written, it is still of value as a milestone in the development of Gibbs' thought. Although a good deal of the contents can be considered little more than a review of well-known principles and although the work proposes some methods which have since been discarded, we can say of it in the words of Professor Waters, "Nevertheless, the author's strict regard for logic, his ability to generalize a problem, and his devotion to the thorough study of a few fundamentals rather than their pursuit into all sorts of imaginable applications, mark his early efforts here as those of no ordinary intellect." [11]

What other lines of study engaged Gibbs' interest and attention during the five years as a graduate student cannot now be determined definitely and must remain matter for speculation. By inference from his interests of the three years following the taking of his degree, he must have given much attention to the study of mechanics and of hydraulics. But this, together with

10. First published in *The Early Work of Willard Gibbs*. As pointed out in the introduction and in the commentary by Professor Waters, it seems probable that the surviving manuscript copy of this work is in the nature of a final draft retained by the author for his own use. This conclusion is based on the fact that the document was found among his papers after his death by his brother-in-law, Addison Van Name, and that it lacked a title page, which would have been expected in a formally submitted thesis. In those days when there was no requirement for the publication of theses and no official depository was designated for them, it is not surprising that the copy actually submitted to the faculty has been lost. The existing copy has been suitably bound and may be seen in the Rare Book Room at the Yale library.

11. *Ibid.*

the certain presumption that he must have done much work in mathematics, is all that can be safely concluded about his graduate work in the absence of definite records.

That Gibbs' life at this period was not however made up solely of work and study *is* a matter of record. In the "Baldwin Papers" are to be found more or less fragmentary and incomplete accounts of vacation parties and trips in which he took part. Thus we find that in the summer after his graduation from college (1858) he took a horseback trip up the Connecticut Valley and through the Berkshires with a small party of college friends. Also in the summer of 1861 a similar party made the trip to Old Lyme and up the Connecticut River as far as Northampton by rowboat. It would appear from the letters describing the return trip down the river that Gibbs must have left the party at Northampton; at least he is not mentioned in these later letters. However, from the incidents of the first part of the trip which have been preserved it is clear that it was a congenial party of friends, with all the "ragging" typical of youthful intimates, and that Willard took his part with the rest in all its pleasures and labors.

It was at some time during the period of his graduate studies that his health began to give him rather serious concern. Physicians were of the opinion that he was threatened with tuberculosis, for which there was apparently some predisposition on his mother's side. Indeed it seems not unlikely that his mother herself died of it. But whether or not the diagnosis was accurate in Willard's case, it seems obvious that, while periodically incapacitated for work, he could not at any time have been very seriously ill, and that such disabilities as he did suffer were surmounted by periods of rest and abstention from work. The fact that his name does not appear in the catalogue for the college year 1861–62 may perhaps be due to the coincidence of one of his periods of enforced rest with the college registration period, and that he took five years to obtain his degree suggests that more than one such interruption of his studies may have occurred. As will be seen later, one similar interruption to his work took place during his European sojourn, but from the time of his return to New Haven in 1869 until his final illness in 1903 his health was excellent. He rarely missed any college appointment, and then only from such minor ailments as colds. He never at any time suffered from the digestive disturbances that so frequently accompany a sedentary life.

However, it would seem certain that the somewhat precarious nature of his health in the 1860's was responsible for his not volunteering to serve in the armed forces in the Civil War. There developed at this time, in addition to the threat of pulmonary trouble, another minor impediment to military service, in his eyesight. This defect, probably aggravated by the close application required in his work in the engineering drafting room, was not then so easily diagnosed and corrected as today; and while it was not by itself an insuperable obstacle, it is reasonable to suppose that with this added to the threat of tuberculosis he did not feel qualified for active service in the army. In any case his name was not reached in the draft. The uncertainty as to the real nature of the eye trouble and a natural dread of the consequences of the lung affection must have given Gibbs much anxiety and added to his cares as head of the household.

The story has come down in the family that Gibbs himself after considerable study and experimentation diagnosed the eye trouble as astigmatism, calculated the lenses for its correction, and had glasses made from his own prescription. There is no reason to doubt the story in spite of its seeming strangeness to a generation accustomed to depend on oculists for such services. This defect of vision had been known to scientists for many years, and the calculation of the necessary cylindrical correcting lenses, while it may seem to the layman a formidable undertaking, would not have offered any insuperable difficulties to a student of Gibbs' training and ability. It is true that physicians of that time may not have had adequate training in the correction of this defect, as the first treatise to give the medical profession any comprehensive description of astigmatism [12] did not appear until 1864. Thus the story that Gibbs was forced to find his own solution for his difficulty is entirely credible and furnishes evidence of his practical experimental ability and resourcefulness. Thereafter Gibbs never experienced any trouble with his eyes and to the end

12. Donder's *Accommodation and Refraction of the Eye* devotes over 100 pages to astigmatism.

of his life never wore glasses except for reading and other close work.

The history of these days of his formal education may fittingly be closed with mention of the influence on his career exerted by the passing from his life of the guiding hands of his mother and father.[13] Never one who wore his heart on his sleeve or committed his emotions to paper, he left no record of the significance to him of their deaths. Yet the cessation of those influences which had been so potent in producing his early maturity could not itself have failed to exert a powerful molding effect on his character. He had adored his mother and was closely sympathetic with the mental and moral qualities of his father. Their passing made him the head of the house, throwing the care and welfare of his sisters upon his shoulders. He passed from boyhood to man's estate, and the clearheaded, competent discharge of the obligations he assumed is not only testimony to the depth of his affection for his sisters but also a tribute to the memory of the parents whose love and wisdom had fitted him for the larger responsibilities. The assumption of these inherited family responsibilities early in life, coupled with the uncertainty of his health throughout the period when most young men have thoughts of founding a family of their own, may well have been the predisposing causes of his bachelorhood.[14]

13. Mary Anna Gibbs died on February 28, 1855; Josiah Willard Gibbs on March 25, 1861.

14. Precarious health is the only cause for this suggested by his nephew W. G. Van Name (See "P.R.I."), but it seems to me that his own family cares must have been a contributing factor.

III

Tutor at Yale and Student Abroad

IN June, 1863, Gibbs was one of three to receive the degree of doctor of philosophy at the Yale commencement. The dissertations of the other two were in classics. This was the third year in which this new degree had been awarded. The first institution in the country to grant it, Yale had established it in 1861. The first year there had been three recipients, one in astronomy [1] and two in classics. In 1862 there was but one awarded, again in classics. Thus Gibbs' doctorate was the second in science and the first in engineering to be given in the United States. For him it marked both the conclusion of prescribed and the beginning of voluntary studies which were to continue throughout his life.

That same year, 1863, he received an appointment as tutor in Yale College, with the customary three-year tenure. The office of tutor was then administered on the old tradition that any graduate so appointed was competent to teach any of the prescribed subjects of the first two years of the college course, whether or not it was in the line of his major interest. To a new appointee fell what remained after the tutors senior to him had exercised such choice among the scheduled courses as the limitations of the curriculum permitted. Thus Gibbs taught Latin (in which his undergraduate record shows he was an entirely competent scholar) for two years and in the third gave instruction in the subject of his own choice, natural philosophy. That he did not choose mathematics in spite of his brilliant undergraduate record in it may possibly be taken as evidence of the strength of his bias toward applied science, although this is necessarily a matter of pure speculation at this late date. It is interesting to note as illustrative of

1. Arthur Williams Wright, later a student of Gibbs in 1871–72, and a colleague on the college faculty throughout his life.

the anomalies inherent in the tutorial system of those days that in the second year of Gibbs' term and while he was still teaching Latin the tutor in the other entry of the dormitory in which he had his office (South Middle College, later Connecticut Hall) was Tracy Peck, who later became head of the Latin Department in Yale College but was then a tutor in *mathematics!*

There have come down from this time rumors (entirely undocumented) that Gibbs had trouble with discipline in the classroom and that he was unsuccessful as a teacher of undergraduates. To evaluate these rumors fairly it should be recalled that those were the times when a college education, formerly almost solely a preparation for the learned professions, was beginning to be sought by those who planned no definite use in later life for the learning so acquired; that the student body included a considerable number of men having no professional incentive to acquire more than passing grades, who came to college primarily for social rather than bookish contacts; and that for such students the baiting of green tutors was a sport offering an outlet to youthful exuberance more attractive than parsing Latin passages or understanding laws of nature of which they expected to make no use in their careers. When it is remembered further that in those days there were almost no organized athletics to afford a safety valve for letting off undergraduate steam, it is not surprising to find that the student body was more unruly than in our day.

Thus it would seem quite possible that Gibbs as a tutor may have had to undergo some disciplinary ordeals, even if nothing to support the rumors has been found in the contemporary records. That he was not temperamentally adapted to the task of forcing knowledge down unwilling throats may also be acknowledged. But that he was a poor teacher for anyone who wanted to learn is unthinkable in the light of the testimony of his students of later days.[2] Also the fact that he served out the full term of his appointment is strong evidence that such classroom disturbances as may have occurred were neither numerous nor very serious.

But the "alarms and excursions" of his classroom experiences of this time have but little interest as elements affecting Gibbs' career. In fact the chief effect of this first teaching experience

2. See Ralph Gibbs Van Name's "Willard Gibbs as a Teacher," as well as the comments of other of his students, in "P.R.I."

now perceptible would seem to be that the blank backs of the Latin and physics examination answer papers afforded him space for notes and calculations on the matters of research which were then interesting him! Curiously enough, these old papers have made it possible, from the names of the students, their college class, and the subject of the examination, to date fairly accurately some of Gibbs' early work. In this way it can be surmised with some confidence that of the three matters on which notes of this time survive [3] the first to engage his attention was the invention of a "center vent" hydraulic turbine, the second the invention of a railway car brake, and the third (although to some extent overlapping the others) a paper on the question of the units in mechanics.

Although Gibbs' work on these three matters cannot be considered to have been of first-rate importance or to have exerted any appreciable influence either on his own later work or in the engineering world, they nevertheless will repay some attention as revealing the immediate effect of his training on an active and ingenious mind. The fact that the first two ventures in research were in applied mechanics and directed toward inventions to effect an improvement in the arts concerned, rather than in matters of purely theoretical interest, is a tribute to the influence of a training which, in the spirit of the times, looked to science almost exclusively as an aid to invention.

The notes on the turbine are quite fragmentary and their importance very difficult to evaluate. They consist of an incomplete draft for a patent specification which in the absence of the drawings for the figures described is not clearly intelligible. Together with this draft is an unfinished mathematical analysis of the theory of the turbine, yielding, however, certain design equations for determining the dimensions to be employed. The theory, seemingly correct as far as it goes and not of a stereotyped textbook pattern, nevertheless does not reveal much of novelty in the treatment. The principal interest of these notes in the present connection lies in the fact that Gibbs' approach to this problem is a purely analytical one as contrasted with the geometrical approach he used in the problems discussed in his thesis. This dif-

3. Preserved in the Rare Book Room of the Yale library.

ference in method is of course largely conditioned by the diverse nature of the problems and is of importance only as showing his competence in the use of both mathematical tools at a time before his studies abroad.

Why this invention was left in an uncompleted state will probably never be known. There is no hint of a reason to be found among the notes, and whether he found that his ideas had been anticipated or he simply put the subject temporarily aside for other matters which ultimately submerged his interest in the problem must remain subjects of speculation. His other invention at any rate was pushed through to completion and resulted in the issue of letters patent by the U.S. Patent Office dated April 17, 1866, for "An Improved Railway Car Brake." This invention is interesting for our present purpose in that it shows an entirely different facet of Gibbs' mind than either his thesis or the notes on the turbine. Here was a problem demanding neither geometrical nor analytical ability but requiring a high degree of mechanical intuition and ingenuity.

The fundamental idea involved in the invention was, briefly, to utilize the application of brakes on the engine pulling the train to actuate the setting of the car brakes by virtue of the train's inertia. Now this basic idea of such so-called "buffer" or "momentum" brakes was not new or original with Gibbs. Indeed the claims made in his original specification in this respect were rejected by the Patent Office as having been anticipated in a patent issued in 1847 and in other applications rejected since that date. What was novel in Gibbs' invention and covered by three of the four claims in the patent as finally issued were devices to make the brakes operate whether the train was moving forward or backward, and with the engine attached to either end. The fourth allowed claim relates to structural means provided for increasing the pressure of the brakes against the wheels. Thus the merits of Gibbs' invention lie in a keen appreciation of the nature of the operative requirements for a brake and in the ingenuity of the mechanical means he provided to implement them. That he had such a clear vision of the problem is, as Dean Dudley [4] points out, quite remarkable for his time and environment, and argues

4. *The Early Work of Willard Gibbs.*

close observation of practical train operation and equipment. Further evidence of the comprehensiveness of his thought on the whole problem is found in some notes, preserved with the patent correspondence, in which he sketches a device for dissipating in friction the energy due to jerks and jars between loosely coupled cars, instead of by the use of coiled springs as was then customary. This idea anticipated by some twelve years a similar suggestion by George Westinghouse, the air brake inventor, and by over twenty years the first practical "friction draft gear" embodying the same principle and now part of standard train equipment. [5]

The third subject to engage Gibbs' thought as shown in the records of this period is illustrative of two fundamental traits characteristic of all of his later work; first, concern for precision in the definition of the underlying basic concepts (in this case of mechanics), and second, a careful exploration of *all* the possibilities involved. This work exists as an incomplete draft entitled "Discussion of a Set of Units of Analytical Mechanics and Examples," and also as the completed manuscript of a paper read before the Connecticut Academy of Arts and Sciences on March 21, 1866, which is bound up in the "Varia" previously referred to, with the title "The proper Magnitude of the Units of Length and of other quantities used in Mechanics." Gibbs had been elected a member of the academy on November 26, 1858, that is, in the fall of his first year as a graduate student; and this paper marking his first appearance before a scientific body must have been an occasion of considerable importance to him. At any rate he took characteristic care in its preparation.

The paper goes at some length into the history of the units which had been used in theoretical and applied mechanics, and the confusion which had resulted in the literature as a consequence of the use in the latter field of the same word to designate the essentially distinct and different concepts involved in the units of mass and force. Gibbs notes for instance that while the French Academy had established a unit of mass, the kilogram, and had formulated no unit for force, French engineers had nevertheless quite generally appropriated the name kilogram for a unit of force. He goes on to point out that the fundamental relation of

5. See Dean Dudley's comments on this point in the reference cited.

mechanics between mass, force, length, and time involves an experimentally determined constant of proportionality, and that to
choose the values of the units concerned so as to give this constant
the value of unity has great advantages in simplicity and convenience. He further points out that some writers have accomplished this by using the usual units of mass, length, and time
together with an altered (decreased) unit of force; while others
have reached the same objective by retaining the customary units
of force, length, and time accompanied by an altered (increased)
unit of mass. Both of these methods, he observes, are at variance
with the common viewpoint (derived from the age-old concern
with but one kind of force—that of gravity) that the unit of force
must be the weight of the unit of mass, and that while such de-
partures from customary usage cause no particular inconvenience
to the physicist, the bar to their universal acceptance is as great as
if it were proposed to abandon the day or the year as units of time.
While this may sound rather far-fetched today, it was nevertheless a valid point under the conditions of the time in which it was
written.

Thus in order to obtain a system of units more generally acceptable Gibbs comes to the main point of the paper, which is a
proposal to give the value unity to the constant of proportionality
in the fundamental equation by retaining the usual units for mass,
force, and time and selecting a suitably altered (increased) unit
for *length*. The adoption of this proposal would then secure the
desired simplification of the fundamental equation without doing violence to preconceptions as to the relations between weight
and mass. So far as I am aware this solution of the difficulties
with regard to the engineering units of mechanics was entirely
novel and original with Gibbs. It has also to the best of my knowledge never been suggested by anyone else, although once having
been pointed out it seems an obvious alternative. That the suggestion has never been adopted is understandable on several
grounds. For one thing it has never up to the present been published,[6] and thus its merits have in general remained unknown and
undiscussed. Also it may very well be that to Gibbs himself, after

6. In view of its interest as Gibbs' first publicly presented paper, as well as because of the
light it throws on his methods of thought at the beginning of his career, it is printed in
full as Appendix II of this volume.

his attention had become focused on the theoretical rather than the practical aspects of physics, the importance of catering to the older preconceptions may not have appeared as compelling as in his younger days, and he was entirely content to allow the suggestion to be forgotten.

However, the evolution of this idea by exhausting *all* the possibilities involved is noteworthy and characteristic of the working of Gibbs' mind. In this case, admitting the impracticability of an alteration in the unit of time, there remained three units any one of which might be altered to yield the desired end—a value of unity for the fundamental constant of proportionality. Two of these alterations had been tried. Why not examine the remaining one? It might (and does) yield certain advantages over the others. This in brief would seem to have been the course of Gibbs' thought on the matter, and the fact that the advantage gained is not of compelling importance in no way lessens the value of the method or precludes (or has precluded) its success when applied to other fields of thought.

In reviewing this early work of Gibbs up to the time of his departure for his European studies, it is interesting to observe how many of the characteristics of the work of his maturity are revealed in these early essays. As we have seen, his grasp of the implications and requirements of a problem, his concern with precise definitions, his geometrical and analytical skills, and his exhaustive exploration of all the possible alternatives involved are all clearly foreshadowed in this work of his graduate student and tutorial days. In addition, the plausible rumor of the self-diagnosis and correction of his astigmatic vision as related in the previous chapter reveals an experimental initiative and ability of no mean order. Thus it becomes apparent that when on the termination of his appointment as tutor in the summer of 1866 he decided to spend the next few years in study abroad in a new academic atmosphere, he went with a mind already sharpened by research and equipped with the tools fitted to make the best use of the broader scientific horizons then available in Europe.

In none of this early work one notes is there indication of an interest shown in any branch of physics other than mechanics.

This may have been due, in part at least, to the inadequate knowledge in this country at that time about the important fundamental developments in the domains of thermodynamics, electrodynamics, and physical optics which had recently taken place in England and on the continent of Europe; and it would seem to be a reasonable inference that a realization of this deficiency and a desire to remedy it formed a principal motive for going abroad. But I believe that this early interest in mechanics has an additional and a deeper significance. It constitutes merely the first evidence of the predilection toward the mechanical explanation for physical phenomena which was to motivate all of Gibbs' work. This trend of thought (incidentally a dominant characteristic of that age) can be discerned in and unites in a common bond of method and aim all of his achievements, whether in electricity, optics, or the properties of matter. It is no matter of chance that his first interest was in mechanics, for that was the core of his intellectual outlook and the key to his accomplishment.

At this time the Gibbs family consisted of Willard and his two older sisters, Anna and Julia, his younger sister Emily having died in 1864. The estate left by the elder Gibbs on his death in 1861 was inventoried at about $23,500 (including the house at 121 High Street) and was now shared by the three children equally. Even allowing for the greater value of the dollar at that time, and admitting that Gibbs, living at home, must have saved something from his salary as tutor,[7] one can see that it might have been impossible for him to go abroad alone for the rather extended period contemplated and at the same time support his sisters at home without serious sacrifices in living comfort for all. In addition, as has been related, Gibbs' health was not rugged, and this by itself would make his sisters loath to be separated from him. Thus it came about that, with their income increased by the rental of the jointly owned house, the three members of the family set sail together for Europe in August, 1866.

They went first to Paris—the gay Paris of the Second Empire —where they boarded at a place on the left bank. It can be pre-

7. Eight endorsed salary checks extending over the years 1864–66 and totaling some $2,137 have been preserved.

sumed that they enjoyed the usual sight-seeing and other attractions of the cosmopolitan capital, although no record is available of such activities. This is not strange, for their being no family left behind at home, there remain no letters such as in other circumstances might have been preserved. But for the present purpose the important aspect of the stay in Paris was its effect on the mind and scientific outlook of Gibbs, and fortunately on these matters we do have some although not a large amount of information. According to the lecture prospectus (copies of which are preserved with the other Gibbs papers in the Yale library), the members of the mathematical and physical science faculties offering lecture courses at the Sorbonne and the Collège de France in the first semester of the academic year 1866–67 included the well-known names of Chasles, Duhamel, Liouville, and Serret in mathematics; Darboux in mathematical and Bertin in experimental physics, and Delauney in applied physics. The courses all consisted of two lectures each week. From Gibbs' notebook of the period (also preserved in the Yale library), which is the sole source of information as to the courses he actually pursued, it is interesting to see that he attended the lectures in all of the courses offered by the above-named professors except those of Delauney on the mechanics of machinery. This may probably be taken as substantiation of the surmise that the principal object of his studies was to strengthen his theoretical rather than his practical knowledge.

The notes which he kept are very meager. Yet from our knowledge of the man and the interests of his later life, it is possible to glean a little as to the influence on his development of his studies of these days in Paris. The courses having the closest connection with his later interests were those of Darboux on the mathematical theory of heat and of Liouville on rational mechanics, and to a lesser extent that of Serret on celestial mechanics and elliptic functions. It would be interesting to find that he here first met with that theorem of Liouville's which occupies such a key position in his development of statistical mechanics, but neither his notebook nor the published description of the course gives any reason to believe that he did. Similarly it is impossible now to connect Darboux's course on heat with Gibbs' own later work on thermodynamics. All that can be said is that the lectures in those courses, as well as those of Chasles in higher geometry, Duhamel in higher algebra, and Liouville in the theory of numbers, must have given him a broader outlook on the fields of mathematics and mathematical physics than he could have obtained at home.

From dates noted in Gibbs' handwriting opposite certain other courses in the prospectus it can be inferred that he occasionally attended lectures in other faculties than that of science. From this and the large variety of the mathematical and science courses which the notebook shows he pursued it would seem that his main objective was to improve his perspective in many branches of learning rather than to specialize in any given branch. That this was the fact is further borne out by the evidence supplied by the notebook as to the considerable amount and the character of the reading he did outside the lecture halls. It was at this time apparently that he began to form the intimate acquaintanceship he later exhibited with the memoirs of those great names in French science, Lagrange, Laplace, Poisson, Fresnel, and Cauchy. In fact it would seem that both here and later in Berlin and Heidelberg his outside reading must have consumed the major part of his time.

One fact that stands out in this Paris experience is the magnitude of the work load assumed by Gibbs. His schedule called for some sixteen hours of lecture appointments a week which, with the large amount of outside reading he undertook, formed a punishing program and undoubtedly contributed to the breakdown he suffered before the close of the first semester. He had contracted a cold early in the winter which he could not shake off and, anxious because of his supposed tendency to tuberculosis, he consulted a French physician who advised him to go to the Riviera and rest. So he and his sisters spent the remainder of the winter and the spring in the south of France where Willard immediately began to improve. On their return north en route to Berlin, he again consulted the same Paris physician, who reported that in spite of his (the physician's) earlier fear of tubercular infection he now found no signs of the disease. This verdict lifted the load of worry which Gibbs had carried for some years. That the whole experience had taught him to recognize his work limitations is evidenced by the much more moderate work loads he took on in Berlin and Heidelberg.

Freed from the fear of the dread disease, Gibbs and his sisters traveled in a leisurely fashion to Berlin in the early summer of 1867. Here they were met by Gibbs' classmate, Addison Van Name, who in 1865 had succeeded Daniel Coit Gilman (later president of Johns Hopkins) as librarian at Yale and who had for some years been engaged to marry Gibbs' sister Julia. The wedding took place on August 19 in the German capital, and the Van Names after a short honeymoon trip returned to New Haven early in October. Anna however remained with Willard in Germany and throughout the balance of his stay abroad.

We have more definite information as to the courses Gibbs pursued in Berlin than for those in Paris, for the *Anmeldungs Buch* (preserved with his other papers in the Yale library) which was issued to him on October 20, 1867, is signed by the professors concerned both at the beginning and the end of his periods of attendance. From this we find that throughout the first semester he attended the lectures of Magnus on general physics, of Kundt on acoustics, of Weierstrass on determinants, of Quincke on optics, and of Kronecker on quadratic forms. In the second semester he followed the courses of Magnus on technology, of Quincke on acoustics and capillarity, of Foerster on least squares, of Weierstrass on analysis, and of Kummer on probability calculations. This list shows more of physics and less of mathematics than did his program in Paris.

The notebook kept by Gibbs on these Berlin courses, while more voluminous than his Paris notebook, is nevertheless quite meager in its contents. This but confirms the impression conveyed by his notes of the previous year that his object was a general survey of the fields of mathematics and physics and not the acquirement of specific techniques. He occasionally goes into some detail on particular subjects, but in general the notes are scanty and of such a nature that they are of little use to anyone but the author, and to him only as an aid to recall the outlines of a lecture discussion. Here as in Paris the bibliographical notes for his own reading indicate that a great part of his time was spent on such study outside of the lecture halls. These reading lists are of two kinds; first, books recommended by a professor at the opening of a course, and second, memoirs and papers compiled on his own initiative. That these latter were not merely noted for future reference but were actually studied at the time is indicated by additional notations calling attention to particular pages or portions of the articles.

These reading lists are informative and instructive both in what they contain and in what is omitted. We find evidence that his earlier interest in applied mechanics and invention was still alive in references to articles in Dingler's *Polytechnische Journal* on the "Use of Reversal of Locomotive to Stop Railway Trains" and on the "Steam Injector," and to one in the *Comptes rendus* on the "Governor." The first of these references was obviously of interest to him in connection with his railway brake invention; the second may possibly indicate that he was already beginning to take interest in the thermodynamics of fluids, which formed the subject of his first published paper; while the third is more certainly the first indication of interest in the problem of the improvement of the Watt steam engine governor, a matter upon which he did some work after his return to New Haven. Of greater interest than these, however, are the considerable number of references to memoirs of Gauss, Jacobi, Hamilton, Dirksen, and Clebsch on the fundamentals of theoretical mechanics and perturbation theory; the equally large number of references to memoirs on electrical theory, by Lipschitz, W. Thomson (Lord Kelvin), Carl Neumann, and Hankel; and the still larger number referring to optics and the relations between electrodynamics and light by Fresnel, Green, Ampère, Hamilton, Lorentz (of Copenhagen), Kirchhoff, and Mascart. It is also of interest to note that at this time he became acquainted with the work of Möbius on lineal geometry, although not with the algebras of Grassmann or Hamilton, which later stimulated his interest in vector analysis and multiple algebra. Two other names, whose omission from these lists is significant in view of the extent to which his later work was influenced by them, are those of Maxwell and Clausius. That there is no evidence to be found that he was at this time acquainted with the ground-breaking work of these two is somewhat strange. It may possibly be due in the one case to the fact that no lecture course in electrical theory was offered during his year in Berlin, and in the other to his not being a regular attendant at Paaljow's course in the theory of heat. But considering that he was acquainted with the work of Lorentz on the relations of electrodynamics and light, the lack of any reference to Maxwell's 1864 paper remains rather striking; and the absence of reference to Clausius raises a suspicion that Gibbs' approach to thermodynamics came ultimately through engineering rather than theoretical considerations.

We have even less information on the studies Gibbs pursued in the two semesters spent in Heidelberg in the year 1868–69 than for those of either of the two preceding years. An *Anmeldungs Buch* for this year either was not issued or has been lost, and there are no notations on the prospectus, which has been preserved, to indicate which courses he actually attended. We only know (from the prospectus) that Kirchhoff, Hesse, Cantor, Rummer, du Bois-Reymond, and Eisenlohr were lecturing in courses on mathematics and mathematical physics; that Bunsen gave a course in experimental chemistry; and that Helmholtz lectured for the first semester in a sort of "orientation" course on the general results of the natural sciences, which was open to students from all of the faculties of the university. The work offered in mathematical physics appears to have been particularly comprehensive and, from the reputations of the lecturers, was presumably rich in content. But as to what part of this feast was enjoyed by Gibbs there is no evidence whatever. Neither have we any clue to the outside reading he did during this time.

We may however assume, without danger of going astray, that the general objectives of his study remained as they were in Paris and Berlin and that the work in Heidelberg suitably consummated the attainment of that perspective on the physical sciences and that insight into the possibilities for research which characterized all the rest of his career. One definite fact stands out from this whole period of European study, namely, that Gibbs cannot be regarded as the student of any *one* master. He undoubtedly gained inspiration from several, but from no one of them predominantly. In my own notes of his lectures in the 1890's I find reference to but one of his teachers of this time, Quincke, and that in regard to a very minor point. His real intellectual heritage stemmed from the

GIBBS THE TUTOR

GIBBS IN BERLIN

THE GIBBS GOVERNOR

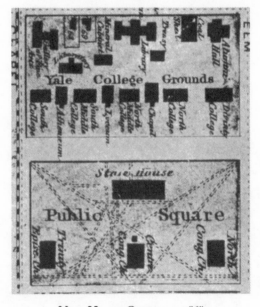

NEW HAVEN CENTER IN 1868

masters of an earlier age, with whom however it is probably true that he first became intimately acquainted through his reading during these student days abroad.

About Gibbs' recreations during this sojourn in Europe we have only scattered recollections which have come down in the family. It is known that between terms he enjoyed short trips and it seems probable that he made excursions on horseback in the picturesque region around Heidelberg. It is also known that he took a few riding lessons at some time during the stay in Germany,[8] and the most likely place would seem to have been in Heidelberg. Hastings in his biographical memoir [9] says that in later years Gibbs would in private conversation occasionally illustrate some point with examples from his personal experiences abroad, and relates one such from the Berlin days which shows that Gibbs had some social contacts outside of the lecture halls and reveals a sly appreciation of German intellectual condescension. But although he and his sisters must have enjoyed the usual amount of sight-seeing, concerts, opera, and theater, the record of this side of their experiences is very meager.

At the close of the second semester at Heidelberg Willard and Anna, after a short return visit in the spring of 1869 to the Riviera, returned to New Haven in June.

8. "P.R.I.," contribution of W. G. Van Name.

9. Charles S. Hastings, "Josiah Willard Gibbs," *Biographical Memoirs* (National Academy of Sciences, Washington, D.C., 1909), VI, 375–393. The story runs that in a conversation with Gibbs about the Connecticut Academy of Arts and Sciences one of his Berlin professors remarked that "its memberships appear to be pretty freely bestowed" if Gibbs himself were a member! Although it is true that the standards for admission to the academy were different from those prevailing in European academies, the implication that they were lower is hardly substantiated by the fact that the memoirs which brought Gibbs lasting fame appeared later in its *Transactions*.

IV

Return to New Haven and Appointment
at Yale

THE New Haven to which the travelers returned had not changed appreciably in outward appearance during their absence—at least in the region around the college. The Green, with its three churches along the Temple Street center line, the State House on its westward rise, and the Franklin Elm sheltering the town pump at its southwestern corner were all as they had been when they left three years before and indeed as they had known them all their lives. Nor were the immediate surroundings of the Green noticeably changed. The old "brick row" of the college buildings bordering its western side, the Methodist Church and the residences facing its northern side, the Court House, City Hall, and the Tontine Hotel dominating the eastern side, and the shops and stores with a few residences and the old New Haven House on the south were all as they had been for many years. The only unfamiliar sight to meet their eyes was the new dormitory, Farnam Hall, then in process of erection on the site previously occupied by the president's house and more recently used as the chemical laboratory. Although the town was growing rapidly, most of the resulting physical changes appeared only in the outlying sections. The original nine squares were as yet practically intact, the old families and solid citizens being still largely housed within their borders and along the two blocks of Hillhouse Avenue to the north. There was some residential expansion taking place northward from the nine squares along Whitney Avenue and Prospect Street and at some distance to the east around Wooster Square—the New Green as it was sometimes called.

The tenor of life in the town however was beginning to change.

During the preceding twenty years there had been effected the first of those steps toward modern conditions of living which have so altered the face of civilization. But the installation of street and house lighting by coal gas, the city water supply, and the inauguration of public transportation by horse-drawn streetcars were all of such recent date that their effects on the manner of living were only just beginning to be felt. Although the city gas service had been started in 1848, few private residences made use of it until after the Civil War.[1] The city water supply, after a lengthy controversy between the advocates of municipal and those of private ownership, had been opened for service by a private company as recently as 1862. The streetcars began operation in 1861, but the development of the system was rather slow, the Whitney Avenue line, for instance, not being completed until the early seventies. But although at the time of the return of the travelers it was somewhat easier to get around the town and the mechanics of living had been materially lightened by the conveniences of running water and gas lighting in the house, the mode of life was still rather primitive from a modern point of view.

For instance, apart from the wholesale and dock districts, and the space between the streetcar tracks on the few thoroughfares they traversed, there was no street paving in the New Haven of that day. This was a factor in everyday living whose significance it is hard for modern city dwellers to realize. Crosswalks were not then relatively broad spaces indicated by white lines painted on asphalt but were narrow strips of flagstone paving raised sufficiently above the level of the rutted mud or dust of the roadways to produce the illusion of tightrope walking for the pedestrian and to act as automatic checks on the speed of vehicular traffic at all street intersections. The scrapers on every doorstep were not there for ornament but of dire necessity, especially in the spring of the year when many of the streets were morasses of mud which sometimes inundated even the raised crosswalks. It is my impression that this archaic condition of the roadways continued rather longer in New Haven than in most cities of the east. At least I remember

1. A notable exception was provided by Professor Benjamin Silliman, Sr., whose house at Trumbull Street and Hillhouse Avenue was the first private residence in New Haven to have gas lighting installed. Its illumination on Thanksgiving eve, 1848, was a great event in the town.

being told by Professor Hastings in the mid-nineties, on his return
from a summer's vacation trip to Castine, Maine, which he and his
companion Dr. Smyth (then pastor of Center Church on the
Green) had made entirely by bicycle, that they had encountered
the worst roads in New England in Connecticut; the worst roads
in Connecticut in New Haven County; the worst roads in the
county within the city limits of New Haven; and that the worst
road in the city was Grove Street, in the old first ward on the
boundary of the original nine squares, passing directly in front of
the Sheffield Scientific School! Whether or not this is a libel on the
city of New Haven, it is certainly within my own knowledge that
the lack of street paving in the nineties together with the prevalence of uneven brick sidewalk pavements made walking a rather
violent form of exercise, particularly if one were in a hurry, and
was the cause of frequent accidents under the snow and ice conditions of winter.

This may seem but a trivial matter incidental to the other inconveniences of living of those times—cooking with wood or coal
stoves, sperm oil lamps or candles for lighting, the absence of cen-
tral heating, and only the most primitive means of sewage disposal
—but we are apt to overlook the influence and importance of
such factors as molders of civilization. After all, the uneven
sidewalks, the muddy or dusty streets, the inadequate street
lighting, the heating by open fires or "airtight stoves," and
the slow and infrequent means of public transportation were
all factors tending to restrict living to the home, to confine recreation to the family circle or with near neighbors, and to
limit outside activities to those connected with providing a livelihood or performance of duty. It was undoubtedly a life tending to
foster provincialism but it was also one which placed a premium
on reading and thinking and the cultivation of one's inner resources. It is true that there were other elements present tending
to combat the growth of too narrow a provincialism. The college
with its annual influx of students from other environments was
one. The international contacts of such scholars as the Sillimans,
Dana, and Marsh and the increasing number of the younger generation of the faculty who had received training abroad were another. Also the country-wide contacts of the town's manufacturing

interests brought a greater awareness of the outside world than was shared by more isolated communities. But by and large the New Haven of that day, while more cosmopolitan in outlook than many New England communities, still shared with the rest of the country a provincialism derived from its geographical isolation from the centers of the development of western civilization in Europe. The life in the college cirele was still largely dominated by the ideas and ideals as well as the inconveniences of living of an earlier period.

However in spite of its limitations New Haven was then as now a very pleasant place in which to live. The college, with its rapidly growing adjuncts soon to convert it into a true university, furnished a stimulating intellectual atmosphere. The simple domestic architecture of many of the homes possessed a quiet dignity, and the glorious arching elms which lined many of the streets—the Gothic arch in nature—made it truly the Elm City and more than compensated for the collegiate Gothic architecture of modern Yale. The real country pressed in much closer to the city limits then than now, and the contrasting beauties of the seashore to the south and the hills, ponds, and streams to the north were a standing invitation to walks and excursions unspoiled by the barbarisms of modern roadside advertising and the ubiquitous hot dog stands and filling stations.

Such in brief were the town and the life to which Willard and Anna returned in the summer of 1869. Julia and her husband Addison Van Name since their return nearly two years previously had been boarding in the then quite fashionable neighborhood of Wooster Square while the house at 121 High Street was undergoing alterations to adapt it for more convenient occupancy by the reunited family. It seems probable that in the course of these alterations the "modern" improvements of gas lighting and running water were installed in the house.

The household slipped back swiftly and easily into the pleasant social routines, not yet much changed from those previously described as characterizing the prewar days. They later acquired a jointly owned horse and carriage, more for recreation and the cult of fresh air than for household necessity, as the close proximity of the house to the shopping center of the town rendered its use for marketing and similar purposes practically superfluous. A pleasant picture of those days of the seventies as they appeared to the younger generation is given in Miss Margaret Whitney's "One of the Prophets":

Though the richer towns-people had carriages of their own, with coachmen complete, like the Trowbridges, the Englishes, the Hotchkisses, the Bishops, the Farnams, and the Salisburys, I can't remember any among the college people. Some of them had a horse and buggy or a canopy top.

President Woolsey and Dr. Bacon and Mr. Henry White were our nearest neighbors on Church Street, all well-to-do, and I don't remember any private carriage among them, except Henry Dyer White's box buggy that took him all over the state searching titles and gathering antiquarian lore, but we all had the one-horse car that plodded through the dusty street to Lake Whitney every half hour.

Mrs. Salisbury lived just across the street, but I don't remember driving in her fine coach, upholstered in brown satin, with Albert and his pendant mustaches sitting in imperturbable dignity on the box. She was a friendly person, so it must have been Albert who disapproved of children in his carriage and behind his slow-moving and well-fed horses; and what Albert didn't want to do, he didn't do.

But the Gibbses and the Van Names who lived together in the Gibbs house on High Street had a horse and buggy and, better still, a cutter in winter.

And Willard Gibbs wanted to take the Whitney children out to drive —all by themselves, as I remember it, and he would turn to tuck us in and see that we were all right with a smile so friendly and re-assuring to the little girl beside him that she felt at once at ease with him. My best memory is driving with him in the winter in a cutter, a rare treat for me. This impression of standing beside the sleigh in the snow, waiting to be lifted in, snow all around, crisp air, sleighbells jingling by, all the world in swift motion, and I to be one of them, this sensation has stayed with me and can always be evoked.

It is well worth a tribute to the kind man who gave it to me.

Emily's best memory is of a Fourth of July picnic at Judge's Cave on West Rock. He carried her all the way down the rock on his back, over a rough trail to the carriage below.

He was of slight build, but evidently did not lack strength, for Marian injured a leg when she was a well grown girl of thirteen, and she remembers Cousin Willard coming day after day to take her out to drive, and that included carrying her downstairs and carrying her up again.

This portrait of a man fond of children and going out of his way to give them pleasure, at a time when he was engaged in the production of one of the most profound and far-reaching works of the scientific imagination, reveals a character simple, kindly, and unpretentious beyond that of the common run of men. A similar impression of his character is given in Miss Whitney's accounts of vacation experiences of the time:

Emily has another vivid memory of returning from the White Mountains on the train in the company of Willard and his sister Anna—his constant companion at home and on such vacation trips. Emily was sixteen then and her impression still remains of a long day of particularly interesting talk. Both Gibbses—all Gibbses—were highly intelligent people. . . .

Another favorite region for vacations was the Adirondacks. Lillie Farnam saw him there when on a trip with her father, William Kingsley. He was on horseback, returning to the hotel and the horse was misbehaving badly. But so firm was his hand on the rein and so good his seat that although they thought the horse might throw him any minute, he was able to control him and bring him quietly to a halt. A fine piece of horsemanship never forgotten. Horse-back riding was the favorite form of exercise for the faculty in those days. What else could they do, but walk? . . .

Another memory of an Adirondack vacation was sent me by Newell Martin, of the class of '75 at Yale . . .

In his own words:

"I am 82 and no longer, to use an old fashioned legal form, 'of sound and disposing mind and memory.' But you ask me to tell you whether I remember anything about Willard Gibbs.

"It must seem to you queer that Willard Gibbs permitted me to walk hand in hand with him when he might have been travelling with Mark Twain or Rogers, of the Standard Oil or that beneficent adventurer, the elder Rockefeller. I profited by the frugality that is so often forced on philosophers. On an evening in July 1873, I drove up, in a ramshackle mail wagon, to Dibble's Tahawus House, in Keene Flats, in the Adirondacks. Dibble's barnlike boardinghouse ceased to exist, many years ago; and Keene Flats became Keene Valley many years ago. The inhabitants of 'Dibble's' came out to get their letters and papers. I was delighted to see Gibbs among them; and it is the most honorable event of my long life that Gibbs was glad to see me. I told him that I was on my way to Beede's and the Maine Woods. He and I stood beside the wagon, in the dusk, and he argued with me. I am, perhaps, the only man left alive in all the world that ever argued with Gibbs. I told him that I was on my way to the Upper Works, to spend two weeks at Mt. McIntyre and in the Indian Pass; and that, at the end of the two weeks, I was to meet a man in the Maine Woods. It should be remembered by my descendants, to the nineth generation, in my honor, that Gibbs took the trouble to persuade me to change my plans. He argued that the huckleberries and porridge of Dibble's were as rich and nourishing as those of Smith Beede's mountain boardinghouse. Defeated in argument I changed my plans and dined, at 'Dibble's,' with him and his sister and a group of young women of extraordinary merit. To that group I have been devoted for 63 years.

"When a philosopher of the first magnitude is associated with anybody less than Lord Rayleigh or Einstein or Bertrand Russell—when he is surrounded by common people—one of the common people does not seem to him any flatter or duller or less instructive than another. Gibbs was one of those that made the summer of 1873 an astonishing delight. I did not know, then, that he was an epoch making philosopher. But all of us younger people had sense enough to see that his mind traveled on serene heights beyond our reach. We climbed, with him, the mild peaks that surrounded us; we rode, with him, on rough farm wagons, to picnic, at all the flumes and glens of the East Fork of the Ausable; and, most immoral of our pastimes, we went with him, to church on Sunday. Our church was a birch grove; and he and I shared, for the singing of hymns, one hymn-book. I knew, quite well, that his calm and contemplative mind did not regard the statements, as to cosmogeny and history, or the theories as to the future, set forth in those hymns, as either accurate or important. But I never ventured to hint that I suspected him of any lack of orthodoxy. . . . Nor did I ever in all the walks and talks that I had with the great Gibbs have any talk with him that was any more intelligent than the talk I had with other educated men. We, younger people, took pleasure in being with him; but we had no suspicion at that time, that he was one of the greatest philosophers; that he was in the class of Newton and Darwin, and greater than Plato."

It must be remembered that these recollections are all those of older persons recalling the days of their youth, and as such are necessarily colored by their knowledge of intervening events. Nevertheless the impression they convey is substantiated by more contemporary accounts. Thus Hastings, who was pupil or colleague through all of Gibbs' active career from these days of the seventies on, says in his biographical memoir: [2]

To me he always appeared . . . perfectly friendly and approachable, ready to talk on any subject, and always equable, he exhibited a flattering welcome to every friend. Effusiveness was as foreign to his nature as insincerity, but cordiality was never wanting. He laughed readily and possessed a lively sense of humor. . . .

No qualities of Professor Gibbs impressed his sympathetic associates and his pupils more than his serenity and apparent unconsciousness of his intellectual eminence. Thoroughly characteristic and delightful is the remark which he once made to an intimate friend concerning his abilities as a mathematician. He said, with perfect simplicity and candor, "If I have had any success in mathematical physics, it is, I think, because I have been able to dodge mathematical difficulties."

Such was the man as he appeared to those who knew him at the opening of his period of great scientific accomplishment, and indeed as he impressed his friends throughout his life. It is well to keep in mind this simple, kindly, happy nature as the background for his scientific achievement. He gave at no time any hint that what he was accomplishing demanded that special privileges be accorded him or that its importance could override the obligations of everyday human relationships. In the inner life of his mind wherein resided his essential happiness he worked and studied on matters that seemed to him of interest or importance, regardless of the opinions or even of the understanding of others. To command his attention a matter must be such as would fill in a gap in previous knowledge or extend it in a new direction. The question as to whether others had the same appreciation of a problem was of little importance to him, and he had none of the advocate's or missionary's zeal to draw attention to his own estimate of the significance of the problem on which he might be engaged, although he did not neglect the customary distribution of reprints of his published papers. Thus, making no demands on other minds either to accept his ideas or to appropriate theirs, he achieved an impersonality in his relationships that to those not knowing him well might seem a contradiction of the warm, friendly nature shown in the recollections quoted above. But the only contradiction was, in the

2. "Josiah Willard Gibbs," pp. 389–390.

words of Hastings, that "He seemed to have absolutely boundless resources within his own mind which would meet every want whether for work or for pastime"; and while this may set him apart in a niche of his own as a scientific worker, the only effect it had on his human relationships was to make him content with a smaller circle of acquaintances and a narrower range of diversions than satisfy most.

What were Willard Gibbs' reactions on his return from the more sophisticated intellectual atmosphere in which he had been living for the past three years? What problems first engaged his attention? There is little to guide us in finding answers to these questions. We can be confident, however, that the period between his return and his appointment to a professorship must have been for him one of a synthesis of the European outlook with that of the more utilitarian and engineering slants of his earlier training. In this period he had no routine appointments or duties outside of the family life, and it is easy and probably correct to visualize him as spending much time in talking over his impressions with his older teachers and friends, and in reflection on the over-all picture of the state of knowledge of physical science which he had attained.

It is probable that one of the first problems upon which he worked at this time, although there is no written record by which it can be dated precisely, was that of the improvement of the Watt conical pendulum governor. We have seen that his attention had been called to the problem during his stay in Berlin; and as the model [3] which was constructed to embody his improvement was probably made about the year 1872, it is reasonable to suppose that the work on its development was one of the earliest to enlist his interest at this time. He had probably observed as far back as his graduate student days that the operation of the device in practice was beset with the disadvantages of sluggishness and a tendency to overcorrect for the changes in speed it was supposed to control. He must also have been familiar, from observation of current practices or from the reference given in his Berlin notebook, with the methods previously employed to minimize these defects.

I have discussed these matters and Gibbs' solution of the problem in some detail elsewhere, and the discussion need not be repeated

3. The model is on permanent exhibition in the Sloane Physics Laboratory.

here.[4] It will suffice to point out that his method of attack was neither empirical nor along lines followed by his predecessors—who had sought to cause the Watt conical pendulum to approximate the action of the parabolic pendulum of Huygens—but through a generalization of the simple conical pendulum by the addition of a third torque to the two inherent in the device. The equilibrium condition which then results immediately suggests practical means for improving the performance of the original form of the governor. These yield increased sensitivity and provide simple methods both for control of the stability and for a higher normal speed of operation. But from the standpoint of the development of Gibbs' thought, the main interest in this invention lies in the method by which he arrived at the result. This shows a close parallel to one which he used later with such success in his thermodynamic studies. For, like the equilibrium of the simple Watt governor which depends on the balancing of two torques—one due to the weight of the "balls" and the other to their rotation—the thermodynamic equilibrium of a simple substance depends on the balance of two entities: the heat energy supplied to and the work energy performed by the substance. In the first case the generalization consisted in the addition of a third torque; in the second, in the addition of energy terms proportional to the masses of other components. In the first case the altered equilibrium condition suggested certain mechanical improvements in the device; in the second it yielded the basis for the determination of heterogeneous, i.e., of all physicochemical equilibria. This latter was of course by far the greater and more important achievement; but the anticipation in the former of the method that ultimately was to bring Gibbs so large a measure of fame lends to the humble governor problem a scientific significance in addition to such engineering interest as it may possess.

What other problems may have engaged his attention at this time or whether he participated in any of the discussions on educational matters then rife in New Haven cannot be determined from

4. See *The Early Work of Willard Gibbs*. Since the appearance of this discussion there has been found a fragment consisting of a single page of equations in Gibbs' handwriting, which gives the first step toward the solution of the problem. The fundamental equation set up is the same as that I have given on p. 73 of *The Early Work of Willard Gibbs*, but the analysis in the fragment is too incomplete to make it suitable for reproduction.

any existing evidence. We do know however that the period immediately following Gibbs' return from abroad was one of much ferment in the world of higher education on both sides of the Atlantic. In England this was evidenced by the legalized relaxation of the medieval restrictions on the academic structures of Oxford and Cambridge; by the establishment at Cambridge of provision for laboratory instruction in physics (the first in England) through the erection of the Cavendish Laboratory and the appointment of James Clerk Maxwell as its director in 1871; and by the growth in the importance and influence of the "provincial" universities, such as those at Manchester and Leeds, with their emphasis on science and engineering, which were enjoying largely increased endowments flowing from the industries profiting from the applications of science.

In America the rigid classical curriculum, which had come down from Colonial days and received its first challenge and tentative expansion with the institution of the Department of Philosophy and the Arts at Yale in 1847, and which had suffered further blows from the subsequent establishment of separate scientific departments there and elsewhere, was beginning to show signs of strain in the colleges of liberal arts. At Harvard the break came with the election of Charles William Eliot as president in 1869 and the inauguration of the "elective" system. No such sharp break occurred at Yale; but the reorganization of the Corporation by the inclusion of alumni in the body, the imminent retirement of President Woolsey after a service of a quarter of a century, and the probability that his successor would be the very conservative Professor Porter led to an effort by some of the more forward-looking members of the faculty to steer the university into more liberal paths. A program for accomplishing this was prepared by a committee [5] and presented by the faculty to the Corporation on July 11, 1871, in a pamphlet entitled *The Needs of the University*.

This pamphlet, intended also to be used in an appeal for funds with which to implement its proposals, went in great detail into the requirements of the library and the necessity for new professorships. It recommended a substantial increase in library appropriations and the establishment of new chairs in Latin, rhetoric, Eng-

5. The committee consisted of Leonard Bacon, James D. Dana, George E. Day, Henry C. Kingsley, Stephen G. Hubbard, William D. Whitney, Hubert A. Newton, Daniel C. Gilman, John F. Weir, and Addison Van Name.

lish literature, French, German, and physics. In regard to the latter it was remarked: "But a field so vast as that of Physics, and one in which the onward march of science is so astonishingly rapid, demands the labors of a professor who shall be permanently and exclusively devoted to it." The whole program involved an increase in endowment funds, in addition to that proposed for new buildings, of more than a million dollars—a very large sum for those days. No specific names of candidates for the suggested new chairs were submitted, but the following paragraph, dated July 13, 1871, occurs in the minutes of the Corporation for a continuation of the meeting at which the pamphlet had been received: "Mr. Josiah Willard Gibbs, of New Haven, was appointed Professor of Mathematical Physics, without salary, in the Department of Philosophy and the Arts."

Aside from its obvious connection with the plan for university expansion, this appointment was unusual in that no formal recommendation for it can be found in the records. In view of the fact that no undergraduate instruction by the appointee was contemplated, it is understandable that no recommendation from the college or the scientific school faculties should have been made. Further, owing to the very loose organization of graduate instruction at the time, it is not particularly surprising that no formal recommendation from the Department of Philosophy and the Arts is to be found. But that Gibbs must, however, have had substantial backing even for an appointment carrying no financial obligation for the Corporation goes without saying.

What this backing was can only be conjectured at the present time. Gibbs had no record of publications on which a judgment of his quality could be based. The only contribution of his that had appeared in print up to that time was the patent specification for the railway car brake, and that could hardly be considered as evidence of competence in mathematical physics. Thus his backing, whether from the committee which prepared the plan of expansion or from the faculties as a whole, must have had its basis in the personal knowledge and confidence of those who had been his teachers and had become his friends. Of those then active on the faculties and in the committee who had themselves the background and the vision either to propose such an innovation as a chair in mathematical physics or to discern that Gibbs was qualified for such a post, one name suggests itself as the most probable prime mover

among his backers. This is that of Hubert Anson Newton. He almost alone in the mathematical faculty had a background of research, he had had the longest experience of anyone as Gibbs'
teacher, and the two men were sympathetic in their ideals and am-
bitions. This is not to say that there were not other backers; Gibbs
seems to have always had the faculty of impressing others with a
sense of his intellectual powers. Thus while it seems probable that
the proposals for the new chair with Gibbs as its incumbent had
quite general if unofficial faculty support, the chief credit for both
the suggestion of creating this unprecedented post and the nomination of Gibbs to hold it is most likely Newton's. There is of course
no way of proving this now, but as his international prestige due to
his work on meteors was very high, his support of the new chair
and of Gibbs must have carried great weight with the university
authorities.

At the same time Gibbs' ability and willingness to serve without
salary were undoubtedly potent factors with the Corporation in
making the appointment. It must be remembered that at that
time the idea of the university as contrasted with that of the college was rather nebulous; the whole proposal before the Corporation involved a formidable financial program; and the main worry
of that body was still to find the funds for teaching undergraduates.
So the opportunity to acquire possible future credit for the institution in exchange for the prestige accompanying a Yale chair, and
with no added financial burden, must have had considerable appeal. As a matter of college finance, the number of graduate students likely to be attracted by a virtually unknown professor was
so small that any salary at all would seem prohibitive in the light
of the ratio of students per teacher which then applied to undergraduate instruction. In fact, for the six of the first nine years of his
service for which records are available it appears that Gibbs had a
total of only seven students, and not more than two in any one
year. In four of these same years he received what the treasurer's
records call "small payments" or "fees." These probably represent
a proportionate fraction of the total fees paid by his students for
their graduate instruction. From the same records it appears that
he actually, in this first period of his research activity, lectured not
more than four times a week in any year. So at a time when the

idea of "research professorships" was not yet born, it is understandable that the Corporation should have acted as it did.[6]

But whatever one may think of this rather haphazard and, from the side of the college, undignified manner of establishing a chair without endowment, from Gibbs' standpoint the appointment offered an opportunity of which he was not slow to take advantage. After all, his income was sufficient to permit him to contribute his share to the expenses of the joint household in which he lived, and beyond that he was indifferent to all but one of the things which money can buy, namely, the opportunity to pursue the work in which he was interested. It was precisely this which the college appointment gave him. He could teach as much or as little as he chose, lecture on whatever subjects interested him, and above all command the leisure for the study and research for which all his training had been a preparation.

Something of what this opportunity meant to Gibbs may be judged from the fact that when some two years later he was invited to consider moving to Bowdoin College on a salaried appointment, he was apparently not seriously tempted. As he never made public the fact of this invitation, the following letter, only recently found among his papers, is worthy of record.

Bowdoin College
Brunswick Maine
Nov 12 1873

Professor J. W. Gibbs, Ph.D.
My dear Sir;

Would you entertain the offer of the chair of Mathematics, or of Physics, at this College?

Our salaries are just at this time low, but we expect to have them raised to about $2000; but perhaps it would be safe to estimate them at $1800, in considerating the actual situation now.

If you can at all entertain the proposition I would be glad to communicate with you further.

I am with high regard,

Yours truly
Joshua L. Chamberlain
President

6. The facts given in the text have been obtained from the annual reports to the Corporation by its secretary, Professor Franklin B. Dexter.

Such an offer might well have tempted one in Gibbs' unremunerated position, even if only to use as a lever to better his position financially at Yale. But there is no evidence that the offer attracted him. It must be remembered that at the time he had just completed his second paper, in which, as we shall see later, he had obtained the first glimpse of the possibility of extending the principles of thermodynamics to the domain of chemistry. The lure of this vision and the greater opportunity for its exploitation in the larger freedom from routine teaching duties afforded by the Yale position, as compared with that in the Maine institution, apparently outweighed the matter of salary for him. Throughout his life financial considerations were always secondary with Gibbs. His mode of living was consistently shaped to the demands of those fundamental intellectual interests which constituted his real happiness.

V

Professor of Mathematical Physics:
Thermodynamics

W ITH his appointment as professor of mathematical physics, the record as to the results of Gibbs' reflections on physical matters which we have postulated becomes definite and factual. We have firsthand testimony from one of the pupils in his first graduate class which, in contrast with the larger and sometimes turbulent classes of his earlier experience with undergraduate instruction, consisted of but two in all, both mature men who had already chosen physics for a profession. They were Charles S. Hastings and Arthur W. Wright, the former of whom gives the following account of Gibbs' teaching in the first two years in the new position:

Professor Gibbs, during his first year in this newly established chair, had only two pupils, both now professors in Yale University and both members of the Academy. In the choice of work for this little class he was absolutely untrammeled either by precedent or by expressed preference of his pupils; hence the character of his teaching possesses a peculiar interest as an indication of the contemporary state of his scientific development which, perhaps, would be sought in vain elsewhere. The text of his choice was the Traité de Mécanique of Poisson, and the works most frequently quoted were those of Fresnel and Cauchy. His lectures were for a considerable period confined to an exposition of the theories of Fresnel concerning diffraction, polarization, and the generalized laws of reflection; but this was followed by a remarkably interesting general treatment of waves, which, in successive chapters, was applied to a discussion of various types, such as water waves and those of light at the boundary in cases of total reflection. Long after this period one of his pupils extorted from him a conditional promise that he would publish this work on waves in book form, and it is much to be regretted that he never found a convenient time to do so; but there is little doubt that the insuperable difficulties in the mechanical explanation of double refraction forced themselves upon his mind at this time and turned his attention in a direction which led him later to his powerful support of the electro-magnetic theory of light. Certain it is that at this period of 1871–2 Professor Gibbs showed his chief interest in the domain of physical optics, and that his inspirations from without were derived from the French school of philosophers rather than from the German.

In the following year, 1872–3, Professor Gibbs chose a little work by Clausius, on the potential theory, as the basis of his lectures, a fact which is worth recording because it indicates that he had become acquainted with the writings of a physicist whose work he was shortly to extend in so remarkable a manner; for it was in April and May of 1873 that he presented before the Connecticut Academy the first of the papers on the mechanics of heat which have established his eminence for all time; and the immediate object of the paper, entitled "Graphical Methods in the Thermodynamics of Fluids," was to exhibit the fruitfulness of the conception of entropy, introduced by Clausius.[1]

Some points in this account merit a little elaboration. Thus it would seem that Gibbs had not yet become acquainted with Maxwell's papers in which the electromagnetic theory of light had been introduced; and this, with the absence of any reference to them in the bibliographies of his Berlin notebook, makes it probable that his first knowledege of Maxwell's epoch-making hypothesis came from the *Treatise* which was published in 1873. At any rate it appears that until 1879—that is until after the completion of his great work in thermodynamics—his teaching was largely confined to the topics described by Hastings. The college catalogues of the time indicate that additional courses on capillarity and the theory of least squares were offered, but there is no evidence that they were actually given. In 1877 he did however give a course on electricity and magnetism based on Maxwell's treatise; and the fact that in 1879 he for the first time offered a course on vector analysis with applications to electricity and magnetism indicates that he must have given much thought and study to Maxwell's development of electrical theory in addition to that devoted to thermodynamics. Thus although it is probably true, as Hastings says, that Gibbs' chief interest was at first centered on physical op-

1. "Josiah Willard Gibbs," pp. 375–376.

tics, it is evident that that interest was soon supplanted by others—at least for the time being.

Hastings' observation as to Gibbs' acquaintance with Clausius' work would seem to be a legitimate inference from the practically simultaneous appearance of his first 1873 paper; at least if he had not then made the profound study of Clausius' work revealed by his later publications, he had acquired a clear and correct appreciation of the concept of entropy at a time when such distinguished physicists as Tait and Maxwell were quite muddled about the matter. Nevertheless I cannot avoid the feeling that the arousing of Gibbs' interest in thermodynamics is due at least as much to an interest in engineering applications of the subject as in its theoretical foundations. A hint to this effect is given by his contemporaneous interest in the problem of governing the speed of steam engines, and is further evidenced by the subject matter of his first paper, on which I will have more to say later. There is of course no question as to the ultimate submergence of his engineering by his theoretical interest, but it seems to me that his initial impulse to research in the field of thermodynamics owed much to the influence of his early engineering training.

Be that as it may, this period—from some time in 1871 or 1872, when he apparently began his serious studies in thermodynamics, to the completion of the monumental third paper early in 1878—was one of Gibbs' great periods of creative activity, perhaps the greatest of his career. The results are comprised in three papers [2] whose bulk in printed pages runs to something more than one third of his total published writings as they appear in his collected works.[3] But the importance of these first monographs lies not in their relative or absolute extent but, as Gibbs has said of Clausius'

2. "Graphical Methods in the Thermodynamics of Fluids," *Transactions of the Connecticut Academy*, 2 (1873), 309–342.

"A Method of Geometrical Representation of the Thermodynamic Properties of Substances by Means of Surfaces," *Trans. Conn. Acad.*, 2 (1873), 382–404.

"On the Equilibrium of Heterogeneous Substances," *Trans. Conn. Acad.*, 3 (1876), 108–248. (1878), 343–524.

3. *The Scientific Papers of J. Willard Gibbs* (New York, Longmans, Green, 1906), 2 vols. *The Collected Works of J. Willard Gibbs* (Longmans, Green, 1928; Yale University Press, 1948), 2 vols.

In each of these editions the paging of Vol. I is the same; the paging of Vol. II of *The Scientific Papers* is the same as that of Vol. II, Pt. 2 of the *Collected Works*.

work,[4] in the impress they have left on the thoughts of men. To gain an adequate appreciation of the reasons for the indelible impression this work has made on the history of physical science or to arrive at a just estimate of the genius of the author and of his place in the history of thermodynamics, it is necessary to have some knowledge of the fundamental concepts of that science. The history of thermodynamics has always seemed to me to be not only one of the most interesting but one of the most dramatic episodes to be found in the story of the intellectual progress of the human mind. Starting in an investigation·of a purely practical problem of engineering economics, it has grown into a body of doctrine of profound philosophical significance, with consequences which permeate the thinking of men on many subjects, from those with the most practical use to the problems of cosmology. Throughout its development it has had to struggle with misconceptions arising from imperfections in our apprehensions of the nature of heat and of the structure of matter. The men who have raised the edifice and who form a considerable part of Gibbs' intellectual ancestry have been men of interesting and most diverse character and experience and were drawn from many professions—the military, the engineering, and the medical as well as that of teaching. No other branch of physics except that of electricity has exerted so profound an influence on the thought of mankind or extended that influence over so vast a domain.

The science of thermodynamics originally comprised only what is implied in its etymology: the relations between heat and mechanical work. In the course of time, and in no small measure because of the work of Willard Gibbs, the meaning of the word has been broadened to embrace the whole field of the transformations of energy between all the forms in which it may be manifested—thermal, mechanical, electrical, chemical, or radiant. In its original restricted significance the development of the theory may be summarized in two distinct steps. The first was taken in 1824 by a young French military engineer, Nicolas Léonard Sadi Carnot.[5]

4. *Proceedings of the American Academy*, N.S., *16* (1889), 458–465. *Collected Works*, II, Pt. 2, 261–267.

5. *Réflexions sur la puissance motrice du feu et sur les machines propres à développer cette puissance*. This scion of a distinguished family whose members played notable parts in French history from the days of the Revolution to those of the Third Republic made

His objective was to determine how the greatest amount of mechanical work can be obtained from a given amount of heat. In the solution of this engineering problem he enriched science with two of its most fertile concepts and a method of reasoning which has become classic. In this essay is to be found the first recognition of the necessity of returning a body to its initial state in order to strike a true balance between the changes it may have undergone. In it also occurs the first formulation of the concept of *reversible* processes; that is, those in which an infinitesimal change in the external conditions to which a body is subject will cause a reversal of the direction of the process. With the aid of these new concepts he proceeded, in one of the most brilliant feats of the imagination in the history of science, to show that with a heat reservoir at a given temperature from which heat could be taken by a working substance, and with another reservoir at a lower temperature into which it could reject heat, the greatest possible amount of mechanical work can be obtained when all the processes undergone by the working substance are reversible. The argument runs, in brief, as follows: Suppose we have an engine whose working substance, e.g., steam, takes an amount of heat (H) from a hot reservoir (such as a steam boiler), does an amount of work (W) on an external load, rejects an amount of heat (h) to a cooler reservoir, and is then returned to its original condition, so that the process can be repeated indefinitely. If all these operations can be imagined to be performed *reversibly* the engine will, when the work (W) is done upon it in each cycle by an outside agency, run in the reverse direction, taking the heat (h) from the cooler and delivering the heat (H) to the hotter reservoir in each cycle. Thus if any engine (reversible or nonreversible) operating between the same two reservoirs can be supposed to be able to perform the same amount of work (W) on a smaller amount of heat than (H), i.e., can be more efficient, it could be made to drive the reversible engine backward; and since the combined engines would in each cycle of operation return to the hot reservoir a larger amount of heat than the driver takes from it, we would have heat continuously transferred from a cooler to a hotter body by a self-contained system receiving no

his sole yet supreme contribution to science when he was but 28 years of age and died when he was only 36.

external aid. As such a result is contrary to all experience, it must be concluded that no engine can be more efficient than a reversible engine when they both work through the same range of temperature; or alternatively, that the maximum amount of work from a given supply of heat is obtainable only by means of a reversible engine.

This conclusion is known as "Carnot's principle." It should be noted that the argument on which it is based is independent of the nature of the working substance or of the particular cycle of operations which it follows. The only things essential to the conclusion are first, the existence of *different* temperatures for the reservoirs; second, the reversible nature of the operations undergone by the working substance; and third, the denial of the possibility that heat can be transferred from a colder to a hotter body by any unaided self-acting contrivance. This third essential element of the argument is known as the "Second Law of Thermodynamics." Although inherent in the derivation of Carnot's principle, it was not specifically formulated by him as a law. Not until more than twenty-five years later did Clausius and William Thomson (Lord Kelvin) formulate it as one of the foundation stones of the science of thermodynamics. The two other essentials of Carnot's argument—the concept of reversibility and the consequence that mechanical work cannot be obtained from heat in the absence of the existence of a temperature difference—are also equally fundamental in the science.

But although Carnot must be regarded as the creator of the new science, he was unable to take the next step: the quantitative determination of the magnitude of the ideal efficiency. This was because of the confusion then existing in the scientific world as to the nature of heat. There is some evidence in the *Réflexions* itself, and still more in his posthumous papers published many years later by his brother, that Carnot was dubious as to the soundness of the then widely accepted "caloric" or materialistic theory of heat and was inclined toward the kinetic theory of its nature. However, the man who first took this second step, and through whom most physicists learned of Carnot's work, Benoit Pierre Emile Clapeyron,[6] was a firm adherent of the idea that heat was a material "fluid."

6. "Mémoire sur la puissance de la chaleur," *Journal de l'école polytechnique, 14* (1834), 170.

He put Carnot's principle in the mathematical form that the efficiency of a reversible engine was a function solely of the temperatures of the two reservoirs (Carnot's function), and proceeded to determine its value by the consideration of a particular reversible cycle applicable to the change of state of a substance (liquid to vapor or solid to liquid). Unfortunately, although his result was correct, in deriving his expression he assumed (as was natural on the caloric hypothesis) that the heat taken from the hot reservoir (H) was the same as that rejected to the cold reservoir (h), the work done being accomplished by the fall in temperature in a manner analogous to that done by a water wheel through the fall of the water because of the difference in height of the intake and the outflow. Now experimental evidence had been accumulating—from that furnished by the work of Benjamin Thomson (Count Rumford) and Sir Humphrey Davy just before 1800 to that of Robert Mayer and James Prescott Joule in the 1840's—that heat and mechanical work are simply two different manifestations of the same entity, that both are forms of energy; and that when one form is transformed into the other the ratio of the amounts so converted is in all cases the same. This statement is an expression of what is known as the First Law of Thermodynamics.

When heat energy is supplied to a body from without, it in general expands (doing work) and grows hotter (increasing its "internal" or "intrinsic" energy). Thus if these three forms of energy are expressed in the same unit and increases in each are reckoned as positive, by the first law for any transformation of energy in either direction the resulting change in intrinsic energy is the difference between the heat energy supplied the body and the work it performs. Where no heat energy is supplied the work is performed at the expense of the intrinsic energy and the stock of mechanical energy external and internal is unchanged or conserved. When a body is put through a cyclic process which returns it periodically to its initial state, there can be no change in its intrinsic energy and hence the net heat energy supplied must equal the work performed; that is, its whole energy in both forms is unchanged or conserved. Hence the first law may be regarded as an expression of the general principle of the "conservation of energy," valid for transformations between the two forms, heat and mechanical energy.

With the final triumph of the first law in the late 1840's, it became necessary to correct Clapeyron's mistaken derivation of the Carnot function. Instead of the relation assumed from the hydraulic analogy that the amounts of heat energy received and rejected by the working substance are equal, the first law requires that their difference be the thermal equivalent of the external work done, or $H - h = W$. On the basis of this relation Thomson showed (in 1848) that by choosing a series of heat reservoirs of uniformly descending temperatures and by supposing that reversible engines each doing the same amount of external work are operated between them in such a manner that the heat rejected by one becomes the heat received by the next in the series, we would ultimately arrive at a point where there would no longer remain any heat to be rejected. The temperature of this last reservoir would then be the lowest conceivable—the absolute zero of temperature. A scale of temperatures thus based on the amounts of work performed by such a series of reversible engines then leads to the reciprocal of the temperature of the hottest reservoir as the value of Carnot's function, and yields for the efficiency of a reversible engine the expression

$$\frac{Work\ done}{Heat\ received} = \frac{Heat\ received - Heat\ rejected}{Heat\ received}$$

$$= \frac{Temperature\ of\ reception - Temperature\ of\ rejection}{Temperature\ of\ reception}$$

The scale of temperature thus specified is variously called the "work," the "absolute," the "thermodynamic," or the "Kelvin" scale. In what follows a temperature is always to be understood as one measured on this scale whose "zero point" is some $273°$ below that of the centigrade or about $460°$ below that of the Fahrenheit scale.

Thus it was twenty-four years after the enunciation of Carnot's principle that it received its exact quantitative expression, and another two years before it can be said to have been placed upon its final firm foundation by Clausius' formulation of a precise statement of the second law. The further development of the fundamental theory consists in the *interpretation* of the equation just given and in the combination of the expressions for the two laws into a single equation. It was from the alternative form of the above expression for the efficiency of a reversible engine,

$$\frac{Heat\ rejected}{Temperature\ of\ rejection} = \frac{Heat\ received}{Temperature\ of\ reception}$$

that Clausius derived the concept of "entropy." This quantity is one of the characteristics specifying the state of a substance, as do its temperature or pressure, its volume or intrinsic energy. It may be defined as the ratio of the heat energy taken in or given out in reversible changes of the condition of a body to the absolute temperature at which the change takes place. Another definition is possibly more instructive. Thus since no actual engine can attain the efficiency of the ideal reversible engine, it follows that in all actual conversions of heat into mechanical energy there is necessarily incurred a waste of energy; and the change of entropy in such conversions may be taken as the measure of this unavoidable waste, or it may be defined as that entity which multiplied by the lowest available temperature gives the magnitude of the necessarily lost energy.

It is difficult to obtain a clear mental picture of entropy, mainly because we have no sensory response to it as we have to other characteristics such as temperature or volume. But it is one of the most useful concepts ever introduced into physics. It permits, for instance, a simplification of the statement of Carnot's principle as great as that resulting from the idea of "absolute" temperature. Thus, as can be seen from the above alternative expression of the principle, the result can be stated simply that for the system of the two reservoirs and the working substance the change in entropy vanishes; or in reversible cycles entropy is *conserved*. Another illustration of the simplification introduced by this concept lies in the conclusion derived by Clausius (and seen most clearly perhaps from the second of the above definitions) that in all nonreversible processes, that is in all natural changes, the entropy must *increase*. This result which he embodied in his statement of the second law, "Die Entropie der Welt strebt einem Maximum zu," together with the equally challenging form he gave to the first law, "Die Energie der Welt ist constant," was placed by Gibbs at the head of his great monograph. They fitly summarize the foundations upon which he built.

A final example of the usefulness of the idea of entropy is afforded by the compactness and simplicity it lends to the combination of the two laws of thermodynamics into what may be styled the "prime" fundamental equation of the science. For reversible processes where the work performed can be expressed as the product of the pressure by the resulting volume change, that is, for fluids (gases, vapors, and liquids) and for noncrystalline and unstrained solids, it reads,

Change in intrinsic energy = Change in heat energy
— Change in mechanical energy
= Temperature × Change in entropy
— Pressure × Change in volume.

This equation is fundamental, in the sense that if from experiment we know for any substance how the change in energy depends on the entropy and volume changes, then the equation suffices to determine all of its thermal and mechanical properties. The equation is of course valid only for bodies uniform in composition.[7]

This fundamental equation formed the starting point for Gibbs' development and extension of thermodynamics. In a sense it may be said to embody the whole of his indebtedness to his predecessors. No one had in the slightest degree anticipated the line of his further development of the subject. Prior to him no one had

7. It should perhaps be emphasized that it is only *changes* in the entropy of a body that can be determined experimentally. Thus the heat required to change one pound of water into steam at the boiling point under normal atmospheric pressure (i.e., at 459°.6 + 212° = 671°.6 absolute Fahrenheit degrees and 14.7 pounds per square inch pressure) is found to be 970.4 British Thermal Units, and hence the change in entropy is 970.4 ÷ 671.6 = 1.445, per pound. This is not however the total entropy of the steam at the boiling point; it is only the *change* in entropy in converting the water into steam at that temperature and pressure. In order to find the total entropy of the steam it would be necessary to add to the above value, first, the entropy change in converting solid H_2O at zero degrees absolute to solid ice at 491.6 F.(abs.); second, that necessary to convert the ice to water at that temperature; and third, that required to raise the water from 491°.6 to 671°.6 F. (abs.). As it is not possible to determine the first of these changes experimentally (absolute zero being an unattainable temperature), the total entropy of steam cannot be determined. This causes no inconvenience in the practical applications, as the entropy may be arbitrarily assigned the value zero at any temperature below the lowest of the useful range of temperatures, without affecting any of the necessary computations the engineer must perform.

realized that the equation could be generalized to include non-homogeneous bodies, or had seen that when so expanded it would hold the key to the great domain of chemical equilibrium. The story of how Gibbs was led step by step with inexorable logic to his great generalization and the completeness with which he explored its consequences and implications form a narrative almost unique in the history of science. "On the Equilibrium of Heterogeneous Substances" appeared upon the scientific horizon in the 1870's as unheralded as had Carnot's *Réflexions* in the 1820's; but whereas Carnot's work required that of Kelvin and Clausius to bring it to fruition, Gibbs' work forms a completed whole in whose framework the developments of the succeeding three-quarters of a century in the fields it covers appear for the most part as necessary and inevitable consequences. Like Sir Isaac Newton's *Principia,* this work of Willard Gibbs stands out in the history of man's intellectual progress as an imperishable monument to the power of abstract thought and logical reasoning.

In the first paper of his trilogy on thermodynamics Gibbs examined the possibilities of representing the properties of bodies, and the work and heat relations of various processes as expressed analytically in the prime equation, by means of diagrams in a plane. Up to the time of the appearance of this paper only a diagram using pressure and volume for the coordinates had been in use. With the skill in the use of geometrical methods which we have seen foreshadowed in his doctor's dissertation, and with that thoroughness in exploring all the avenues of a field manifested in his essay on the units of mechanics, he studied the advantages and disadvantages of using as coordinates other pairs of the five variables of the prime equation. Of the five new diagrams whose merits he discusses, three are of value only for rather limited engineering applications, for which analytical methods are on the whole more suitable, and have not come into use. Of the other two new diagrams discussed, the one using temperature and entropy as coordinates has had a wide use in engineering, although probably not as a direct result of its description in this paper but because of independent recognition of its merits at a later time by others. In this respect Gibbs' priority in calling attention to this diagram has suffered the same fate, as will be seen later, as some of his other thermodynamic discoveries.

The last of the new diagrams discussed in the paper—that using entropy and volume as coordinates—is in a different category from the pressure-volume or the temperature-entropy diagrams, in that in it areas are not linearly related to either heat or work, and both coordinates instead of but one are proportional to the amount of the substance present. Gibbs shows that this last feature permits the adequate representation of the properties of a body when it exists partly as solid, partly as liquid, and partly as vapor, and that this cannot be accomplished with the other diagrams. Thus for all problems involving the properties of bodies and where those of the conversion of heat to work are a secondary consideration, the entropy-volume diagram is the more perspicuous. In his study of this diagram is to be found the germ of his later development of the problem of the thermal equilibrium of bodies. In fact, his first discussion of stability and equilibrium occurs in the last three pages of this paper.

This first paper can be regarded as exhibiting the transition of Gibbs' interests from the applied to the purely scientific points of view. Starting with the object of generalizing the graphical methods more extensively used in applied than in theoretical science, he concludes with matters not at the time of engineering interest, which yielded him his first glimpse of a broad field not previously explored. While the subsequent influence of this paper has not been great, it is certain that its results were of moment in starting the author on his path of discovery, and as such still repay consideration.

The second paper of the trilogy, which appeared in the fall of the same year, forms a logical sequel to the first, extending its methods to the representation of the properties of a body by a surface in three dimensions. To the two coordinates of the entropy-volume representation of the first paper Gibbs added the third coordinate—the energy of the body. With this extension of the picture he found it possible to cover in greater generality the determination of the conditions of equilibrium for any body of invariable composition, and in particular to take account of those states of the body which are not homogeneous (i.e., those consisting of a mixture of more than one state), although still in equilibrium. It is impossible to describe this thermodynamic surface in detail without considerable prolixity and use of the notions and terms of higher geometry. However, the principal features—and those of the most significance for the later work—are capable of description in fairly simple terms. In the first place, it follows from the prime equation that the inclinations of a plane tangent to the surface at any point will indicate the temperature and pressure of the body in the state represented by the point. In the second place, the surface must be of such a form that if the tangent plane is rolled over it it will be in contact with the surface at one point or at two or three points simultaneously. The portions of the surface over which the plane can roll without touching it at more than one point yield the range of temperature and pressure through which the body can be varied and still remain in a single state—solid, liquid, or vapor. Those portions of the surface over which the plane can roll with two points simultaneously in contact represent the range of the variables through which the body can exist in two states at the same time, in contact and in equilibrium—solid and liquid, liquid and vapor, or solid and vapor. Where the rolling plane comes to touch the surface at three points it becomes fixed, and the three points define a plane triangle every point of which represents some mixture of the three states at the same temperature and pressure.

Third, by defining the concept of a surface of minimum or *dissipated* energy as that surface made up of the envelope of all the positions which can be assumed by the rolling tangent plane, Gibbs was enabled to express the equilibrium of any point on the thermodynamic surface by means of its position with respect to the surface of dissipated energy. If the point lies above that surface, the equilibrium is stable; if it lies on that surface, it is in neutral equilibrium; if it lies below that surface, its equilibrium is essentially unstable. Thus the surface of dissipated energy represents the limit for the stable existence of a substance when the temperature and pressure are varied.

These are the principal though by no means all the results of the second paper. By means of this method of approach to the problem of equilibrium, many questions as to the behavior of bodies which, as Maxwell [8] said, had seemed almost impossible of solution, received simple and direct answers. Maxwell's appreciation of the importance of this contribution of Gibbs' was such that he constructed a model of the thermodynamic surface for water,[9] a plaster cast of which he presented to Gibbs. Photographs of four aspects of this model (which is on permanent exhibition at the Sloane Physics Laboratory in New Haven) are shown in the plate facing page 86. In the fourth edition of his textbook, *Theory of Heat,* Maxwell also devoted some thirteen pages to a description of the surface and an account of some of the problems which can be solved with its aid. Recognition of the importance of his work by this distinguished physicist was the first mark of public appreciation that Gibbs received, and was undoubtedly responsible for several of the other early tributes which followed.

But from the standpoint of Gibbs' later development the most important point in this second paper is contained in its final footnote. Here is shown his first recognition of the fact that the results obtained in the paper were valid even if the substance for which the model was formed was not homogeneous in nature; that for a body made up of heterogeneous substances a surface of dissipated energy could be constructed yielding entirely similar criteria of stability and equilibrium. Here is to be found the maturing of that germ seen in his study of the entropy-volume diagram of the first paper. Here we see becoming clear before his eyes the vision that led him on to the exploration of the whole domain of chemical equilibrium.

It is significant of the appreciation that Gibbs himself had of the importance and complexity of field opening before him that he abandoned the purely geometrical approach which hitherto had served so well. In the coming developments he was faced with

8. In a lecture before the Chemical Society of London.

9. The Reverend Alexander Freeman, at that time a student of Maxwell and also a fellow and junior bursar at St. John's College, Cambridge, in a letter to Gibbs requesting reprints of the first two papers, tells of the making of the model. The letter is dated February 18, 1875, and is preserved in a bound volume of the Gibbs scientific correspondence assembled by Addison Van Name and now deposited in the Yale library. As I shall have occasion to refer to letters in this volume rather frequently, it will be designated as "Scientific Correspondence." A catalogue of these letters will be found in Appendix III.

the problem of portraying the relations between not five but an indefinite number of quantities; instead of dealing with two, he had to take into account two plus a number of independent variables as great as the number of components in the heterogeneous mixture to be considered.

Thus it is that the great third paper of the trilogy on thermodynamics, "On the Equilibrium of Heterogeneous Substances," is almost entirely analytical in form. Starting with the two laws of thermodynamics as stated by Clausius, Gibbs first gives a rigorous derivation of the general mathematical conditions of equilibrium and stability to which they lead. He then proceeds methodically to the discussion of the necessary modifications of the prime equation and the particular forms the equilibrium conditions take on when there is brought into the picture, first, the presence of matter of different kinds and states; second, the presence of gravitational forces; third, the effects of a state of strain in the solids which may be present; fourth, the effects of surface tensions in the bounding surfaces between various portions; and fifth, the effects of electrical forces. Each one of these five divisions of the work contains results which have had a profound influence in the formation of the science of physical chemistry, but it is undoubtedly the first that is of the greatest importance. The stroke of genius by which Gibbs showed how the prime equation must be modified to take account of the presence of components differing in their nature furnished the key for all that followed. And this key, like all the other great ideas which have given a new direction to men's thinking—like Newton's idea of universal gravitation, Carnot's of a reversible engine, Maxwell's that all electric circuits must be *closed* circuits—is an essentially simple one and not difficult to understand.

What this idea was may be seen by considering an ideal experiment. Suppose we have a large, rigid, closed tank with walls made of a material which will not conduct heat, and filled with a solution of several salts in water, all at a given temperature and pressure. Further imagine that somewhere inside there is a box completely enclosing a homogeneous portion of the fluid, and that the walls of the box are of negligible weight and made of a material which is elastic and a perfect conductor for heat but will not permit the passage of any of the fluid. Then suppose the condition of the fluid in the tank to be slightly altered, say by a change in its temperature at some point, so small that the average temperature of the fluid is not sensibly affected. What can happen to the energy in the portion of the fluid in our imaginary box? Obviously heat may enter or leave it and the walls may buckle in or out, changing its volume. This results in a change in its energy which may be computed from the prime equation since all of the conditions under which that equation is valid are fulfilled in the experiment. From that equation then, the change in energy in the box is given in terms of the two independent variables, entropy and volume; its temperature by the change in energy per unit change in entropy if the volume had been held constant; and the pressure by the change in energy per unit change in volume if the entropy had remained constant.

Now suppose that the imaginary box is constructed with walls which in addition to being elastic and thermally conducting are also porous, so that the solution can pass freely through the pores in either direction—from inside out or from outside in. Then if the condition of the fluid is slightly altered as before, the change in energy in the box will depend not only on the heat which may enter or leave and the volume change due to the buckling of the walls but also on the masses of the components of the fluid going through the pores. Thus this energy change cannot be computed by the prime equation as it stands. It must be altered by the addition of as many energy terms as there are components of the fluid passing through the walls. If there are n such components, the generalized prime equation will express the change in energy in terms of $n + 2$ independent variables. Each of the added energy terms, in analogy to those in the prime equation, Gibbs expresses as the product of two factors, one an intensity and the other an extension factor. Thus just as the heat term is expressed as the product of temperature and the change in entropy, and the work term as the product of pressure and the change in volume, so an energy term due to the added mass of any component was expressed as the product of what Gibbs termed a "potential" and the change in mass. Hence his generalized prime equation reads:

Change in energy = Temperature × change in Entropy
            — Pressure × change in Volume
            + Potential × change in Mass (1st comp.)
            + Potential × change in Mass (2nd comp.)
            + -------------------------------------
            + Potential × change in Mass (nth comp.).

This equation embodies Gibbs' great contribution to thermo-dynamics and marks the birth of the theory of chemical equi-librium. It is a fundamental equation for a heterogeneous system in the same sense that the prime equation is for a homogeneous body. From it can be deduced all the thermal, mechanical, and chemical properties of a complex system by the same procedures that the thermal and mechanical properties of a simple body of invariable composition are derived from the prime equation. The important new concept introduced by Gibbs, which for definite-ness we will call the "chemical potential," is defined from the equation as being the change in energy per unit change in the mass of any component which would occur if the entropy, the vol-ume, and the masses of the other components remained un-changed. The importance of this concept lies in the fact that it plays the same role for chemical that temperature and pressure do for thermal and mechanical conditions of equilibrium. Chemi-cal equilibrium in a heterogeneous mixture is determined by the equality of the values of the chemical potentials for the separate components, just as the thermal and mechanical equilibrium is given by the equality of temperature and pressure throughout the mixture.

Thus the possibility of finding expressions from which the chemical potential can be calculated becomes a matter of great importance. Gibbs approached this problem, together with that of finding more convenient methods of expressing the conditions of equilibrium and stability, by developing other fundamental equations employing other independent variables. This led to the introduction of the famous ψ, χ, and ζ functions, which under various and sometimes conflicting names have found extensive use in several branches of physical chemistry and must be considered as contributions of importance second only to the concept of the chemical potential. In addition to these better-known fundamental equations, Gibbs developed another—a fifth [10]—which has been found to be one of the most fertile of his contributions in ever-increasing and widening fields of application, although its importance was not as immediately recognized as in the case of the others. This equation expresses the pressure in a heterogeneous mixture in terms of temperature, the chemical potentials and densities of the components, and the entropy per unit volume. Not only did Gibbs base on this equation his derivation of the celebrated "phase rule" but from it he obtained an important integrated expression for the chemical potentials of the components in a mixture. The limitations of experimental knowledge at the time were such that he could only evaluate this expression in the case of an "ideal" gas mixture and for that of the dissolved substance in very dilute solutions, although he makes it plain that it might have a much wider validity. That he was correct in this expectation has since been amply proven, and it is now recognized that Gibbs' fifth fundamental equation leads simply and directly not only to the conditions for coexistent phases but also to van't Hoff's law of osmotic pressure, to the effects of added substances on the melting and boiling points of solutions, and indeed to the whole modern theory of solution. The importance which Gibbs himself attached to this one of his developments is indicated by the fact that the meager notes which he left for additional chapters of the "Equilibrium of Heterogeneous Substances" are almost wholly concerned with matters stemming from this fifth fundamental equation.

In the last few paragraphs I have attempted to give an idea of the basically new concepts introduced by Gibbs. But it would be impossible to set down in any reasonable compass an adequate account of the influence of these new concepts as developed in the five divisions of his great monograph. Some idea of its extent and variety may perhaps be gathered from the fact that in 1936—sixty years after the appearance of the first part of the "Equilibrium of Heterogeneous Substances"—a *Commentary* [11]

10. Equation 98, *Collected Works*, I, 88.
11. F. G. Donnan and A. Haas, eds., *A Commentary on the Scientific Writings of J. Willard Gibbs* (New Haven, Yale University Press, 1936), 2 vols.

was published under the auspices of Yale University which ran to over thirteen hundred pages, of which some eight hundred are devoted to the "Equilibrium" monograph. In these pages eleven well-known mathematicians, physicists, and chemists have contributed critiques and appraisals of Gibbs' accomplishment in thermodynamics and have traced its influence in the later development of both pure and applied science. While these contributions are by no means exhaustive as to all of the applications that have been made of Gibbsian thermodynamics—scant attention being given to the industrial applications—nevertheless they form the best survey which has yet appeared of the astounding scope of the influence of Gibbs' great monograph.

It is possible to mention here only the more significant of these developments. The most publicized of both the theoretical and the industrial and manufacturing applications are those which have followed in the train of the phase rule. This celebrated law, which gives for any mixture the relation which must hold between the number of components, the number of coexistent phases, and the number of possible variations of phase [12] that can take place, has found innumerable applications in metallurgy, mineralogy, and petrology as well as in theoretical chemistry. It has elucidated the problem of the formation of the oceanic salt deposits such as those at Stassfurt; it has been invoked to explain certain phenomena of volcanology; it has furnished the guide to the production of new alloys and to the explanation of the effects of heat treatment on the properties of metals; it has unraveled the constitution of portland cement and standardized its method of production; it has made possible the interpretation of the complicated phenomena of solid solutions; and it has been invaluable in the manufacturing processes of the heavy industries. In view of this bewildering variety of applications it is interesting to note that the phase rule itself is a simple result of the routine process—automatic with any mathematician—of determining the "degrees of freedom" of a system from the difference between the number of variables required to specify the system and the

---

12. By a phase Gibbs means a portion of a mixture which is uniform in composition and physical state; by coexistent phases those which can exist together in thermodynamic equilibrium.

number of relations necessary to express the conditions to which it may be subject. That the simple relation thus obtained should have had such a large effect on the development of a science is a striking example of the difficulty of foreseeing what results in pure science are going to be most valuable in its applications. I have no doubt that Gibbs himself was surprised at the magnitude and diversity of the developments that stemmed from the phase rule even during his lifetime when such application had scarcely more than begun to appear.

Of equally great theoretical and industrial importance have been the applications of Gibbs' contributions to electrochemical theory. This development, which like that of the phase rule occupies but a few pages of the monograph, corrected the misapprehensions which had previously existed as to the relations holding between the voltage developed and the heat changes occurring when an electrical current passes through an electrolyte. Gibbs obtained the correct result by a simple and comprehensive extension of the principles of equilibrium previously derived, so that they would include the transport of ionic charges through the solution. His equations have yielded a fertile method for the determination of chemical potentials in terms of the electromotive force of reversible electrolytic cells—one which has profoundly affected the development of physical chemistry. They have been a potent factor in raising the industrial processes of electrolytic separation and synthesis from the realm of empiricism to that of an art governed by law, and thus have had a part in the expansion of the electrochemical industry to its present vast proportions.

So great has been the influence of these results on our civilization that to many they would seem to comprehend the most important of Gibbs' achievements in thermodynamics. It is true that the developments outlined above are those which have most affected our mode of living, and their monuments—our concrete highways, our purer and cheaper materials, and the lighter, stronger structures and tools which have resulted in so many of our "modern improvements"—are easily perceived by all. But in the final analysis the greater achievement was in the methods of *thought* applicable to all problems of equilibrium, which we owe to Gibbs. These are the heritage of greatest value to the race which Gibbs has left. And their results in the explanations they afford of the phenomena of phase equilibrium, of electrolytic processes, of surface tension and capillarity, of solution, of catalytic action, of gaseous mixtures and diffusion, as well as the insight they give into the problems of the molecular constitution of bodies, are monuments more enduring than concrete or alloy steels.

From this point of view one of the most striking aspects of the Gibbsian thermodynamic methods is the simple and natural manner in which they apply to the discoveries and problems that have arisen since his death, and of which consequently he himself could have had no inkling. Such discoveries as that embodied in the Nernst heat theorem (or the third law of thermodynamics as it is sometimes called) and such problems as those connected with the specific heat of solids, where the reconciliation of theory with experiment has involved invoking the revolutionary "quantum" idea of a discrete structure for energy as well as for matter, have for the most part merely yielded evaluations of the undetermined integration constants in the fundamental equations of Gibbs; or else Gibbs' equations are found to give the correct results when for the expression for the partition of energy derived from the classical kinetic theory there is substituted that required by the quantum hypothesis. The fundamental equations and the conditions of equilibrium have required no alteration or amendment.[13]

A still more striking example of the power of Gibbs' thought to embrace developments beyond the horizons of his time is to be found in his discussion of the diffusion of gases. Here (in 1876) he came to the conclusion, by an argument based on the result that the increase in entropy in gaseous diffusion is independent of the nature of the gas, that a decrease in entropy is not impossible but only highly improbable. Or, in his own words, "the impossibility of an uncompensated decrease of entropy seems to be reduced to improbability."[14] This often-quoted prevision of the limitations of the second law is so closely in accord with the most modern ideas on the subject, corroborated as these have recently

13. For a detailed account of these matters see Paul S. Epstein, "Article O," *A Commentary*, Vol. II.

14. *Collected Works*, I, 167.

been by the finding of actual cases in which entropy really does decrease,[15] that it has been stated that Gibbs' 1876 formulation still holds as the best expression of the facts.[16] The concept of a basis in *probability*, thus foreshadowed, somewhat mitigates the otherwise rather gloomy philosophy embodied in the doctrine of the increase of entropy. This envisions an ultimate state of nirvana for the universe, in which although possessing the same amount of energy it has none of it available for useful work. Together with the modern speculations based on the facts of radioactivity both natural and artificial and on the hypothesis of the convertibility of energy into mass, it has profoundly modified our ideas of the cosmos, and that in a direction away from the almost Calvinistic determinism so prevalent in the scientific thinking of the nineteenth century. Gibbs' contribution to this modern viewpoint was further elaborated in his *Statistical Mechanics*, as we shall see later; but his early recognition of the true significance of the second law is a tribute to the acuteness of his perceptions and the accuracy of his thinking, which is no small part of his title to fame.

Finally, it should be pointed out that it is probable not all the implications of the ideas and methods embodied in the monograph "On the Equilibrium of Heterogeneous Substances" have been as yet exploited. As a single instance, it would seem that Gibbs' conclusions as to the possibility of the formation of previously nonexistent phases and a following up of the methods he developed to explain the phenomena of surface tension and capillarity may have important consequences, as yet imperfectly explored, for the biological sciences. Prediction is a risky business, and no one can discount in advance the effects of new discoveries on the course of scientific progress, but where the master key furnished by Gibbs has opened so many doors (including some to which separate individual keys exist and others to which none had been discovered), it would seem fairly safe to believe that not all of the doors it is capable of opening have yet been found.

When we survey this monumental work of Gibbs, which in its penetrating physical intuition, its profound philosophical develop-

15. In the phenomena of the "Brownian" movements and of the "opalescence in the critical state" of a gas.
16. Epstein, *A Commentary*, II, 112.

ment, and its exhaustive comprehensiveness has few counterparts in the realm of physical science, and realize that it came from an environment which furnished no precedent for work of this nature, we begin to appreciate that only a character like Willard Gibbs' could have produced it. It exhibits detachment, intellectual independence communing with the inner essence of things rather than with personalities, and devotion to an austere, rigorous method. A genius that required stimulus from outside—whether from the laboratory, from the pressures of life, or from other minds—could scarcely have achieved it. A simple, contemplative, serene nature undistracted by personal ambition and unconcerned with rewards, such as we have seen was Gibbs', was the only soil from which it could have sprung. There is no finer example of the revelation of character in scientific writing or of scientific achievement conditioned by personality, than is to be found in this great monograph.

Gibbs' attitude toward his discoveries is also illuminating as to his character. This was, as I observed it in later years, always purely objective. In discussions on thermodynamic problems in the classroom or privately he never differentiated between his own contributions and those of others. Both were facts of greater or less bearing on the particular point then at issue, and to one not conversant with their history no hint would be given that he personally had had anything to do with their establishment. He would, for instance, stress the importance of the concept of the chemical potential with the same impersonality that he did that of entropy. With the exception of the preparation of an abstract of the third paper,[17] he made no effort to "sell" his discoveries (aside from the usual distribution of reprints of his papers) or to popularize the results. He was so confident of their rightness and ability to stand on their own feet that he was entirely content to let their value and importance be "discovered" by others. The fact that *he* had made a discovery was to him an irrelevant matter; the important thing was the truth established.

17. *American Journal of Science*, ser. 3, Vol. *16* (December, 1878).

VI

Recognition

THE publication by the Connecticut Academy of Gibbs' three thermodynamic papers and particularly of the third was in itself something of a tribute to the author. For the academy had no publication funds and all of its financial support came from membership dues which, at $5.00 a year with a list of some one hundred names, were entirely inadequate for the costs involved in the composition of such an extensive and mathematical paper as "On the Equilibrium of Heterogeneous Substances," which, moreover, none of the publication committee professed to understand! The president of the academy at that time was the zoologist Addison E. Verrill. He has told [1] of taking up a subscription among the faculty and businessmen of New Haven to defray the expense of publication of the monograph. Verrill states that Professors Loomis and Newton of the mathematical faculty, who were also on the publication committee, both said they did not understand Gibbs' papers, and that one of the two said that no man who ever lived except Maxwell could, and he was dead! While it is probable that Professor Loomis might have made some such remark at some time, it is plain that Professor Verrill's memory was at fault as to its having been made on this occasion, since Maxwell was *not* then dead.[2] But it is nevertheless understandable that a work containing so much that was absolutely new to science and clothed in such a rigorous and mathematical form should have been caviar to Gibbs' colleagues. Thus the decision of the committee to go ahead with the publication because, in the words of Verrill, "we knew Gibbs and took his contributions on faith," was a recognition which must have been

1. *Science* (January 9, 1925).
2. Maxwell died November 5, 1879.

as pleasing to the author as it was fortunate for the world of science.

It is true that at that time there were very few either in this country or abroad who were capable of understanding or appreciating Gibbs' work. It broke new ground and founded a new science which required for its comprehension either a physicist with mathematical and chemical leanings or a chemist with some knowledge of mathematics and physics. Neither of these combinations of skills was as common then as today. Scientific training tended to be more strictly compartmentalized than it has since become, and in this new borderline science there were few workers with the background necessary for the appreciation of these papers. Thus we should expect to find a considerable time lag before full recognition and acknowledgment of his achievement came to Gibbs. And in general this was the fact, although not to the extent sometimes affirmed.

As was pointed out in the last chapter, there was one man with the necessary background and vision, who almost immediately acclaimed Gibbs' work and whose recognition of its value called the attention of others to it. There is no record of Maxwell's having corresponded with Gibbs on this (or any other) occasion, although one would expect that his gift of the model of the thermodynamic surface would have been accompanied by a letter of transmittal. This was either lost in transit or later mislaid by Gibbs, as no such letter is included in the volume of his correspondence assembled by his brother-in-law nor did Gibbs ever allude to it as far as is known. But there is no lack of evidence in the letters of this time which have been preserved of Maxwell's influence in spreading the knowledge of Gibbs' work. Of the fifteen letters on thermodynamic matters in the "Scientific Correspondence" prior to 1882, twelve are from students or colleagues of Maxwell. There are five from Alexander Freeman, one of which was referred to in the last chapter. It is of interest to quote those from G. Pirie and M. M. Pattison Muir as affording the contrasting aspects of appreciation of different types of mind.

Queens' College
Cambridge
England
Jan 16th 1878

Dear Sir

I have the loan for a few days of your papers on the "Equilibrium of Heterogeneous Substances" from Prof. Clerk Maxwell. I should like very much to have a copy myself. It is not in our University Library.

I should be much obliged if you would present me with a copy or put me in the way of getting one.

I am

Yours very truly
G. Pirie
Math. Lecturer in Queens' College

Queens' College
Cambridge
Ap 10th 1878

Dear Sir

I have to thank you for your letter which I received in February. By means of it I found your paper on the Equilibrium of Heterogeneous Substances.

I congratulate you heartily on the introduction of the method of potentials.

I have applied it to saturated saline solutions and I find that it establishes the known law according to which the solubility depends on the pressure.

It also points to many conclusions for the verification of which experiments are wanting.

I am

Yours very truly
G. Pirie

GONVILLE & CAIUS COLLEGE
CAMBRIDGE

Feb. 14, '80

Prof. J. Willard Gibbs
    Yale College
Sir

I have ventured to send you copies of papers by Mr. Slater and myself on "Chemical Equilibrium," considered from a purely experimental and chemical point of view.

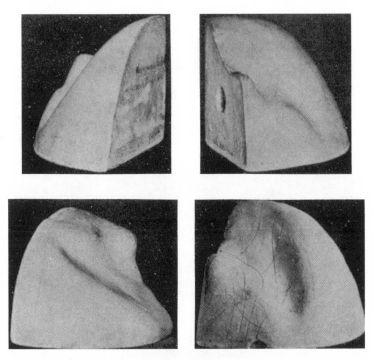

Thermodynamic Surface for Water
Photographed from Maxwell's model

Old Sloane Laboratory
Gibbs' office was on the second floor, right of the tower.

PORTRAIT IN THE GRADUATES CLUB

PORTRAIT TABLET IN THE SLOANE PHYSICS LABORATORY

I was told of your paper on the "Equilibrium of Heterogeneous Substances" but being no mathematician (as you will perceive by my papers) I did not venture to read it.—But recently I found Clerk Maxwell's translation of your paper into ordinary language, in the Science Conference at South Kensington (1876). Will you allow me as a chemist to thank you most sincerely for the very wonderful work you have done for us who, without the aid of mathematics, must needs grope so much in the dark?

Your results seem to throw light on very dark spots in chemical theory. I had been dimly groping after some connection between entropy and Chemical Equilibrium; but you have told me what my gropings meant.

Believe me Sir

Sincerely Yours

M. M. Pattison Muir

In these letters we see the cold clear vision of the mathematician penetrating to the heart of Gibbs' achievement and the warmer admiration of a nonmathematical chemist who grasps its significance almost as aid from another world. Both, it is to be observed, owe their acquaintance with Gibbs' work to Maxwell; and the same is true of the other English writers represented in the "Scientific Correspondence." Thus it is evident that, thanks to Maxwell, Gibbs received in England at least more immediate recognition than might have been expected from the abstract nature of his work.

Nor was he without prompt recognition elsewhere than in England. Thus we find under the date of October 9, 1878, a cordial letter from M. Massieu, who had partially anticipated Gibbs' ψ and ζ functions; and on March 3, 1879, one from his own countryman, Professor Henry A. Rowland of the Johns Hopkins University. The following quotation from the latter is of particular interest in view of the oft-repeated assertion that Gibbs was a prophet not without honor save in his own country:

I have also to thank you for sending me some time since your papers on Thermodynamics. I have been so busy this year that I have almost entirely neglected my correspondence and must beg your pardon for not having written before.

Mathematical physics is so little cultivated in this country and the style of work is in general so superficial that we are proud to have at least one in the country who can uphold its honor in that direction.

But it is not only in his private correspondence that evidence of prompt and adequate recognition of Gibbs' genius is to be found. It was just one year after the appearance of the second part of the monograph "On the Equilibrium of Heterogeneous Substances" —when he was barely forty years old—that he was elected, on April 21, 1879, to membership in the National Academy of Sciences. This body, born in the stress of the Civil War to act as a scientific adviser to the government, had become in the days of peace a society of the "elder statesmen" of science, and membership in it connoted the highest honor in the country for a man of science. The average age of election was at that time about forty-four, and was usually made only on a considerable record of publications, so that Gibbs' election at the relatively early age of forty and with a record of but three published papers would seem to be a rather unusual testimonial to the esteem in which his work was held. Further, it was in 1880 that he was elected to membership in the American Academy of Arts and Sciences of Boston, which on January 12, 1881, awarded him its Rumford Medal. This medal has always been considered among the outstanding rewards of achievement for an American scientist. It is true that the citation for this award reveals an imperfect appreciation of Gibbs' achievement and relied rather heavily on Maxwell's judgment; nevertheless the correspondence with the academy and particularly with Professor Trowbridge, who owing to Gibbs' indisposition acted as his proxy at the actual ceremony of award, shows a real esteem and a sincere recognition of his quality.

Gibbs' letter of acceptance of this award is worthy of reproduction here both as an example of his clear and felicitous style and as the only public comment on his own thermodynamic work he ever made.

TO THE AMERICAN ACADEMY OF ARTS AND SCIENCES:—

Gentlemen,—Regretting that I am unable to be present at the meeting to which I have been invited by your President, I desire to express my appreciation of the very distinguished honor which you have thought fit to confer upon me. This mark of approbation of my treatment of questions in thermodynamics is the more gratifying, as the value of theoretical investigation is more difficult to estimate than the results obtained in other fields of labor. One of the principal objects of theoretical research in any department of knowledge is to find the point of view from which the subject appears in its greatest simplicity. The success of the investigations in this respect is a matter on which he who makes them may be least able to form a correct judgment. It is, therefore, an especial satisfaction to find one's methods approved by competent judges.

The leading idea which I followed in my paper on the Equilibrium of Heterogeneous Substances was to develop the *rôles* of energy and entropy in the theory of thermo-dynamic equilibrium. By means of these quantities the general condition of equilibrium is easily expressed, and by applying this to various cases we are led at once to the special conditions which characterize them. We thus obtain the consequences resulting from the fundamental principles of thermo-dynamics (which are implied in the definitions of energy and entropy) by a process which seems more simple, and which lends itself more readily to the solution of problems, than the usual method, in which the several parts of a cyclic operation are explicitly and separately considered. Although my results were in a large measure such as had previously been demonstrated by other methods, yet, as I readily obtained those which were to me before unknown, I was confirmed in my belief in the suitableness of the method adopted.

A distinguished German physicist has said,—if my memory serves me aright,—that it is the office of theoretical investigation to give the form in which the results of experiment may be expressed. In the present case we are led to certain functions which play the principal part in determining the behavior of matter in respect to chemical equilibrium. The forms of these functions, however, remain to be determined by experiment, and here we meet the greatest difficulties, and find an inexhaustible field of labor. In most cases, probably, we must content ourselves at first with finding out what we can about these functions without expecting to arrive immediately at complete expressions of them. Only in the simplest case, that of gases, have I been able to write the equation expressing such a function for a body of variable composition, and here the equation only holds with a degree of approximation corresponding to the approach of the gas to the state which we call perfect.

Gratefully acknowledging the very favorable view which you have taken of my efforts, I remain, gentlemen, very truly yours,

J. Willard Gibbs

New Haven, Jan. 10, 1881.

It is significant that among the new results "readily obtained" by his method and not further commented on are included those as to osmosis, the phase rule, dilute solutions, capillarity, and electrolysis—that is, nearly all of the matters on which his fame as a thermodynamician rests. Here, quite characteristically, he confines himself to emphasizing his fundamental method and to pointing out that the challenge of the yet remaining difficulties could only be met by experiment. It is almost as if he had said, "I have given the theory as completely as it can be done in the present state of experimental knowledge. Further progress lies in the laboratory."

Still another form of recognition, more rare in American university circles at that time than now, came to Gibbs thus early in his career. In May, 1879, he received an invitation from Daniel Coit Gilman, president of the Johns Hopkins University, to come to Baltimore and give a course of lectures during the following academic year. Gilman, who after leaving Yale in 1872 to take the presidency of the University of California had returned to the East as the first president and organizer of the new institution in Baltimore, had of course known Gibbs during his days at Yale. In fact, as noted in a previous chapter, Gilman had been one of the committee whose labors were at least partially responsible for Gibbs' appointment as professor of mathematical physics, and he thus had personal knowledge of Gibbs' quality. Professor Rowland, who had been Gilman's choice to head the Physics Department at the new university, was also as we have seen above appreciative of Gibbs' eminence, and it was through Rowland that the arrangements were perfected for Gibbs to give a course of lectures on analytical mechanics in Baltimore. The course was given during the months of January and February, 1880, and was notable for his first public use of vector methods.[3]

That this course was otherwise a success and that he had strengthened the impression of his abilities which had been responsible for

3. The synopsis of this lecture course as it appeared in the Johns Hopkins University circular (presumably prepared by Gibbs himself) is as follows: "The principle of virtual velocity will be taken as the point of departure and the subject will be treated somewhat on the plan of the *Mécanique Analytique,* but other modes of developing the subject will be noted and critically compared with that of Lagrange. The notation generally known as the quaternionic, in which direction and magnitude are expressed by a single letter, will be used to a considerable extent, but not so as to presuppose any knowledge of Quaternions, as all notions and notations borrowed from that science will be fully explained and the essential propositions demonstrated. The object of the course will be to develop the general principles of mechanics in their mutual connections, and to explain the most important methods."

the original invitation is shown by the fact that before his return to New Haven he was invited by President Gilman to become a member of the faculty of Johns Hopkins, at a salary of $3,000. This further recognition of his work and the opportunities for wider scientific contacts which the new position would offer, together with the fact that his ten years of work at Yale was so little appreciated by the authorities there that he was still paid no salary, must have given the invitation a strong appeal. He did not, however, discuss the matter with anyone in New Haven outside the family circle, except in confidence with Newton on the eve of the latter's departure for Europe on sabbatical leave.

It was not an easy decision to make. Against the manifest attractions of the offer there were balanced those of long-established habits of working by himself and a satisfying home life. The balance was however tending toward acceptance of the offer, and plans were being made for his sister Anna to accompany him to Baltimore, when in some manner not now entirely clear [4] the news of the offer reached the university authorities, and they were persuaded to promise Gibbs a regular salary of $2,000 per annum in the future, with prospects of an early increase. This belated recognition of the value of his services to the university, and still more the expressions of esteem and of concern at the prospect of his leaving Yale which he received from his colleagues, finally decided the question for him. The following letter from Professor James Dwight Dana so aptly summarizes Gibbs' prestige in the faculty and the reaction of his colleagues to the threat of his departure, as well as picturing clearly the strain on the loyalty of progressive faculty members under a too conservative administration, that it is worth quoting in full.

New Haven, April 26, 1880

My dear Prof— Gibbs:

I have only just now learned that there is danger of your leaving us.— Your departure would be a very bad move for Yale. I have felt, of late, great anxiety for our University (using a name we are striving to deserve) because there seemed to be so little appreciation among our Graduates as to what we need, and so few benefactions in our favor; and now

4. According to the account of Miss Whitney in "One of the Prophets" it was Professor Thacher of the Latin Department who stirred the authorities to action.

the idea of losing the leading man in one of our departments is really disheartening. I do not wonder that Johns Hopkins wants your name and services, or that you feel inclined to consider favorably their proposition, for nothing has been done toward endowing your professorship, and there are not here the means or signs of progress which tend to incite courage in Professors and multiply earnest students. But I hope nevertheless that you will stand by us, and that something will speedily be done by way of endowment to show you that your services are really valued.

Johns Hopkins can get on vastly better without you than we can. *We can not.*

Sincerely yours
James D. Dana

The feeling expressed in this letter was so general that Gibbs came to appreciate that if he stayed in New Haven he would no longer be merely an appendage but really a part of Yale, necessary to its well being, and this was an essential factor in his decision to remain. Other considerations were undoubtedly influential. Thus the fact that his life in Baltimore, with a semi-invalid sister to care for, would be more circumscribed than in New Haven, both socially and in his freedom to work, must have carried some weight, as would also the fact that his previous habits of work would have to be modified in the more vigorous intellectual atmosphere then prevailing at Baltimore. But the main reason was that as an acknowledged responsible member of the Yale family he was at *home.* His letter finally declining the call is characteristic in its definiteness, its restraint, and its courtesy. As taken from a draft copy [5] recently found among his papers it reads:

New Haven
Apr. 29 1880

My dear Sir

Within the last few days a very unexpected opposition to my departure has been manifested among my colleagues—an opposition so strong as to render it impossible for me to entertain longer the proposition wh you have made. I had not previously spoken of the matter outside of my own family except in confidence to Prof. Newton, as he

5. This and other draft copies of Gibbs' letters quoted here and later are reproduced exactly as written, with all the abbreviations he habitually employed. Only where the meaning of an abbreviation might not be immediately obvious to the reader is the full word added in brackets. The few errors in spelling which occur have been corrected.

was leaving for Europe. I only mention this to explain why after so long a time I have arrived at a decision contrary to that to wh I was tending.

I remember your saying that you told Prof. Sylvester that you thought it would be hard for me to break the ties wh connect me with this place. Well—I have found it harder than I had expected. But I cannot omit to say that I am very sensible of the cordial sentiments wh have been expressed by yourself as well as by other members of your University, I mean especially Professors Sylvester & Rowland.

Very truly yours
J. W. G.

Pres. D. C. Gilman
Johns Hopkins University
   Baltimore

It is significant that the larger salary offered at Baltimore carried little or no weight with Gibbs. Here as in the case of the previous offer from Bowdoin the decision turned upon the consideration of his real intellectual happiness. When it became clear that that condition could be fulfilled best at New Haven, nothing else counted, the salary differential least of all.

Although it is evident from the facts already cited in this chapter that Gibbs received in some quarters at least prompt and adequate recognition for his work, it is nevertheless true that for quite a long time it did not begin to bear fruit in the experimental work which it suggested and invited. Much has been written on the causes for this delay. It has generally been ascribed to one or more of the following four reasons: first, to a lack of interest on Gibbs' part in calling the attention of scientists to his work; second, failure on his part or on that of his colleagues to popularize the work; third, to the logical severity and mathematical conciseness of the style in which it was clothed; and fourth, to the inadequate circulation it received by reason of its publication in the relatively obscure *Transactions* of the Connecticut Academy.

The first of these alleged reasons has no foundation in fact. It is purely a legend arising probably from Gibbs' well-known modesty, his solitary habits of work, and his reticence on all personal matters. That, contrary to what has been thus inferred, Gibbs took rather unusual pains in the distribution of copies of his papers, is amply proven by his mailing lists for reprints (in his own handwriting) which include the names of practically all the contemporary mathematicians, astronomers, physicists, and chemists who could possibly have had an interest in his work. The principal list, which indicates the particular papers sent to each individual, comprises 160 names from this country and Canada, 119 from Great Britain, 104 from Germany, 57 from France, 11 from Italy, 10 from Holland and Belgium, 10 from Austria, 8 from Russia, 8 from Switzerland, 6 from Norway and Sweden, 5 from Poland, 3 from Denmark, 2 from India, and one each from Spain, Brazil, China, and Japan— a total of 507 names. Distribution of the first two thermodynamic papers was made to 73 and 76 names respectively; copies of the first and second parts of the "Equilibrium of Heterogeneous Substances," of the abstract in the *American Journal of Science,* and of the paper on vapor-densities were sent to 99, 102, 127, and 141 names in that order; the paper "On the Fundamental Formulae of Dynamics" went to 87; the two parts of the pamphlet *Vector Analysis* were sent to 81 and 52 persons, while the complete pamphlet went to an additional 84; the first three of the optics papers were distributed to 127, while the last two went to 174 and 168 respectively; the Buffalo address "On Multiple Algebra" was sent to 276 names and the paper on orbits to 199. From other lists we find that copies of his book *Elementary Principles in Statistical Mechanics* were sent to 21 individuals in addition to 22 copies furnished to scientific journals and learned societies.[6]

In the light of these formidable lists, which read like a directory of the eminent in the physical sciences of the times, it becomes evident that an indifference to the spreading of a knowledge of his work among those presumably competent to understand it was not among Gibbs' failings. Indeed he went further than most to insure a hearing in that he records that he sent proof sheets of certain parts of the "Equilibrium of Heterogeneous Substances" in advance of publication to Maxwell, William Thomson, and Clausius.[7] This rather unusual procedure on the part of a young

6. The complete lists are given in Appendix IV in this volume.

7. In addition to these three celebrated names Gibbs adds that of Rühlmann as a recipient of proof sheets. The name Richard Rühlmann also appears in the principle mailing list as having been sent reprints of ten papers. Although not of the eminence of the other three to whom proofs were sent, Rühlmann was the author of a *Handbuch der mechanischen Wärmetheorie,* and it would seem possible that Gibbs included him in this distribution as the result of an acquaintanceship formed during his student days in Germany.

and unknown scientist is proof not only of his desire to make his work known but also of his confidence in its importance.

However, the charge that the absence of any attempt to popularize his work was a factor in delaying a general appreciation of its value is without question valid. Aside from the abstract in the *American Journal of Science* already mentioned, Gibbs made no effort to call attention to his work. He did however expand the monograph by the publication of a paper [8] giving a comparison of the previously derived formulas for gas mixtures with convertible components with the results of all the pertinent experiments then known; but this can only be regarded properly as an addendum to the former work. Whether he should have made an effort to popularize his work, or whether his colleagues might have been more alert to follow up the wealth of experimental leads implicit in the great monograph and thus have hastened its ultimate fruition, the fact remains that neither he nor they did so. It was simply not in Gibbs to blow his own horn, and the necessary combination of training and vision was not present among his chemical colleagues.

The allegation that Gibbs' prose style was a deterrent to his prompt recognition also possesses a measure of truth. There is considerable testimony from eminent men that they found the "Equilibrium of Heterogeneous Substances" very difficult reading. But that it is obscure or lacking in clarity of style is untrue. It is logical, terse, and requires unrelieved concentration of thought; but there is nowhere any possibility of misunderstanding his meaning, no loose statement of facts, or any other defect in clarity. Gibbs' style has been contrasted with the "sparkling clarity" of Maxwell's,[9] a comparison which seems to me to reveal a fundamental ignorance of the styles of both masters. Maxwell's popular writings are undoubtedly clear and relatively easy to read, but so are the comparable writings of Gibbs—in the biographical notices of Clausius and Newton for instance. And in his serious work Maxwell's style is no more intelligible and his pages no easier to read than Gibbs'. Neither is easy reading; no scientific work which forces a revision or radical extension of previously held ideas *can* be easy to read; the difficulties, which are real, lie in the mind of the reader. But from a considerable experience in teaching gradu-

8. "On the Vapor-Densities of Peroxide of Nitrogen, Formic Acid, Acetic Acid, and Perchloride of Phosphorus," *Am. Journ. Sci.*, ser. 3, Vol. *17* (1879).

9. Muriel Rukeyser, *Willard Gibbs* (New York, Doubleday, Doran, 1942), p. 251.

ate students both from Maxwell's *Treatise* and from Gibbs' equilibrium monograph, I can testify that the latter occasioned no more difficulties for the classes than did the former. Thus it seems to me that it has been more the lack of suitably prepared mental soil than the want of perspicuity that has been involved in the difficulties which undoubtedly have been experienced by many of Gibbs' readers, particularly among the chemists.

The fourth of the reasons which have been put forward to explain the slow acceptance of Gibbs' work—that of inadequate circulation—would seem to have been somewhat overemphasized, although it must be given some weight. The first two papers were of a length which would have permitted their publication in a scientific journal where they might have received a somewhat wider distribution. But the extent of the third paper precluded any other manner of publication than one similar to that actually used. From the annual reports of the then librarian of the Connecticut Academy, Addison Van Name, we find that in 1875–76 its *Transactions* were exchanged with those of 170 other learned societies, of which 140 were in foreign lands. Thus it would seem that the distribution was sufficiently large to have permitted anyone abroad who so desired to obtain access to Gibbs' papers, even if he had not been included in Gibbs' personal distribution of reprints. The truth would seem to be that when, with the gradual increase of interest in the no man's land between physics and chemistry, some of Gibbs' results were independently rediscovered, and attention had been drawn to the fact that these were not new discoveries but were all contained, along with much else of even greater significance, in Gibbs' monograph, the natural human reaction of blaming someone or something else for the oversight came into play. Thus the alleged "inaccessibility" of the *Transactions* of the Connecticut Academy became a sort of scapegoat for those Europeans who, perhaps not altogether unjustifiably, were then apt to ignore North America as a possible source of anything of theoretical interest.

Thus it would seem that while the failure immediately to follow up Gibbs' work with the experimental investigations it suggested was due partly to a lack of any interpretation of it in a language that chemists could understand and partly to the somewhat restricted circulation of the papers, the fundamental reason is to be found in the fact that the work was ahead of its time and necessarily had to wait for the evolution of interest in the border-line field it exploited and for the appearance of the physical chem-ist.

It is interesting to note in this connection that the earliest appre-ciation of the significance of Gibbs' work came mainly from physi-cists and mathematicians, that is, from those who by training and habit talked a similar language. In addition to those mentioned previously there is found in the "Scientific Correspondence" under the date of July 13, 1884, a letter from J. J. (afterward Sir Joseph) Thomson touching on a confirmation he had secured of Gibbs' re-sults as to the effect of the relative quantities of the combining sub-stances on chemical equilibrium, and commenting on the value of that section of the monograph which deals with electrolytic equi-librium. Another physicist who according to the testimony of Professor Michael Pupin [10] must have become acquainted with Gibbs' work in the mid-eighties was Herman von Helmholtz. In 1882 the latter had published a derivation of an equation giving the rate of change of the electromotive force with temperature for a re-versible electrolytic cell which became generally known as the Gibbs-Helmholtz equation after it was pointed out that it was im-plicit in and more readily derivable from Gibbs' work of some four or five years previous. Helmholtz like Maxwell never became per-sonally acquainted with or, as far as is known, corresponded with Gibbs, although it is known (from a letter of Professor Ogden N. Rood of Columbia University in the "Scientific Correspondence") that Helmholtz on his visit to the United States in 1893 expressed his regret at missing an opportunity for a talk with Gibbs.

Another German physicist who knew and appreciated Gibbs' work during the eighties was Heinrich Hertz, the discoverer of the physical existence of electromagnetic waves. The letter from him in the "Scientific Correspondence" is worth quoting both for its frank acknowledgment of Gibbs' priority and for the estimate of Gibbs' achievement. It is one of the few letters in the collection from a German scientist which is written in English.

10. In an address at the Graduates Club, New Haven, in the presentation ceremonies accompanying the gift of a portrait of Gibbs to the club.

Karlsruhe 3 Mar. 89

Dear Sir

I give you my best thanks for the papers you were so kind to send me. I beg to accept in return those of my electrical papers of which I have copies left. It is with great pleasure that I seize the opportunity to give expression to the very highest esteem I have since long for your thermo-dynamical work. I did not master it absolutely but I mastered it enough to see how fundamental it is. Many things which I thought had been first done by Helmholtz I found in your paper. And I think it is quite a mine which is yet not at all explored. If it took much time that your paper was fully appreciated here I think it is because the Cambridge [!] Transactions are only with difficulty to be had here.

As to your papers on the electric theory of light I did not yet come over them and as I see they cannot be read in little time I will not post-pone this answer till I have done it. Repeating my very best thanks I remain

Yours truly
H. Hertz

A Dutch physicist who according to the testimony of his son [11] came to an early appreciation of Gibbs' work in thermodynamics was J. D. van der Waals, most widely known for the development of an equation of state for fluids which was the first to compre-hend both the liquid and the vapor phases. It was for his attempts to extend the results of this characteristic equation to mixtures of several substances that Gibbs' work furnished the key and con-tributed to his success. To van der Waals' influence, together with that of the chemist J. H. van't Hoff, is to be attributed the inspira-tion which initiated the great Dutch school of physical chemistry which has done so much to develop and apply Gibbs' ideas.

Electrochemistry was very much to the fore in the minds of both physicists and chemists during the late eighties and early nineties, and it is a striking testimony to Gibbs' reputation that he was twice invited in that period to attend and participate in the discussions of the British Association for the Advancement of Science (B.A.A.S.), in 1886 and 1893. Although he did not attend on either occasion, he did contribute to the discussions in two letters to the secretary of the Electrolysis Committee, Oliver J. (afterward Sir Oliver) Lodge, which were included in the reports of that committee for

11. *Chemisch Weekblad* (September 18, 1926).

1886 and 1888.[12] Other English physicists with whom Gibbs is known to have corresponded on similar subjects during this period, although no record of his part in them now remains, were R. T. Glazebrook and E. H. Griffith. Thus as far at least as physicists are concerned, it is evident that Gibbs' thermodynamic work received, from Maxwell onward, a cordial and ever-growing tribute of admiration and respect.

The recognition he received from the chemists was only a little less prompt and general. The first chemist after Muir who showed interest in Gibbs' work would seem to have been Professor Wolcott Gibbs of Harvard. There is a letter from him in the "Scientific Correspondence" dated December 4, 1881, in which he suggests possible applications of Gibbs' methods to problems in thermoelectricity and in chemical combination. He does not however seem to have followed up these matters with experimental work. In 1884 we find two letters from Professor William (afterward Sir William) Ramsay, telling, among other things, of his experimental confirmation of Gibbs' formula for the density changes in a vapor (peroxide of nitrogen) which occur on dissociation. In this connection it may be mentioned that there is in the notes left by Gibbs and preserved in the Yale library a considerable volume of computations from his equations as compared with the later experimental results of Ramsay and Young on ether. In these he assumed that the vapor obeyed the equation of van der Waals rather than that of a perfect gas. While these computations were never published, they were used as illustrative material in his later lectures.

But the man who did the most to arouse interest in Gibbs' work among chemists was undoubtedly the pioneer physical chemist, Wilhelm Ostwald. In the second volume of his autobiography he tells of the growth of his interest in and appreciation of Gibbs' thermodynamic papers and how he came to undertake their translation into German. I have translated freely.

While still in Dorpat, Oettingen had recommended to me the thermodynamic works of the American J. Willard Gibbs as especially significant but formidable investigations.

In order to obtain for myself greater clarity on this most important of all aids to the explanation of the doctrine of transformations, I began to

12. Printed in the *Collected Works*, I, 406–412.

study the papers after I had, not without difficulty, unearthed them. Like Oettingen I found them formidable, but recognized their undoubtedly great significance. Before myself few had appreciated them, only the physicists Maxwell and van der Waals had mentioned or utilized them.

To penetrate their meaning better I found no more effective means than to translate the works word for word. Abstracts of them could not be made, for they were written in such compact form that any further compression was impossible. Also I thought that through the German edition which would thus result, this long-overlooked treasure would finally be uncovered and converted into the current coin of progress.

This work had the greatest influence on my own development. For, although he does not especially emphasize it, Gibbs deals almost exclusively with energy and its factors and holds himself free from all kinetic hypotheses. Because of this, his results possess a certainty and a lasting quality of the highest degree humanly attainable.

In fact, not a single error either in his formulas or conclusions or, what is most remarkable, in his assumptions has yet been discovered. For one finds among scientific writings not a few whose logic and mathematics are irreproachable but which yet are worthless because their assumptions and postulates do not correspond to reality.

While this account with its naïve assumption that it needed only a German translation by Ostwald to insure Gibbs' immortality may be somewhat irritating, it is nevertheless valuable both as to the origin of that translation and for its comments on Gibbs' eminence. That Ostwald underestimated the extent of the reputation already attained by Gibbs in his own country and in England is sufficiently evident from what has been previously related in this chapter; but that he overestimated the influence of his translation on the development of physical chemistry is more questionable. It certainly made a knowledge of Gibbs' work more available in that part of the world where professional physical chemists first appeared, and to that extent was a significant contribution both to that subject and to Gibbs' growing reputation. The fact that at that time students were flocking from all over the world to Germany as the principal place in which physical chemistry was being cultivated may perhaps to a certain extent justify Ostwald's assumption that it was only in Germany that the founder of that subject was appreciated.

There is in the "Scientific Correspondence" considerable material bearing on this translation of Ostwald's. The first proposal for a translation occurs in a letter from Ostwald dated November 14, 1888. In a draft for a reply, which has been preserved, Gibbs tentatively agreed to the proposal pending the receipt of further details. These were furnished in a postcard of December 25 and a letter of January 30, 1889, Ostwald's proposition being to bring out the translation of "Equilibrium of Heterogeneous Substances" as one of the series of *Classiker der exacten Wissenschaften* which he was then editing. In the meantime Veit & Company, the Leipzig publishers, had made a proposal (dated December 30, 1888) to publish in either English or German at Gibbs' pleasure a reprint of all three of his thermodynamic papers, under the German sponsorship of Professor Felix Klein of Göttingen. This second offer made the greater appeal to Gibbs as evidenced by the drafts of his letters to Veit, Ostwald, and Klein, which have been preserved. He preferred a German reprint, but declined a suggestion made in February, 1889, that he write a commentary to accompany the German edition, on the ground that this would come more appropriately and possess more value if prepared by the translator or one of the proposed Göttingen sponsors who then included Professors Klein and Riecke.

There follows here a gap in the record of nearly two years which, judging from the letters after its resumption, was occupied on the part of Veit in seeking for a competent translator and in negotiations to that end with Ostwald, and on the part of Ostwald in actually making the translation. The matter was finally settled by Veit's assigning all their rights to Ostwald and his publisher W. Englemann. A draft of a reply to a letter of Ostwald's announcing this pending arrangement (March 3, 1891) and offering to include a translation of the second with that of the third paper is worth reproducing because it is the only comment on his own work in thermodynamics which Gibbs ever made, as far as I have been able to determine, aside from his letter of acceptance of the Rumford Medal. .

New Haven Mch 27, 1891

Dear Prof. Ostwald,

If Veit & Co (not finding a suitable translator) are disposed to give up the matter to you, & you are still disposed to undertake it, I think that you had better do so, & should be very glad to have you.

I think that your proposal to include the paper on the "Geometri.

Rep by Surfaces" is a judicious one. That is doubtless the most important of the minor papers. It contains, I believe, the first solution of a problem of considerable importance, viz: the additional condition (besides equality of temp & press) wh is necessary in order that two states of a substance shall be in equilibrium in contact with each other. The matter seems simply enough now, yet it appears to have given considerable difficulty to physicists. (See Clausius Wied Ann ix p 355, 1880, where he gives the solution in a somewhat different form.) I suppose that Maxwell referred esp. to this question when he said (Nat. xi, 359) that by means of this model, problems wh had long resisted the efforts of himself and others, could be solved at once. In the 4th Ed. of his "Theory of Heat" he gives several pages to this geom. rep.

Moreover the treatment of a homogeneous body in this paper is really identical in spirit with my treatment of heterogeneous bodies in the larger paper, (except that the latter does not admit of the simple geometrical representation) & I think its previous perusal is very well adapted to diminish the difficulties wh students may feel in reading the latter.

In regard to notes, I cannot make any engagement at present, but I will think about it, & write to you again, at least if I hear that the matter has been definitely arranged between you & Veit & Co.

Yours faithfully
J. Willard Gibbs

The final agreement with Veit & Company was announced in a letter from Ostwald on April 12, 1891, in which he expresses his thanks for Gibbs' cooperation and his hope that the book will appear in the fall. The further correspondence has to do only with details of format and a few matters which came up in reading proof. The book was finally published in the spring of 1892 under the title *Thermodynamische Studien* and is signalized in the "Scientific Correspondence" only by one from the publishers covering the transmittal of complimentary copies to Gibbs and notifying him as to the American agency arrangements for the volume. The book as finally published comprised translations of all three of Gibbs' papers.

But there were other European chemists who appreciated and were influenced by Gibbs' work even before Ostwald's translation appeared. Thus the Dutch chemists Bemmelen and Roozeboom in the mid- and later eighties and the Viennese Meyerhoffer in the early nineties were working on applications of the phase rule. A letter from Meyerhoffer preserved in the "Scientific Correspondence" is worth quoting, if only as evidence that not all chemists agreed with Ostwald that there had been an undue delay in the appreciation of Gibbs' work. (The translation is mine.)

Wien 23—6—1893
20 Schwarzspanierstrasse 20

To Herr Prof. J. Willard Gibbs
New Haven.

Permit me, honored Herr Professor, to offer you the accompanying brochure, which may give you further evidence how quickly and completely your ideas have conquered the old world. The little book contains indeed only a small selection of all those matters which are brought together under a single viewpoint by your law. But these few examples are sufficient to show that the phase rule is one of the most fortunate generalizations on which theoretical chemistry can congratulate itself.

With distinguished respect,
Dr. Wilhelm Meyerhoffer.

But although there were, as we have seen, quite a number of both physicists and chemists who recognized Gibbs' genius and the importance of his work within a relatively short period after its publication, nevertheless its full fruition began only with the emergence of physical chemistry as a profession. This may be approximately dated from the appearance of the *Zeitschrift für physikalische Chemie,* sponsored by Ostwald and van't Hoff, in 1887. From that time onward there has been an ever-growing volume of work published which has found its inspiration in Gibbs' work in thermodynamics, and in particular in applications of the phase rule to ever-widening fields of use. The Dutch school with van't Hoff, Roozeboom, van Laar, Schreinmakers, Smits, Cohen, and others; the German school from Ostwald and Meyerhoffer to Tammann; the British school with, among others, Findlay, Freeth, Guggenheim, and Donnan; the Frenchmen Le Chatelier and Duhem; and the Americans Bancroft, Trevor, and Morey, to name but a few, have all produced a great volume of work and many discoveries inspired and guided by Gibbs' pioneering research of the 1870's. The sheer volume of the literature on the phase rule, to which Gibbs devoted some four pages, is overwhelming. In the bibliography attached to the jubilee number of the *Chemisch Weekblad* there are listed 42 books by 27 authors with a total of some 11,000 pages, and covering applications ranging from problems of mineralogy, petrography, geology, and metallurgy to those of technical processes and manufacturing methods. A truly tremendous sweep of matters to spring from a more or less routine check of the disposable variables in a mathematical investigation having no other than a purely theoretical motivation.

The beginnings of physical chemistry in this country were marked, as they had been a decade earlier in Germany, by the establishment of a medium for publication, the *Journal of Physical Chemistry*. This was founded by Professors Wilder D. Bancroft and Joseph E. Trevor of Cornell University in 1897. Both editors maintained a considerable correspondence with Gibbs, and it was in connection with that of Bancroft that Gibbs prepared some material which, at the time of his death, he was considering as a supplement to the "Equilibrium of Heterogeneous Substances" and which is included in the *Collected Works*. In the correspondence with Trevor the proposal from Le Chatelier for a French translation of his thermodynamic papers is to be found. This translation appeared in 1899 under the title *"Equilibre des systèmes chimiques,* and together with a French translation by G. Roy of the first two papers under the title *Diagrammes et surfaces thermodynamiques,"* and the German translation, furnished the principal means by which Gibbs' thought was made available to the world, until the appearance of *The Scientific Papers* in 1906. The Le Chatelier translation, however, included only the first part of the third paper, up to p. 184 of *The Scientific Papers*.

It was also in the year 1897 that Gibbs' last published work on thermodynamic matters appeared. This took the form of a letter to the editor of *Nature*,[13] in reply to a problem posed in a previous issue of that journal by Lord Kelvin. This reply provides a comparison between a mechanical derivation of van't Hoff's law of osmotic pressure and one employing Gibbs' own method of the chemical potentials. The directness and simplicity of the latter method, which requires only the assumptions that a dissolved sub-

13. 55 (March 18, 1897), 461–462.

stance shall be capable of existence in the ideal gaseous state and shall not be dissociated in the solution, are brought out strikingly, and the generalizations which the law permits are clearly indicated. This paper together with the fragments included in the *Collected Works* (or *The Scientific Papers*) gives the principal definite indication of the lines along which Gibbs' intended supplementary chapters to the "Equilibrium of Heterogeneous Substances" would have proceeded. But it seems doubtful if anything he could have added would have materially increased his reputation as the foremost thermodynamician of his age. At the time of his death Gibbs' position in the scientific world was such a commanding one that it is certain his least word would have been eagerly pursued. And yet it seems to me that from its very nature little of a fundamental character remained to be added to his work of the seventies. Certain matters with respect to the functional form of the chemical potentials for fluids could have been restated with greater definiteness and generality; the treatment of solid-fluid equilibrium might possibly have been given a greater elegance by expression in terms of dyadics; but by and large all that could have been accomplished would seem to have been a further development of applications along lines already pointed out. Had he lived longer he would undoubtedly have contributed further to our knowledge, but possibly more significantly in other domains. His work in thermodynamics was essentially complete.

VII

Professor of Mathematical Physics:
Mathematics

DURING the early years of his professorship, in spite of the
magnitude and extent of his work in thermodynamics
Gibbs found time for other activities and studies. In
November of 1877 he founded the Mathematical Club at Yale,
an organization for the presentation and discussion of papers by
faculty members and graduate students. This was the second
of such discussion groups to be formed in the university [1]
and for a long time it formed almost the only connecting
link between the individual departmental faculties of the college
and the scientific school. For the first ten years of its life Gibbs
served as its executive officer, and in that time, although no record
of the actual titles of his contributions remains, it is known that he
gave before the club the first public accounts of his mathematical
researches in vector analysis and of its applications in the fields of
astronomy and physical optics. Whether he also thus first presented the studies in multiple algebra, to which the work on vector
analysis naturally led, is not known with certainty, although it is
probable that at least some phases of it were given to the club.

The origin of Gibbs' interest in the algebra of directed quantities,
(vectors) is to be found in his studies of Maxwell's *Treatise on
Electricity and Magnetism*. This work, which appeared in 1873, is
one of the great landmarks in the history of electrical science. It
translated Faraday's ideas on the role of the medium surrounding
conductors in the production of electrical effects into mathematical
language with the aid of the concept of dielectric displacement;
and it established, at least to a first approximation, that the phe-

1. The first was the Classical and Philological Society; the date of founding is uncertain,
but according to the late Professor Franklin B. Dexter it held meetings as early as 1864.

nomena of optics must have an electromagnetic origin. But it was not only in its physical concepts that the *Treatise* presented novelties. In order to put the results in a móre compact form than is possible with the usual Cartesian analysis, Maxwell utilized some of the ideas of Sir William Rowan Hamilton's calculus of quaternions, in which attention is focused on the quantity considered rather than on its components. That it was the critical study of the quaternionic methods of representing the phenomena of electricity and magnetism which led him to his vector analysis we have first-hand evidence in Gibbs' own words. This occurs in the draft of a letter preserved in the "Scientific Correspondence" which he wrote in 1888 to Dr. Victor Schlegel in reply to one calling his attention to a certain pertinent publication of Schlegel's. This draft answers so explicitly several questions which have arisen with regard to Gibbs' system of vector analysis and its relations to other systems that it is worth while to reproduce it in its entirety in spite of its length.

Aug. 1, 1888

My dear Dr. Schlegel,

I am glad to hear that you are pleased with my address on Multiple Algebra. My object in writing it was threefold; to vindicate the value of the methods of Multiple Algebra, to call attention to the fundamental importance of Grassmann's work in this field, & lastly, to express my own ideas on the subject, i.e., to give a brief résumé of those notions wh seem to me fundamental & in the mutual connection wh seems most natural and fruitful. That I was not acquainted with your work at that time (or rather that having only seen the first part, I had hastily concluded that it contained only geometrical applications) was a matter of regret to me subsequently when I found that I had made a serious omission.

Your apt characterization of my Vector Analysis in the Fortsch. Math. suggests that you may be intersd to know the precise relation of that pamphlet to the work of Ham. & Grass. with respect to its composition.

My first acquaintance with quaternions was in reading Maxwell's E. & M. where Quaternion notations are considerably used. I became convinced that to master those subjects, it was necessary for me to commence by mastering those methods. At the same time I saw, that although the methods were called quaternionic the idea of the quaternion was quite foreign to the subject. In regard to the products of vectors, I saw that there were two important functions (or products) called the vector part & the scalar part of the product, but that the union of the two to form what was called the (whole) product did not advance the theory as an instrument of geom. investigation. Again with respect to the operator ∇ as applied to a vector I saw that the vector part & the scalar part of the result represented important operations, but their union (generally to be separated afterwards) did not seem a valuable idea. This is indeed only a repetition of my first observation, since the operator is defined by means of the multiplication of vectors, & a change in the idea of that multiplication would involve the change in the use to the operator ∇.

I therefore began to work out ab initio, the algebra of the two kinds of multiplication, the three differential operations ∇ applied to a scalar, & the two operations to a vector, & those functions or rather integrating operators wh (under certain limitations) are the inverse of the said differential operators, & wh play the leading roles in many departments of Math. Phys. To these subjects was added that of lin. vec. functions wh is also prominent in Maxwell's E. & M.

This I ultimately printed but never published, although I distributed a good many copies among such persons as I thought might possibly take an interest in it. My delay & hesitation in this respect was principally due to difficulty in making up my mind in respect to details of notation, matters trifling in themselves, but in wh it is undesirable to make unnecessary changes.

My acquaintance with Grassmann's work was also due to the subject of E. [electricity] & in particular to the note wh he published in Crelle's Jour. in 1877 calling attention to the fact that the law of the mutual action of two elements of current wh Clausius had just published had been given in 1845 by himself. I was the more interested in the subject as I had myself (before seeing Clausius' work) come to regard the same as the simplest expression for the mechanical action, & probably for the same reason as Grassmann, because that law is so very simply expressed by means of the external product.

At all events I saw that the methods wh I was using, while nearly those of Hamilton, were almost exactly those of Grassmann. I procured the two Ed. of the Ausd.[2] but I cannot say that I found them easy reading. In fact I have never had the perseverance to get through with either of them, & have perhaps got more ideas from his miscellaneous memoirs than from those works.

I am not however conscious that Grassmann's writings exerted any particular influence on my V-A, although I was glad enough in the in-

2. The two editions of the *Ausdehnungslehre* of 1844 and 1862.

troductory paragraph to shelter myself behind one or two distinguished names in making changes of notation wh I felt would be distasteful to quaternionists. In fact if you read that pamphlet carefully you will see that it all follows with the inexorable logic of algebra from the problem wh I had set myself long before my acq. with Grass.

I have no doubt that you consider, as I do, the methods of Grassmann to be superior to those of Hamilton. It thus seemed to me that it might [be] interesting to you to know how commencing with some knowledge of Ham's methods & influenced simply by a desire to obtain the simplest algebra for the expression of the relations of Geom. Phys. &c I was led essentially to Grassmann's algebra of vectors, independently of any influence from him or any one else.

In the meantime however, I had learned from Grassmann, that this is all special, only a small part of a large field. How that larger field appears to me, you may see in my Mul. Alg. where the notions, mainly Grassmann's, are presented with a slightly different perspective & notation.

To return to my V-A.—My dyadic ex[pressions] are not *algebraic* products but the most general kind of product mentioned by Grassmann, those having no *special* laws, say *indeterminate* products. In the principal use I make of them they correspond I think to his open or lückenhältige products as I think you will see on closer examination. In my V-A. I use no sign for this product wh is philosophically appropriate as corresponding to the absence of *special* laws. Sometimes however I have found it convenient to have a special sign as in my M.A. where I used a | wh serves to keep the letters apart, the union being less close in a certain sense, than in other products.

The first pages in Chap III in my V-A. give I think exactly the way in wh I was led to this product. It was not the abstract def wh first presented itself, but the expression presented itself & demanded interpretation.

These dyadic expressions or sums of indeterminate products again correspond to what are generally known as Matrices, a subject wh as you know has been considerably discussed of late. That my notation is not bad, I have been led to believe, from the fact that I have been able to obtain with the greatest ease results wh others have apparently had considerable difficulty in obtaining. I dare say however that the same could be said of notations more strictly conformed to Grassmann's.

This draft is not signed, but even if the internal evidence of Gibbs' authorship were not indubitable, it would be positively confirmed by the references to it contained in a later letter from Schlegel.[3]

3. In the "Scientific Correspondence."

One point with regard to Gibbs' pamphlet on vector analysis which has aroused considerable comment and some criticism is settled unequivocally by this letter. Bumstead for instance has expressed the opinion [4] that Gibbs' reluctance to publish the work was due to his opinion that it was not sufficiently original and consisted too predominantly of adaptations and applications of the work of others. But this Schlegel letter makes clear that it was only hesitancy as to the best notation to be used and not any question of the propriety of publication that dictated his course of action or inaction. It should be borne in mind that at the time he wrote the pamphlet the only algebra of vectors in use among physicists (as in Maxwell's *Treatise,* for instance) was one which tied it to the quaternion, and Gibbs was the first to perceive that this was a totally unnecessary and complicating attachment, at least from the point of view of physical applications. Thus it is apparent that Bumstead's supposition is not supported by the facts.

Further evidence on this point is afforded by a draft of another letter in the "Scientific Correspondence." This one, dated December 1, 1881, is to C. S. Peirce, in reply to one from him criticizing Gibbs' notation. In this draft reply Gibbs states that the notation of the dot (.) and the cross (x) for the scalar and vector products of vectors, which he used in the pamphlet, were those he had first employed in his initial studies of quaternions; that he had replaced the dot by the line (|) for the scalar product in his lectures at Johns Hopkins; and that on preparing the manuscript for the printer he had at first used no symbol to denote the scalar while retaining the cross for the vector product, but had finally reverted to the original notations although still not entirely convinced that it was the best for all purposes. He then goes on to say:

It is really this hesitation in regard to the merits of dif notations wh has kept me from publishing anything on the subject before, & wh has now kept me from any form of permanent publication. I mean that while I might have saved myself a trifling expense by printing in the transactions of some society (where I would not have felt cramped for space) I was deterred by a certain feeling of crudeness in my use of symbols. I felt that before a year should pass I would very likely want to change the whole and should feel sorry to have it on permanent record.

4. In the biographical sketch prefaced to *The Scientific Papers,* I, xix.

Similar hesitation in regard to matters of detail prevented me from
adding a IIId Chapter on linear vector functions of wh I had worked
out the plans.[5] The trouble was that I had worked out the plan from
two dif points of view, & could not tell which to choose. So I concluded
to follow Horace's advice & lock up my poem in my desk for a year.

The specter of notations has haunted the algebra of vectors from
the beginning. The original quaternionic notations of Hamilton
and Tait were undoubtedly clumsy and never gained much head-
way among physicists, except for a slightly modified version sponsored by Oliver Heaviside,[6] whose introduction of Clarendon type
to denote vector quantities was his most valuable contribution to
this matter of notation. Although there has been a steady increase
in the use of the vectorial methods of Gibbs through the years until now they may be said to be practically universal, there is less
unanimity in the use of his notations. The employment of both the
methods and the notations was however considerably accelerated
with the appearance in 1901 of E. B. Wilson's *Vector Analysis,
Founded upon the Lectures of J. Willard Gibbs;* but many a mathematical page is still sometimes defaced with the unmathematical
appearing "div," "rot," or "curl" in place of the more suitable and
convenient notations of Gibbs.

But of more importance than the elucidation of the reasons for
his failure to publish his vector analysis or the question of the best
notation is the revelation in the Schlegel letter of the development
of Gibbs' thought on vector algebra and its relation to other algebras. That his first object was the purely practical one of expressing the physical relations of electromagnetic theory in suitable
mathematical language and that this was accomplished by taking
from the quaternionic theory only so much as subserved this end
is made abundantly clear. This pragmatic viewpoint is characteristic of Gibbs' whole philosophy. He repeatedly expressed the
view—as in his letter of acceptance of the Rumford Medal—that
the simplicity of a theory was of the essence of its verity, and he
made this criterion a touchstone for judgment on many occasions.
Thus in regard to the objections to his procedure in basing his

5. The first 36 pages of the pamphlet, containing chaps. i and ii, were printed in 1881
and the remainder, including chaps. iii, iv, and v and a note on bivector analysis, in 1884.
6. *Electromagnetic Theory*, Vol. I.

vector analysis on the definitions of the two kinds of products of vectors as arbitrary and violating certain shibboleths of the pure algebraist,[7] his defense always rested on the fact that this manner of presentation yielded the simplest expression of the phenomena involved and hence had the highest justification. What difference did it make if in his analysis the product of two vectors was not always another vector (as required in linear associative algebras), when such a result corresponded to a physical reality which demanded expression? Or what did it matter if another product of two vectors yielded a third vector instead of a quantity of the second order (as in Grassmann's geometrical algebra), when phenomena of electrodynamics were thereby correctly and simply portrayed? His object was not the formulation of rules for an abstract intellectual game, however interesting or important such a task might be; his purpose was the interpretation in the simplest possible manner of certain laws revealed by experiment in external nature. And as no one any longer questions the usefulness of his methods, who, in this pragmatic age, remains to quibble at their origin?

But if Gibbs in the development of his system of vector analysis was actuated by considerations of practical utility, it is not to be inferred that he was indifferent to the beauties and potentialities of the more abstract and general algebraic systems to which his own was related. As he says in the Schlegel letter, he not only perceived that his methods, although developed independently, were more akin to those of Grassmann than to those of Hamilton but he also recognized that they were only a small part of the great system envisioned by the former. His admiration for that system led him to those studies in multiple algebra in which, he frequently said in later life, he had obtained greater pleasure and satisfaction than in any of his other activities. The principal monument to these studies in pure mathematics is to be found in his vice-presidential address "On Multiple Algebra" before the American Association for the Advancement of Science (A.A.A.S.), Section of Mathematics and Astronomy, in 1886 at Buffalo.

The term "multiple algebra" denotes the algebra of quantities which require more than a single term for their definition. Thus the algebra of complex numbers is a *double* algebra, that of vectors

---

7. See, e.g., Schwarz's criticism as reported by Irving Fisher in "P.R.I."

a *triple* algebra, and that of quaternions a *quadruple* algebra. The great merit and power of Grassmann's system, as set forth so cogently in Gibbs' address, lies in its generality and inclusiveness. It is an *n*-fold algebra where *n* is any finite number and provides for several kinds of products of the *n* elements. It is in the recognition of different kinds of products that Grassmann's system differs most radically from the multiple algebras of others, such as those of Hamilton and Peirce. And it was in connection with this concept of a plurality of multiplications that Gibbs founded his principal contributions to the subject. His dot and cross products were analogous to Grassmann's "internal" and "external" products, and his indeterminate dyadic product to Grassmann's "open" product (as made clear in the Schlegel letter). The development of the dyadic analysis undoubtedly forms Gibbs' most significant contribution to multiple algebra. His recognition of the key position of the indeterminate product in the Grassmannian system and its relation to the theory of matrices, as well as his demonstration that both the algebraic and the external or combinatorial products (to which Grassmann had given the greater emphasis) could be derived from the indeterminate product, was an original contribution of great value.

As stated in the first paragraph of the Schlegel letter, one of Gibbs' principal objects in the vice-presidential address was to call attention to the fundamental importance of Grassmann's work. In preparing this address he had been handicapped, as he says in a letter of 1888 to Thomas Craig (then professor of mathematics at Johns Hopkins and editor of the *American Journal of Mathematics*), by being unable to establish Grassmann's priority over Hamilton, because a thesis of Grassmann's of 1840 on the "Tides" had never been published. As Hamilton's first paper on quaternions appeared in the same year, 1844, and one month earlier than the *Ausdehnungslehre,* Gibbs did not feel that he could publicly dispute Hamilton's priority, although he was morally certain that the ideas of Grassmann did antedate those of Hamilton. This led Gibbs to get in touch with the surviving members of Grassmann's family and to urge them to publish the thesis of 1840. A draft of a letter to one of Grassmann's sons [8] puts the whole matter so clearly that it is worth while quoting in full.

8. In the "Scientific Correspondence."

New Haven, Connecticut
Febr. 2, 1887

Dr. H. Grassmann,
    My dear Sir
    Please accept my thanks for the copy of your paper, wh I shall take pleasure in studying.

Permit me to take this opportunity to express my hope that the publication of another edition of the Ausdehnungslehre of 1862, will not be long delayed. Using that treatise in one of my classes two years ago, I had great difficulty in collecting 3 or 4 copies by borrowing, &c.

Another matter has long been on my mind. Your honored Father, in the preface to the first Ausdehnungslehre, mentions a work on the *tides* in wh he used the principles of the Ausdehnungslehre prior to its publication. If the manuscript of that work is in existence, it seems to me that its publication would be an important contribution to the history of the development of mathematical ideas in this century.

In the preparation of an address which I made recently, & of which I send you a copy, as I had occasion to trace the development of multiple algebras, it was strongly impressed upon me, that while Hamilton has given a very detailed account of the invention of his "Quaternions," & while he, very naturally and properly, hastened to put his discoveries on record, your Father, writing at the same time, more anxious to perfect his work than to place it on record, published nothing until he was able to give the world a complete treatise. This makes it, perhaps, no more than is due to his memory, & to justice, with respect to certain questions of priority, that any such work prior to the publication of the first Ausdehnungslehre, should be now published, if it is in existence. It should, I think, be published with scrupulous fidelity, & every care taken to ensure the manuscript against any danger of loss or injury while in the hands of the printer.

In any case, the manuscript should be preserved where it will be secure against accident. The next century will demand its publication, if it is in existence, & not published before.

I trust that you will excuse my urgency, attributing it, as you may, to my deep appreciation of your Father's unrivalled services, & to my interest in the cause of historical justice.

Hoping that I may soon see the essay, either in some mathematical journal, or as a separate pamphlet, or as an appendix to the next edition of the Ausdehnungslehre, which I suppose will soon appear, I remain
                                    My dear Sir
                                    very truly yours
                                    J. Willard Gibbs.

Six years elapsed before the project urged by Gibbs was consummated. Some difficulty was experienced in locating a copy of the manuscript, which was finally found in the archives of the University of Berlin where the thesis had been presented. In addition the Grassmann family was dubious as to the acceptability of the project to German publishers, in view of the scant appreciation afforded their father in that country during his lifetime. This latter obstacle led Gibbs to persuade Professor Craig, in the letter already mentioned, to agree to publish the thesis in the *American Journal of Mathematics* in case the publication in Germany proved impossible. Although this ultimately did not become necessary, the following brief excerpt from the draft of the letter to Professor Craig [9] is pertinent and interesting in further clarification of Gibbs' attitude in the matter:

I believe that a Kampf um Dasein is just commencing between the different methods and notations of multiple algebra, especially between the ideas of Grassmann & of Hamilton. The most important question is of course that of merit, but with this questions of priority are inextricably entangled, & will be certain to be the more discussed, since there are so many persons who can judge of priority to one who can judge of merit. Those who are to discuss these subjects ought to have the documents before them, & not be handicapped as I was two years ago, for want of them.

The final outcome of Gibbs' interest and activities in this matter is best told in a letter from Dr. H. Grassmann in the "Scientific Correspondence," of which the following is a free translation.

Halle a/S 23 F. 1893

Highly honored Professor:

As I learn from Professor Engel of Leipzig, he has communicated to you the manner in which the publication will be made of my father's work on the Ebb and Flow, which you in recent years have instigated. Perhaps he has not written you that now also the original of the work on the Ebb and Flow has been turned over to my brother by the Scientific Examining Board in Berlin.

For the completion of a collected edition of the mathematical and physical works of my father we have to thank primarily the energetic labors of Professor F. Klein of Gottingen, who through his wide con-

9. *Ibid.*

nections has supplied the necessary driving force for the undertaking. However the credit for stirring up interest in the matter is exclusively yours. And hence our family feels the obligation of expressing its lively gratitude. To this end therefore, in the name also of my sister, I express our combined thanks for your friendly labors in the interest of the works of our father, and sign myself

with the highest respect
most humbly
H. Grassmann

The letter from Professor Engel referred to here and one from Professor Klein, both expressing warm appreciation of Gibbs' interest in the matter, are also preserved.[10]

How right was Gibbs' opinion, as expressed to Professor Craig, that a period of "struggle for existence" between the methods and notations of Grassmann and Hamilton was imminent in the late eighties is shown by the rather acrimonious attacks upon his *Vector Analysis* which broke out in various quarters in the early nineties. Gibbs' part in this controversy [11] was sustained with vigor and cogency, but without the vituperation indulged in by his opponents, Professors Tait, Knott, and McAulay. Today these attacks appear rather puerile, motivated by a naïve belief in the sacrosanct nature of Hamilton's work, and marked by an imperfect realization of the relation of that work to the broader field of multiple algebra.[12] In these letters to *Nature* Gibbs was still handi-

---

10. *Ibid.*

11. *Nature*, Vol. *43* (April 2 and May 28, 1891; March 16 and August 17, 1893).

12. The most notorious of these criticisms was that in the preface to the third edition of Tait's *Quaternions*, in which appears the following passage: "Even Prof. Willard Gibbs must be ranked as one of the retarders of quaternion progress, in virtue of his pamphlet on *Vector Analysis*, a sort of hermaphrodite monster, compounded of the notations of Hamilton and Grassmann." Gibbs' reply to this (April 2, 1891) may be found in the *Collected Works*, II, 155–160. The passage below is worth quoting both as an example of his command of the English language and as an effective and dignified retort to an attack lacking in at least one of these qualities: "The merits or demerits of a pamphlet printed for private distribution a good many years ago do not constitute a subject of any great importance, but the assumptions implied in the sentence quoted are suggestive of certain reflections and inquiries which are of broader interest, and seem not untimely at a period when the methods and results of the various forms of multiple algebra are attracting so much attention. It seems to be assumed that a departure from quaternionic usage in the treatment of vectors is an enormity. If this assumption is true, it is an important truth; if not, it would be unfortunate if it should remain unchallenged, especially when supported by so high an authority. The criticism relates particularly to notations, but I believe that there is a deeper question of notions underlying that of notations. Indeed, if my offence had been

capped on the question of priority by the delay in the publication of Grassmann's work on the tides, and his discussions are hence almost exclusively confined to the matter of merit, both in regard to Grassmann's ideas and to his own notations. The limited outlook of Gibbs' opponents in this controversy is aptly characterized by Oliver Heaviside in a letter to Gibbs: [13]

No one would imagine from Prof. Knott's abuse of your Vector Analysis, that you had carried the theory of linear operators far beyond anything in Prof. Tait's Treatise. . . . It is curious to think that a simple matter like V.A. should be, in a sense, more advanced than the highly developed Quant^{ics}; that men should go through the latter to get to the former!

In his communications in *Nature* Gibbs employed the strategy of defense by attack in introducing a further extension of the methods and notations of his pamphlet. These additions, which he had long used in his courses at Yale and had first briefly mentioned in the Buffalo address, were concerned with the matter of double multiplication, which forms a convenient and powerful tool in the theory of rotations and strains. His researches in this field were first given in extenso in Wilson's *Vector Analysis* which was issued as one of the Yale Bicentennial Publications in 1901. With this exposition the tale of Gibbs' original contributions to mathematical theory is completed, insofar as published work goes. And with the vindication of his methods and notations afforded by the vogue of Wilson's book, we may allow the dust to settle once more on these now almost-forgotten polemics of the nineties.

There remains to be told here the story of the work in mathematics which Gibbs might have given the world if he had lived longer. It is known that shortly prior to his death he was con-

---

solely in the matter of notation, it would have been less accurate to describe my production as a monstrosity, than to characterize its dress as uncouth."

13. In the "Scientific Correspondence." With reference to this same incident Oliver Heaviside remarks on p. 138 of his *Electromagnetic Theory:* "Prof. Gibbs has recently (in the pages of *Nature*) made a powerful defence of his position. He has by a long way the best of the argument, unless Prof. Tait's rejoinder has still to appear. . . . I am able (and am happy) to express a general concurrence of opinion with him about the quaternion, and its comparative uselessness in practical vector analysis."

templating further publication in the field of multiple algebra. Professor Wilson's recollections [14] on this point are corroborated by my own. In what direction such further developments might have proceeded is of course now largely a matter of speculation. The only possible source of information on the matter available at this time lies in the notes that Gibbs left, which are preserved in the Rare Book Room of the Yale library. The pertinent material there falls into three categories. The first consists of more or less fragmentary notes covering what he was accustomed to present in his courses on vector analysis and multiple algebra. There is nothing to be found in the notes on vector analysis which is not treated in his pamphlet or in Wilson's book. The material on multiple algebra covers substantially the same ground as that presented by Wilson from lecture notes taken by G. P. Starkweather [15] and E. L. Dodd,[16] but contains additional illustrative matter. In the second category we find notes on quaternionic theory, the *Ausdehnungslehre,* Peircian analysis, etc., which were apparently made either during his early studies in multiple algebra or in preparation for the Buffalo address or the communications to *Nature* discussed above. There is nothing in the material in either of these categories that is new or that suggests any lead for further development.

There exists however—filed not with the other multiple algebra notes but with those on statistical mechanics—material of a third category in a folder labeled "Multiple Algebra for Dynamics," which contains an incomplete development of an idea that is entirely novel so far as I can ascertain, and which it seems to me may very well be the nucleus of the further publication of which Gibbs spoke to Wilson and myself. This material, whether owing to the place of its filing or to some other cause, apparently has been entirely overlooked by all of those who have previously examined the Gibbs papers. In brief it can be said that in this folder there is developed, with the aid of the invention of two new kinds of multiplication, a method of deducing the fundamental equilibrium equation of Gibbs' statistical mechanics from the

14. *The Scientific Monthly* (March, 1931).

15. "On the Theory of Double Products and Strains in Hyperspace," *Trans. Conn. Acad.,* *14* (1908), 1–57.

16. Donnan and Haas, *A Commentary,* II, 127–160.

point analysis of Grassmann. This approach, so different from that via the generalized coordinates and momenta and Hamilton's form of the equations of motion, constitutes, it seems to me, an innovation of considerable significance. The manuscript of this folder, comprising some fifty pages and bearing the two dates 1896 and 1899, is not in a form or a state of completion suitable for publication, and any detailed description of its contents would be inappropriate in the present place, and, I fear, somewhat beyond my own competence to undertake. However, that it does embody a novel point of view and one which moreover connects the two greatest interests of Gibbs' later intellectual life—multiple algebra and statistical mechanics—seems to me indubitable and worth further study by a competent scholar. Its significance will appear more clearly when we come to consider in a later chapter the other of the two topics—statistical mechanics—which are united in the material of these unpublished notes.

Aside from his work in the field of multiple algebra, Gibbs made but one contribution to mathematical theory. This consisted in the recognition and clarification of a phenomenon of the convergence of a Fourier series, the nonrecognition of which had led to some confusion and misunderstanding on the part of some physicists as to the significance of the summation of such infinite series. Gibbs' contribution was embodied in two brief letters to the editor of *Nature* in the issues of December 29, 1898, and April 27, 1899, the second of which corrected an error in the first. This error is, so far as I have been able to ascertain, the only one (aside from typographical mistakes) which occurs in any published work of Gibbs. The phenomenon which he elucidated in these two short letters has since become quite generally known among mathematicians as the "Gibbs phenomenon."

Although not a matter of pure mathematics Gibbs' paper "On the Fundamental Formulae of Dynamics" may be mentioned here. This was published in the *American Journal of Mathematics* in 1879. The form into which Gibbs here throws the indeterminate equation of motion may be regarded as a generalization of the Gaussian principle of least constraint. Aside from the applications which he makes of his equation in this paper, I know

of none which is not equally amenable to treatment by the Gaussian principle directly. Hence I believe that the novelty he introduced is of quite limited utility. But for a comparison of the
different forms into which the equations of motion may be put
there is nothing anywhere more perspicuous or enlightening.
Gibbs prepared an abstract of this paper for Königsberger's
*Repertorium reinen und angewandten Mathematik, Original-
berichte der Verfasser,* in which the abstract of the "Equilibrium
of Heterogeneous Substances" (from the *American Journal of
Science*), had previously appeared. It was never published however, owing apparently to the suspension of Königsberger's journal. As Gibbs' original abstract has been preserved and as it is the
only one of his completed manuscripts which has never before
been published, I include it as Appendix V at the end of this volume.

Although it cannot be said that Gibbs' achievement in mathematical theory was of a significance or importance equal to that
of his contributions to thermodynamics or statistical mechanics,
nevertheless it reveals entirely similar mental qualities and attitudes. Wilson says: [17] "He had a very even balance between the
intuition of the geometer and the instinct of the algebraist; a notion must be simple, fundamental, and wholly germane to the
subject; a notation must be simple, flexible, and suggestive of the
operations which would have to be carried out in numerical cases."
This carefulness in precise definition and preoccupation with the
niceties of notations were part of a conscious effort to avoid adding
to the difficulties of a physical problem any unnecessary complexity in the mathematical aids to its solution. It is something of
this sort that he meant by his remark which we have previously
quoted from Hastings: [18] " 'If I have had any success in mathematical physics, it is, I think, because I have been able to dodge
mathematical difficulties.' " Gibbs was primarily a physicist, for
whom mathematics was a tool and not an end in itself; and his
eminence in mathematics lies in his shaping of those tools to an
almost perfect adaptation to the ends for which they were designed.

17. *Ibid.,* II, 160.
18. "Josiah Willard Gibbs," p. 392.

VIII

Professor of Mathematical Physics: Optics

WE have seen from the recollections of Professor Hastings quoted in Chapter V that at the beginning of his teaching career Gibbs' chief interest was in the domain of physical optics. That this interest did not immediately find expression in research in this field was undoubtedly largely due, as Hastings suggests, to the formidable difficulties surrounding the then orthodox elastic-solid hypothesis as to the mechanism of propagation of light waves. It is true that what to certain types of mind was a way out of these difficulties had been elaborated by MacCullagh as early as 1839. The special assumptions inherent in MacCullagh's rotationally elastic ether would however have offered little attraction to Gibbs' type of mind and habits of thought even if he had been at that time acquainted with Mac-Cullagh's work—for which there is no evidence. It must be remembered that in all of his creative work Gibbs avoided reasoning based on special hypotheses as to the intimate structure of matter and consciously limited himself to problems whose solution could be based on broad general principles and the most certainly ascertained facts. Thus it is not surprising to find that he turned away from his earlier interest in physical optics, where future progress seemed to involve rather extensive speculation on the structure of matter, to his thermodynamic studies where the raw material of research comprised only the two great generalizations from experience—the first and second laws of thermodynamics.

When however he had become acquainted with Maxwell's great contribution to electrical theory—which must have been soon after the appearance of the *Treatise* in 1873—and had worked out its expression in the vector language, which exhibits its essence so perspicuously and compactly, he returned to his interest in the problems of physical optics. With this new background the solution of certain of these optical problems no longer required detailed speculation on the structure of matter but could be regarded as originating in the broad general laws of the electromagnetic field. Thus here again was a field attractive to Gibbs' peculiar genius.

Ever since the time of Young and Fresnel at the beginning of the nineteenth century the phenomena of light have been recognized as consequences of a *transverse* wave motion, that is, one in which the wave displacements take place at right angles to the direction in which they are progressing. This concept, originally sponsored by Huygens toward the end of the seventeenth century but for more than a hundred years overborne by the weight of Sir Isaac Newton's objections based on difficulties connected with the explanation of why light travels in straight lines, was finally established on a firm foundation by the work of Young and Fresnel and has since remained an unquestioned premise in all theories of light. This concept sharply differentiates light waves from those responsible for acoustic phenomena, where (in air) the wave displacements lie in the direction of propagation (longitudinal waves), or from those resulting from shocks or distortions set up in fluids or elastic solids, in which in general both transverse and longitudinal waves exist.

Thus the first task imposed on any theory of light is the explanation of the absence of the longitudinal wave in optical phenomena. It was assumed because of its finite speed that there must exist a medium through which light is propagated. But this invisible medium could not have the elastic properties of any known fluid or solid without entailing the presence of longitudinal waves. Hence the light medium or "ether" had to be endowed with properties unlike those of ordinary matter as otherwise known to us. Much ingenuity has been exercised in the specification of the properties of the ether and in attempts to reconcile its peculiarities with our innate mechanical perceptions. Only one of these attempts, that of MacCullagh, was in any degree satisfactory or successful, and they are all now only of historical significance. The electromagnetic theory which has replaced them, and according to which light waves consist of an electric field propagated from oscillating electric charges, has the great advantage that in it the possibility of a longitudinal wave is automatically eliminated. There is no necessity to invent any special mechanism to insure this condition as there was on the elastic-solid theory, for here the transversality is a simple consequence of the same laws of electricity and magnetism that govern the behavior of electric motors and dynamos. This fact, together with the result that the velocity of propagation of electromagnetic waves is the same as that of light waves, lent a great weight of a priori probability to the electromagnetic theory.

But although certain optical phenomena such as those of polarization and interference require only this transverse property for their explanation, others—particularly those involving the passage of light through solid materials—require more of a theory, inasmuch as they involve the interaction of the hypothetical ether with ordinary matter. Thus the theory must be competent to yield the conditions at the boundary between different media demanded by the well-known laws of reflection and refraction. That these conditions are also inherent in the laws of the electromagnetic field was first shown by Helmholtz in 1870. Again it is necessary that a theory give an adequate explanation of the phenomenon of double refraction exhibited by certain crystals in which we find two refracted rays instead of one, a phenomenon which Fresnel had shown could be accounted for if the wave surface in the crystal had the form of a certain ellipsoid. That this surface is a consequence of the different velocities which on the electrical hypothesis would exist owing to the different values of the dielectric constant found in three separate directions in the crystal was first shown by Maxwell in 1869.

None of the phenomena just mentioned require any special hypothesis as to the structure of the material medium. They are simple consequences of the transversality of the waves and of the dependence of their velocity on the dielectric properties of matter, both of which are implicit in the electromagnetic hypothesis. When we come however to such phenomena as dispersion—the breaking up of white light into the prismatic colors—some assumption as to the connection between the electric force in the waves and the atomic or molecular structure of the medium would seem to be necessary. The assumption usually made predicates the existence of electrical charges within the atoms or molecules which, reacting to the electric force in the wave, alter the period of vibration and thus produce the colors. This type of mechanism is that first proposed by Maxwell (1869) and is essentially the same as that invoked in the modern electron theory. In its earlier form it simply presupposed the existence of electrical charges bound to the ultimate particles which were assumed to constitute the medium, and these charges were supposed to be set into forced vibration by the alternating electrical field of the light waves. In the more modern form much that was formerly purely speculative has become experimentally established fact; the "bound" charges have become electrons whose properties and functions in the structure of matter, learned largely from other fields of experiment, have found detailed application in the derivation of formulas for the dispersion of colors. But the fundamental idea that the explanation of dispersion lies in the sympathetic vibrations of atomic or molecular charges remains as Maxwell conceived it.

However at the time Gibbs turned his attention to the problems of physical optics the idea of the electron in the modern sense had not been born, and even Maxwell's great contribution to electromagnetic theory—the idea of dielectric displacement—had not yet won universal acceptance. While the phenomena of electrolysis had from Faraday's time pointed unmistakably toward an atomic structure for electricity, the connection between such a conception and that of displacement had not been clarified nor had the role of such elementary particles in the structure of matter been visualized. Thus the orthodox explanation of dispersion (and other phenomena) seemed to Gibbs to be based on too speculative a foundation and led him to seek another method of attack on these problems as free as possible from unverifiable assumptions as to the structure of either matter or electricity. His results were published in three articles in the *American Journal of Science* in April and June, 1882, and in February, 1883.[1] The methods he developed in these papers were highly original and

1. He had also presented his results before the National Academy in November, 1882.

radically different from those used by other investigators before or since. They have not had an influence on the development of scientific thought comparable with that exerted by his work in thermodynamics or statistical mechanics, but nevertheless the results he obtained were decisive as to the validity of the electromagnetic theory. As Bumstead says in the biographical sketch prefaced to *The Scientific Papers*, in commenting on these papers and two others which compare their results with those of other theories: [2]

Of all the arguments (from theoretical grounds alone) for excluding all other theories of light except the electrical, these papers furnish the simplest, most philosophical, and most conclusive with which the present writer is acquainted; and it seems likely that the considerations advanced in them would have sufficed to firmly establish this theory even if the experimental discoveries of Hertz had not supplied a more direct proof of its validity.

In addition, this work in physical optics serves in some ways even better than that in other fields to give an insight into Gibbs' mental processes and powers, and will prove rewarding to consider in some detail.

The first assumption that Gibbs makes, that concerning the structure of matter, is that the medium must be fine grained but not infinitely so. Specifically, he considers it to be made up of exactly similar unit volumes or elements whose dimensions are small with respect to the wave length of the light traversing it (say, of the order of a fifty-thousandth of an inch) but still large enough to contain many of the ultimate particles of which it is constituted (say, having dimensions of the order of a fifty-millionth of an inch). Within each of these units the average of the motions of the particles set up by the radiation passing through may be expressed by the ordinary equations of wave motion, but the motion of an individual particle may (owing to the interaction of unknown molecular forces) differ greatly from that given by such a simple description. He thus postulates the motion in each unit volume as the sum of two parts, the average or regular motion, and the irregular motion, whose average over

2. *The Scientific Papers*, II, 223, 232. *Collected Works*, II, Pt. 2, 223, 232.

any wave plane or throughout the volume of the unit necessarily vanishes.

The next postulate of Gibbs' development, that specifying the identity of the period of the light vibrations with that of the motions set up in the medium through which it is propagated, is best stated in his own words: [3]

Let us suppose that luminous vibrations of any one period are somewhere excited, and that the disturbance is propagated through the medium. The motions which are excited in any part of the medium, and the forces by which they are kept up, will be expressed by harmonic functions of the time, having the same period, as may be proved by the single principle of the superposition of motions quite independently of any theory of the constitution of the medium, or of the nature of the motions, as electrical or otherwise. This is equally true of the actual motions, and the averages which we are to consider.

In neither of these postulates is there anything less valid now than when it was written. While the point of view embodied in both may not have been previously stated so explicitly, there is nothing in them to disturb the orthodox or to which anyone then or now could object. It was in his third assumption, that defining the relation between the electric force in the wave and the resulting motion in the medium at a given point, that Gibbs broke from precedent and employed a novel concept of the quantity "displacement." This term, introduced by Maxwell, was used by him to denote only that motion of electricity in response to electric force which results from the elastic reaction of the medium, and did not include those motions of convection of charge which constitute electric currents. In Gibbs' use of the term he includes both the elastic and the convective parts of the resulting motion, thus making the relation between force and displacement in electric waves an exact analogue of that holding in the case of mechanical and acoustic waves. Although subsequent writers have preferred to retain Maxwell's definition, that of Gibbs is dynamically sound and leads, as he showed, without further detailed assumptions as to the structure of matter, to a correct portrayal of the results of experiment.

Gibbs' final postulate has to do with the relation between the

3. *The Scientific Papers*, II, 213. *Collected Works*, II, Pt. 2, 213.

regular and the irregular displacements. In the first of his three papers he makes the assumption that the irregular are linear functions of the regular displacements, and shows that no further assumptions are necessary in order to explain all the optical properties of transparent bodies except that of circular polarization. In the second paper he shows that the explanation of this last phenomenon is obtained if the irregular are supposed to be linear functions not only of the regular displacements but also of their space rates of change.

The method by which these results are obtained is as ingenious as it is simple. The actual displacement is considered as due to a *stationary* wave system in the medium, and the kinetic energy at the instant of maximum velocity is equated to the potential energy at the instant of zero velocity. From this equation can be found the velocity of the progressive waves of which the stationary system is compounded. Now if in the expression for the kinetic energy only that due to the average or regular displacement is taken into account, then the velocity thus found will represent only the average velocity of the light through the medium and will not show any of the effects attributable to its molecular structure. But if in the expression for the kinetic energy there are included those terms due to the irregular displacement, then there appear in the expression for the velocity of the radiation additional terms which are shown to yield explanations of those phenomena that depend on molecular structure. The expressions found are in accord with experimental results, and the phenomena elucidated include those of double refraction occurring in certain crystals, the dispersion of colors (including that of the optic axes in double refracting crystals), and those of the natural rotary polarization shown by some substances such as the sugars. These diverse phenomena are deduced from the postulates simply as logical consequences of general dynamical principles applied to the action of electrical forces.

In the third paper the restriction to transparent media is removed and there is deduced a general equation governing the propagation of monochromatic radiation (that having a single frequency) through media of every degree of transparency. The development is made in terms of the average or regular displacement, and the explanation of the phenomena treated in detail in the two previous papers is made to depend on a suitable definition of the relation between the electric force, the displacement, and its rate of change. The propagation equation of Gibbs differs (except in the case of transparent media) from that of Maxwell, owing to the different definition of electric displacement. The Maxwellian equation for absorbing media (i.e., those possessing some degree of electrical conductivity) yields results in terms of the experimentally determined dielectric constant and conductivity of the medium; but without the aid of additional assumptions, such as were later furnished by the electron theory, is incompetent to explain certain of the dispersion phenomena associated with absorbing media. With Gibbs' equation, on the other hand, all of these phenomena receive an adequate explanation without further assumptions. His formula however does not yield results directly in terms of experimental parameters. They are thus not immediately comparable with the results of experiment. Nevertheless in no case do they contradict the experimental findings, as do those of the Maxwellian equation unmodified by the special assumptions of the electron theory.

In these three papers we see the working of a mind that sought to synthesize the diverse phenomena of the extensive field of physical optics through the principles of dynamics alone, the electrodynamic force and the electric displacement being related in an analogous manner to that subsisting between mechanical forces and displacements. In a domain and at a time when other investigators were content to develop the theory piecemeal and to rely on special assumptions to meet the difficulties as they arose, Gibbs showed, in his own words,[4] "how a point of view more in accordance with what we know of the molecular constitution of bodies will give that part of the ordinary theory which is verified by experiment, without including that part which is in opposition to observed facts." In none of his work in other fields is this power of all-embracing synthesis in terms of fundamental dynamical principles shown in a more striking manner. Here is seen clearly a basic trait of all of Gibbs' thinking: the avoidance

4. *Collected Works*, II, Pt. 2, 221.

of guesswork or any form of wishful thinking. He seems to say here more plainly than anywhere else, let us explore *all* of the possibilities of the known methods to see if it is necessary to invoke speculation about the unknown.

The failure of later investigators to make use of Gibbs' methods in this field and in particular to adopt his definition of displacement is probably to be attributed to the prestige of Maxwell's name, together with the fact that most physicists are less allergic than was Gibbs to speculation based on uncertain though not impossible grounds. Also the emergence of the electron theory into the realm of established fact has radically changed the picture and caused Gibbs' objections to the Maxwellian point of view to lose some of their force. Nevertheless, the simplicity of his assumptions and mathematical methods and their freedom from the necessity for any particular structure for matter would seem to indicate that Gibbs' method of attack will still repay study in an age which has discarded the ether and when the subject is more beset by mathematical than by physical complications.

The decade of the 1880's was the last in which the old mechanistic point of view for the explanation of physical phenomena reigned supreme and virtually unchallenged. In the 1890's with the determination of the physical properties of the electron and the discovery of the X rays and radioactivity a new era in physics was ushered in. But in the eighties, although the mechanical elastic-solid theory of light was putting up a losing fight for acceptance, the underlying idea that there must be a mechanical explanation of the phenomena also permeated the electromagnetic theory and dominated the development of the conceptions of the light medium or ether. This mechanistic basis of scientific thought, solidly founded on the many successes it had achieved in the past in unraveling many of nature's secrets in diverse fields, gave way but slowly to the realization that electricity and not matter was the fundamental entity and that instead of an ether, with all its difficulties from the mechanical standpoint, empty space through which electrical forces could act might suffice.

Although to the best of my knowledge Gibbs never abandoned the idea of an ether, he did combat the ultramechanistic interpretation of its properties as those of an elastic solid. In addition to the three papers already discussed another was published in June, 1888,[5] in which he showed conclusively, as indeed he had previously, though in less detail, in a review of Ketteler's *Theoretische Optik*,[6] that an elastic-solid theory in which the longitudinal wave was disposed of by supposing its velocity to be infinite (the medium absolutely incompressible) could not yield the Fresnel ellipsoid in doubly refractive media, whereas that ellipsoid was a direct consequence of the electromagnetic theory. In this paper he also reiterated the objections to the elastic-solid theory which he had elaborated in more detail in his 1882 paper, based on its inadequacy to explain the phenomena of dispersion without further special assumptions.

However in the fall of the same year (1888) new life was breathed into the body of the elastic-solid theory by a brilliant suggestion of Sir William Thomson. Sir William, who confessedly had never understood Maxwell's theory, now proposed in a paper in the November issue of the *Philosophical Magazine* that the bête noir of the elastic-solid theory—the longitudinal wave—be met by supposing the ether to be indefinitely compressible (in which case the velocity of the longitudinal wave would vanish), and that the resultant instability of such a medium be counteracted by supposing it to be attached to and supported by the boundaries of space. In answer to this new, and as it has turned out to be, final form of an elastic-solid theory Gibbs published the last paper he was to write on optical matters.[7] In this paper, after showing that (except for the dispersion of colors) the new version of the elastic-solid hypothesis led to the same results as did the electromagnetic theory, he concluded with the following two paragraphs[8] which state the case as between the rival theories as compactly and cogently as can be found anywhere:

It is evident that the electrical theory of light has a serious rival, in a sense in which, perhaps, one did not exist before the publication of Sir William Thomson's paper in November last. Nevertheless, neither surprise at the results which have been achieved, nor admiration for that happy audacity of genius, which, seeking the solution of the problem pre-

5. *Am. Journ. Sci.*, ser. 3, *35*, 467–475. *Collected Works*, II, Pt. 2, 223–231.
6. *Am. Journ. Sci.*, ser. 3, *31*, 62–67. *Collected Works*, II, Pt. 2, 249–252.
7. *Am. Journ. Sci.*, ser. 3, *37*, 139. *Collected Works*, II, Pt. 2, 232.
8. *Collected Works*, II, Pt. 2, 245–246.

cisely where no one else would have ventured to look for it, has turned
half a century of defeat into victory, should blind us to the actual state
of the question.

It may still be said for the electrical theory, that it is not obliged to invent hypotheses, but only to apply the laws furnished by the science of
electricity, and that it is difficult to account for the coincidences between
the electrical and the optical properties of media, unless we regard the
motions of light as electrical. But if the electrical character of light is
conceded, the optical problem is very different from anything which
existed in the time of Fresnel, Cauchy, and Green. The third wave, for
example, is no longer something to be gotten rid of *quocunque modo,*
but something which we must dispose of in accordance with the laws of
electricity. This would seem to rule out the possibility of a relatively
small velocity for the third wave.

In these modern times when through the medium of radio
broadcasting the idea of electromagnetic waves has become a
commonplace even to the man in the street, and when to the
physicist they have become such an unquestioned element in the
background of much of his thinking that the recent discovery of
the wave characteristics of the electron and the development of
"wave mechanics" have come simply as necessary extensions of the
older ideas, it is somewhat difficult to realize that the electromagnetic theory ever had to fight for acceptance—that the question of the possible existence of the "third wave" was ever a live
issue. The notion of electric waves has become so fundamental
in so many domains that the controversies of earlier times possess for us somewhat of an archaic flavor, an aura of unreality.
But in the 1880's and before the significance of Hertz's discoveries
had been assimilated the issue was real and of a compelling interest, and nowhere is this more vividly shown than in these
papers of Gibbs. Further evidence of the contemporary importance of the question is to be found in Gibbs' interest in finding
experimental as well as theoretical grounds for denying the existence of the compressional or longitudinal wave in optics. This is
described by Hastings in his *Biographical Memoir* as follows: [9]
When he was engaged upon his recondite analysis of the elastic theories
of light he found what looked like a possible way of eluding the very
great difficulties which come from the apparent non-existence of the com-

9. "Josiah Willard Gibbs," p. 388.

pressural wave system; the tentative explanation, however, involved the occurrence of certain phenomena in specular reflection which had never been seen or, at least, recorded. As it did not seem to him that such negative evidence was conclusive, he constructed an apparatus with his own hands so perfectly adapted to the end in view that his observations afforded the proof sought. A striking light is thrown upon the character of the great physicist by the fact that no reference to this theory, which must have cost much critical study, appears in his writings, nor is it known that any one except the present writer ever saw the apparatus and made the experiment for which it was designed. Its only lasting effect was to add to the conviction, not at that time invincible, that the electromagnetic nature of light must be accepted as a verity.

The above is the only account that survives of this sole known excursion that Gibbs made into the field of experimental physics. The apparatus itself has not been preserved, and the only hint as to its nature is in a recollection of Gibbs' nephew, Professor Ralph G. Van Name,[10] who says that when he was a boy some ten years of age his uncle showed him a piece of apparatus he had built which may possibly have been that to which Hastings refers. However it is difficult to see from Professor Van Name's description of the contrivance how it could have been used to demonstrate any new or unrecorded phenomena of specular reflection; at least neither I nor any of the others with whom I have discussed the matter have been able to reconstruct in what the experiment could have consisted. As to Gibbs himself having left no reference to the experiment, the most probable explanation would seem to be that he soon came to realize that the direct experimental proof of the existence of electromagnetic waves by Hertz (1887), together with the theoretical considerations already published, was adequately conclusive on the matter without further appeal to experiment.

One further matter, to conclude the account of Gibbs' contributions in this field, may be mentioned here. This though not strictly a question of optics is still a matter of electromagnetic waves. It arose from another of Lord Kelvin's attempts to cast doubt on Maxwell's theory, and is particularly vivid in my memory as the incident occurred while I was still a student in Gibbs'

10. "P.R.I.," contribution of Ralph G. Van Name.

classes. In February of 1896 Kelvin suggested the problem of determining the effect on a spark gap of the discharge of another gap at a distance from the first. Gibbs' solution, which he presented first in his course in electricity and magnetism, was published in the issue of *Nature* for April 2 of that year. It contains in a very compact vector form all the essentials of the theory of the radiation from a Hertzian oscillator, with its three systems of spherical waves near the origin and its single system of plane waves at a distance, all propagated with the velocity of light. From this it follows that the answer to Kelvin's problem is that the discharge of the first gap will take place on the arrival of the wave originated at the discharge of the distant gap. Today this answer is sufficiently obvious, but at a time when an experimental answer was beyond the available technical resources and when there were still those who like Kelvin were unconvinced of the validity of Maxwell's formulation of the electromagnetic field equations this solution of Gibbs was an effective contribution to their ultimate acceptance.

IX

Widening Contacts

I T was during the year 1883, in which the third of the papers on the electromagnetic theory of light appeared, that the first Sloane Physics Laboratory was built, and in it Gibbs' study and classroom were located for the remaining twenty years of his life. He had previously occupied a study in one of the dormitories of the Old Brick Row,[1] but it is not known definitely where he met his classes before Sloane was erected. According to a story told by the late Dean Wilbur Cross, these classes probably used a room on the ground floor of the old Treasury Building, which stood near the middle of the Old Campus.[2] The story runs that as Henry A. Beers, then professor of English, was passing along the corridor which ran through the building and formed a part of one of the main cross-campus walks he heard some peculiar whimpering noises coming from one of the classrooms. On opening the door Professor Beers found three people inside, two seated and writing furiously in notebooks and the third, Professor Gibbs, standing at a blackboard, covering it with minute characters and *crying* over them! Beers' description is as understandable as it is amusing if one keeps in mind that Gibbs had a naturally rather high-pitched voice, and probably happened to be suffering from a cold in the head.

But wherever Gibbs' study or classroom may have been located before 1883, his quarters in the new laboratory building were pleasant and commodious. As I remember it, his study on the second floor (which he also used as the meeting place for his

1. Personal recollection of Willard Gibbs Van Name.

2. This building was originally erected in 1831 from money raised largely through the efforts of Professor Benjamin Silliman, Sr., to house the Trumbull paintings. After the removal of the Trumbull collection to the Art School in 1867 the offices of the president and the treasurer were located on the upper floor, while classrooms (in my time used by the Department of Music) occupied the ground floor. The building is no longer standing.

smaller classes) was a bright room with three large windows, one on the north and two on the east side. It was plainly, not to say severely, furnished with tables, chairs, bookshelves, and a large movable blackboard. There was no desk and Gibbs did all of his writing at a large table in the northeast corner. The blackboard was usually placed across the northwest corner and as occasion might demand a second portable blackboard was brought in. There was no apparatus of filing cabinets, desk memorandum pads, or pen and inkstands. He used for the most part a stylographic pen, and his notes were kept in Manila folders and stored in drawers in the table or in orderly piles on the bookshelves. One unusual piece of desk furniture was a small black sphere resting in a cradle formed of two wooden crosspieces with semicircular cut-out portions to receive the sphere, and on which great circles, spherical angles, triangles, et cetera could be drawn with chalk. In my recollection this was usually present on the table and was constantly used to aid in visualizing spatial relations. Other models, such as plaster ellipsoids of Fresnel's wave surface in uniaxial and biaxial crystals, and of course the thermodynamic surface, were kept on the bookshelves and displayed on the table as the course he was giving might require; but the little black sphere was practically continuously in evidence. The writing table always presented a neat and orderly appearance whether one entered by appointment or unannounced. There was never any sign of the confusion associated in the popular mind with the surroundings of the "absent-minded professor" busy with thoughts beyond others' comprehension.

Such was Willard Gibbs' sanctum. In a sense this room with its simple utilitarian furnishing and the bright, clear light from its ample window spaces was symbolic of the mind of its occupant, where no shadows blurred his intellectual vision and no distractions of immaterial things confused the picture. It is in these surroundings that he should be visualized, as with much pacing back and forth he pursued, in the words of Wordsworth, his "Voyaging through strange seas of thought alone."

From this time on he was not as isolated in his intellectual life as he had been previously. It is true that he continued to the end to perform his creative work with little if any stimulus from other living minds. But from the mid-eighties on his advice and co-operation on scientific matters were increasingly sought both by scientific bodies and by individual scientists. In the "Scientific Correspondence" there are preserved some forty-five letters bearing signatures well known in the scientific world and containing requests for advice on technical matters or for discussion of points of current scientific interest. The subjects covered in this correspondence range from mathematical points raised by J. J. Sylvester, E. H. Moore, H. Buchholz, and A. McAulay, through the meteorological and aerodynamical queries of Cleveland Abbe and S. P. Langley, the thermodynamic questions propounded by G. F. Becker, E. H. Griffiths, W. D. Bancroft, and J. E. Trevor, problems in the theory of light discussed by Langley, A. A. Michelson, and Lord Rayleigh, to points in kinetic theory and statistical mechanics suggested by S. H. Burbury and Lord Kelvin.

Unfortunately few of Gibbs' replies to these letters have been preserved. Two of them have been published in the *Collected Works*—one to Bancroft on thermodynamic matters as the ninth item of Volume I and the other to Buchholz on the vector method for the computation of orbits as the sixth of Volume II, Part 2. Two others, the first a reply to Lord Rayleigh's questions on certain points in optical theory and the second in reply to Langley's problem on the possibility of the soaring flight of an unpowered plane, have recently been published by E. B. Wilson in the *Proceedings of the National Academy of Sciences* for January and August, 1945. Aside from these four, only three additional replies in this category are preserved in the "Scientific Correspondence." One contains a rather destructive criticism of two manuscripts submitted by G. F. Becker; the second, to A. McAulay, is an unimportant footnote to the controversy over vector notations alluded to in Chapter VII; [3] and the third is a discussion of a

3. This letter closes with a sly bit of humor about the limitations of the quaternionic as contrasted with the flexibility of his own notations, which is perhaps worth quoting: "In quaternion analysis the ∇ and the σ are like the fox and the goose in the story wh could not be left alone together." The purpose of the letter as stated at the beginning was to illustrate in greater detail than would have been appropriate in a published article some of the points he had made in his letter of April 2, 1891, to *Nature*. That the above quotation did not appear in print is illuminating both as to Gibbs' sense of dignity in public controversy and as to his gift for homely and apt retort in private.

point in kinetic theory raised by Lord Kelvin which, as its interest lies in its connection with statistical theory, can be more appropriately treated in the following chapter.

Of the published replies those in the *Collected Works* are undoubtedly the most important as containing expansions and clarifications of his ideas in thermochemistry and the theory of orbit computation. That Gibbs himself regarded the letter to Bancroft as of some importance may be inferred from the fact that it was included among his manuscript notes for additional work on thermodynamic theory which he was contemplating at the time of his death. It is also known that he had in mind at that time [4] certain improvements in the vector method for the computation of elliptic and parabolic orbits which he had published in 1889; [5] and the letter to Buchholz may very well have served as an introduction to this. Incidentally it may be remarked that among the notes in the Yale library there is included a very large amount of computational work which Gibbs had carried out in the course of testing his method and which may possibly include some embodying the improvements mentioned to Wilson.[6] At any rate the volume of this material is evidence of the importance which he attached to the vector method. That he was not alone in his appreciation of "the convenience and perspicuity of vector notations in this subject," as he expresses it in the Buchholz letter, is shown by the work of W. Fabritius [7] and by the fact that the National Academy paper was reprinted in the third edition of Klinkerfues' *Astronomy*. That Gibbs was at some pains to call the attention of

4. E. B. Wilson, *The Scientific Monthly* (March, 1931).

5. *Memoirs of the National Academy of Science* (1889), Vol. IV, Pt. 2.

6. These notes and calculations on orbits left by Gibbs have recently been carefully scrutinized by Dr. Samuel Herrick in connection with a monograph on Gibbs' method to be published shortly. He has found among these notes what is apparently an unfinished manuscript of a further publication on the method. This is undated, but from a letter of Professor B. A. Gould (then editor of the *Astronomical Journal*) dated October 16, 1889, to Gibbs in the "Scientific Correspondence," which cordially welcomes a paper on the subject (or any other subject) from Gibbs, it seems a safe inference that the material identified by Herrick is the manuscript of the projected paper. Why it was never published is still not clear, but the reason may be connected with the opinion expressed to Wilson, (*Scientific Monthly*, March, 1931) that astronomers had not enough interest in the method to make its publication worth while.

7. "Ueber eine leichte Methode der Bahnbestimmung mit Zugrundlegung des Princips von Gibbs," and "Weitere Anwendungen des Gibbs'chen Princips," *Astronomische Nachrichten*, Nos. 3061, 3065 (1891).

practical computers to the method is evidenced by his sending reprints of the paper to no fewer than 199 persons, and also by a letter
(included in the "Scientific Correspondence") from the astronomer
Asaph Hall who remarks:

You need have no fear, I think, that astronomers will not adopt any
real improvements in their methods of computing. In fact it is curious to
see how a set of computers will find out the easiest way to do a piece of
work. This way is not always the shortest, but it is the one requiring the
smallest amount of physical and mental labor. The computer is a real
mercenary, and does not care for the reputation of anybody. He is like
a stream finding its way down a mountain side,—a good illustration of
the principle of least action.

That Gibbs' method has not attained a wider acceptance may very
well be due to the fact that, although a shorter road, it requires too
much mental labor for the "mercenary" computer in acquiring
facility in the use of vectors.

Of the two letters recently published by Wilson that to Lord Rayleigh (dated June 27, 1892) is of interest in its showing Gibbs' continued partiality for his heterodox point of view with regard to
electric displacement as affording the simplest way of accounting
for dispersion. It also possesses some interest for his comments in
reply to one of Rayleigh's queries as to the expression for the
potential energy in Lord Kelvin's quasi-labile theory of the ether
which Gibbs had recently (1889) published and upon which I
have commented in the last chapter. This letter also contains an interesting and characteristic reply to a suggestion that Gibbs bring
out a book on thermodynamics, on the ground that the "Equilibrium of Heterogeneous Substances" was too condensed to be
easily understood. Gibbs' reply was: "I thank you very much for
your kind interest in my 'Equilib. Het. Subst.' I myself had come
to the conclusion that the fault was that it was too *long*. I do not
think that I had any sense of the value of time, of my own or of
others', when I wrote it."

It may seem strange that Gibbs should express such an opinion
in view of the fact that at the time of his death he was contemplating a revision and extension of his thermodynamic work. But it
may be that Rayleigh in his suggestion and Gibbs in his reply were

thinking about two different things: that the former was referring to an expansion of the relatively quite condensed first part of the memoir, published in 1876, and the latter to the elaborately developed sections on solids and surface phenomena of the second part. On the other hand, the explanation may lie in a change in viewpoint due to events of the interval between 1892 and 1902. It must be remembered that the former date came at the close of a period during which he had given scant attention to thermodynamic matters. In the following year (1893) he first began to lecture regularly on the subject of his own researches, and it is not impossible that his experience with his classes in the course on thermodynamics and the properties of matter in the next decade may have caused him to change his opinion as to the necessity for a fuller exposition of the subject. Further, a perusal of some of his later correspondence, particularly that with the editors of the *Journal of Physical Chemistry,* suggests the surmise that in this correspondence he found confirmation of the need for more explanation, with examples, to bring to chemists a realization of the usefulness of the concept of the chemical potential. It seems to me that while a sense of overelaboration in the second part of the memoir may very well have determined the form of his reply to Rayleigh in 1892, it was his subsequent experiences which finally decided him to expand his thermodynamic contributions into book form.

Another interesting point in this exchange is the evidence it affords of the esteem in which Gibbs was held by one of the greatest of English physicists. In it Rayleigh approaches Gibbs with the deference accorded a master who would know all the answers, and Gibbs replies with an assurance and a clarity that completely justify Rayleigh's attitude.

The letter to Langley (dated May 30, 1894) is of interest as embodying an ingenious and simple method of attack on the problem of free-soaring flight. Considering the embryonic state of aerodynamic theory at this early date we cannot fail to admire, with Langley, Gibbs' "original and distinctive" solution of the problem. That the formula Gibbs obtained was not easily amenable to development in a form suitable for design purposes accounts for the fact that Langley apparently made little use of it, although in a later letter [8] he continued to express his interest in it. In this problem, so foreign to his other interests at this time, the working of Gibbs' mind shows a clear resemblance to that of the young inventor of the 1860's.

Among the letters in the "Scientific Correspondence" to which no answers have been preserved the most important are the six from Albert A. Michelson. Both from the historical significance of the questions he raises and from the fact that Gibbs' views on these questions are nowhere a matter of record, it is unfortunate that the replies, particularly to the first one of the series, have not been preserved.[9] The queries in this first letter, as containing one of the earliest descriptions of the famous Michelson-Morley experiment which became ultimately so large a factor in the development of Einsteinian relativity, make the letter worthy of quotation in full.

CASE SCHOOL OF APPLIED SCIENCE

Cleveland, O. Dec 15 1884

My dear Professor Gibbs,

I have delayed so long the acknowledgement of your kindness in sending me your papers on "Electromagnetic theory" and "Vector Analysis," that I am a little in doubt whether it is still "better late than never."

I have had such a press of work that thus far I have not had leisure to study them but hope to do so soon.

I had the pleasure of talking with Sir William Thomson and Ld. Rayleigh, on the subject of influence of motion of media on propagation of light, and they both seemed to think that my first step should be to repeat Fizeau's experiment.

I have accordingly ordered the required apparatus and hope to be able to settle the question within a few months.

Meanwhile, I should very much like to have an opinion from you concerning the feasibility of the experiment which I described to you rather hastily at our last meeting,[10] namely:—

1st. Granting that the effect of the atmosphere may be neglected, and supposing that the earth is moving relatively to the ether at about 20 miles per second would there be a difference of about one hundred-millionth in the time required for light to return to its starting point,

8. In the "Scientific Correspondence."

9. I have made every effort to locate these replies. The authorities at the University of Chicago, with which Michelson was connected at the time of his death, have been most cordial in aiding in the search, but to no avail.

10. Probably at the National Academy meeting in New Haven in November, 1883.

when the direction is parallel to the earth's velocity—and that when the direction is at right angles? 2nd. Would this necessitate a movement of the interference fringes produced by the two rays?

3rd. If these are answered in the affirmative, provided the experiment is made so far above the surface of the earth that solid matter does not intervene, what would be the result if the experiment were made in a room?

Trusting that I am not imposing on your good nature by propounding these conundrums and hoping to hear from you

I remain

Very sincerely yours

Albert A. Michelson

Now Gibbs to the best of my knowledge never discussed in public or in private the theory or the implications of this celebrated experiment, the first results of which were published some three years after the date of this letter. In fact his silence on these matters even in the classroom would seem almost to amount to a conscious avoidance of any discussion of the electrodynamics of moving media and that at a time when the subject was a very live one in the world of physics. This reticence on a scientific matter, like that we have seen him exhibit on political and religious topics, is probably to be ascribed to an innate tendency to avoid an expression of opinion on anything where he had not thoroughly explored all the implications or where for any other reason he was not entirely sure of his ground. Nevertheless it would be more satisfactory if in this instance we were in possession of the more positive evidence which it would seem possible might have been contained in his part of the Michelson correspondence. That he did reply to this letter is a fairly certain inference from the cordial tone of the remaining letters of the series. These are mostly concerned with answers to inquiries from Gibbs as to the numerical results obtained in the repetition of the Fizeau experiment. These data Gibbs used in his review of Newcomb and Michelson's determination of the velocity of light which was published in 1886 in the *American Journal of Science* [11] and also in his letter that same year to *Nature* [12] on the question of whether it is the group or the phase velocity that is measured in the revolving-mirror method of Foucault.

11. *Collected Works*, II, 247.
12. *Ibid.*, p. 253.

Another case in which the absence of Gibbs' replies is regrettable occurs in the correspondence with his former pupil Professor Eliakim Hastings Moore. In a letter dated June 21, 1902, Moore asks if Gibbs can supply a proof for a theorem in multiple algebra which he says Gibbs had sent him in a letter written when Moore was a student in Berlin in 1886–87. He states that he had frequently reread this letter and had unsuccessfully attempted to find a proof for the theorem himself. It is possible that the further work in multiple algebra of which Gibbs spoke in the conversation with Wilson mentioned in Chapter VII may have included a proof of this theorem, concerning which Moore remarks, "This is certainly a very general theorem and as you said, one with the widest application."

Gibbs' response to requests for advice or cooperation from scientific bodies was apparently less cordial than to those from individuals. Given his character as we have seen it, the reasons for this are not far to seek. Such requests usually involved travel, of which he was not fond, or implied participation in a public discussion of matters on which he had already published all that he felt he had to say, or were concerned with subjects of which he felt incompetent to speak—at least without more study than the work upon which he happened to be engaged would permit. The sole appointment to an important committee which he accepted was that as Commissioner to the National Conference of Electricians at Philadelphia [13] in 1884, and this only on the urgent insistence of Professor Rowland, who wrote, "Can you not accept even if you cannot come as we wish the weight of your name?" In that same year he declined an appointment to the board of examiners for the International Electrical Exposition.

He showed a similar reluctance to accept invitations to attend or address large meetings or conventions. Thus he refused two separate invitations to meetings of the British Association for the Advancement of Science, one extended in 1887 by Oliver Lodge and the other by R. T. Glazebrook in 1893, although he did, as noted on p. 98, contribute to the discussions of the earlier meeting in writ-

13. The certificate of appointment, over the signature of President Arthur, is preserved in the Yale library, together with the diplomas, membership certificates, and other honors received by Gibbs.

ing. At the same period he also declined to participate in the mathematical exhibition of the German Mathematical Society and the Association of German Naturalists and Physicians held in Nürnberg (1892), to which Ludwig Boltzmann sent him a personal invitation. In fact the only large conventions he is known to have attended were the Montreal meeting of the B.A.A.S. in the summer of 1884 and the A.A.A.S. Buffalo meeting in 1886, where he served as one of the sectional vice-presidents.

Further evidence of his avoidance of public appearances, except when little travel was required or he had some original matter to present, may be seen in the record of his attendance at the meetings of the National Academy of Sciences.[14] In the twenty-three years of his membership in that body he is recorded as attending but seven of the forty-six scheduled meetings, and four of those seven were held in New Haven. In that time he read but three papers: one at a New York meeting (1882) entitled "On the General Equations of Optics as Derived from the Electromagnetic Theory of Light," at a time just prior to the publication of the studies discussed in the last chapter; one at a Washington meeting (1887), with the title "On the Determination of Orbits of Planets and Comets," on which, as we have seen, his published work appeared in 1889; and the third at the New Haven meeting in 1894, "On a Certain Theorem in Theoretical Mechanics," which formed part of the material for his *Statistical Mechanics,* published in 1902. In fact, the record shows that he attended but one meeting held outside of New Haven at which he did not read a paper and that the three papers read were all reports of important new and unpublished material.

Several requests for his cooperation during the years he was engaged in preparing the *Statistical Mechanics* for the press were quite understandably declined. One (1899) was an invitation from J. J. Thomson to contribute to a volume of the *Proceedings of the Cambridge Philosophical Society* celebrating the jubilee of Sir George Stokes as secretary of the Royal Society. Another later in the same year invited Gibbs to participate in an international congress on philosophy in Paris by a contribution to its *Proceedings* even if he could not attend. And in 1900 and 1901 he was asked by Professor H. Kammerlingh Omnes for contributions to anniver-

14. These data were obtained for me through the kindness of Professor E. B. Wilson.

sary volumes in honor of Professors H. A. Lorentz and J. Bosscha. Acceding to even one of these requests would have interrupted the work on his book which he had agreed to have ready for publication as one of the series to be issued in celebration of the two hundredth anniversary of the founding of Yale College.

When it came however to cooperation which did not include a scientific contribution or the necessity for travel, the invitation met with a prompt and cordial response. Among such as are preserved in the "Scientific Correspondence" may be mentioned a request for advice on the selection of honorary members from the secretary of the American Academy (Boston) in 1889; an appeal from Professor H. P. Bowditch of Harvard for aid in raising money for a Helmholtz memorial in 1891; and a proposal to act as one of the sponsors in establishing a medal and a prize in honor of J. J. Sylvester in 1897.[15] In such matters it appears that his advice and co-operation were sought not only for the weight and prestige which his name would contribute but also for the practical utility of his suggestions. This side of Gibbs' character—his efficiency in the practical affairs of life—is one that has been little appreciated outside of his immediate family. Nevertheless there is ample evidence attesting his competence in such matters. Within the family not only was he the handy man who could be relied upon to meet household emergencies adequately as they arose but it was his advice and counsel that were depended upon in the matter of investments and on financial matters in general.[16] Outside of the family his sagacity and competence in mundane affairs were recognized by his appointment as a trustee of the Hopkins Grammar School in 1881 and as the secretary and treasurer of that body in 1886, in both of which offices he served for the remainder of his life. Thus both in his professional relationships and in those of the family and community we get a picture of a well-balanced mind as efficient in the ordinary affairs of life as it was in scientific research.

15. It may also be mentioned that Gibbs had earlier cooperated in the establishment of a memorial to Maxwell. A letter from A. Freeman dated July 9, 1880, acknowledges the receipt of a contribution of five guineas from Gibbs for that purpose.

16. "P.R.I.," contributions of W. G. Van Name and R. G. Van Name.

X

Professor of Mathematical Physics: Statistical Mechanics

THE question how far it is possible, given adequate tools and vision, to subdivide a given piece of matter has always exerted a fascination on the mind of man. From the earliest times the advocates of infinite divisibility—those postulating that bodies form continua so that there could be no limitation (in the imagination) on the process of division—have been vocal and persistent. And indeed there is considerable justification for this view. Many of the properties of liquid bodies are even today simply, accurately, and fully expressible in terms of this hypothesis. But it is also true that the opposing idea of a limited divisibility, although not yielding so simple an explanation of the properties of liquids, nevertheless does furnish an account of those properties which is equally accurate and complete and in addition supplies a more adequate theory of the properties of other forms and states of matter. Hence in portraying the basis of our modern conceptions of matter and in trying to make clear the relation to them of Gibbs' work in statistical mechanics, it is with this opposing point of view that we have to deal.

The idea that matter is not indefinitely divisible—that every material body consists of enormous numbers of discrete particles or atoms—is one of the oldest physical speculations of which we have a record. It first appears in the teachings of Leucippus and Democritus in the fifth century B.C. although most of our knowledge of these early conceptions is derived from the poem *De rerum natura* of Lucretius, dating from the first century B.C. From this work we can infer that the notion owed its origin to an attempt to explain such things as the existence of the various crystalline forms exhibited by gem materials, the diffusion of odors, and the pressure of gases. No experimental evidence, in the modern sense, was adduced for these speculations. They consisted for the most part of dogmatic assertions such as "No atom can ever stop giving up its motion to its neighbor." No attempt at a quantitative formulation of the properties of bodies in terms of the hypothesis was made. And yet the basic conceptions as set forth in Lucretius' poem are in general still essential parts of the modern kinetic theory of matter.

But although the atomic hypothesis may thus be said to be now some two and a half millennia old, it cannot be said to have had a period of development of any such extent. With other scientific ideas dimly adumbrated in Greco-Roman times and forgotten during the intellectual stagnation under the authoritative domination of the long "age of faith," it had to await its fruition after the rebirth of individual initiative which followed on the fall of the Byzantine empire and the rediscovery of the science of the classical age. Even if with Schuster [1] we date the birth of the modern scientific method with the publication of Galileo's *Dialogues* in 1632, we must still wait more than a century to read the next chapter in the development of the atomic idea. For although it was anticipated qualitatively by Gassendi and Hooke in the seventeenth century, it was not until 1738 that Daniel Bernoulli, last of the great triumvirate of the celebrated Dutch-Swiss family, first derived an exact expression for the pressure exerted by a gas in terms of the motions of its assumed constituent particles or atoms, and thus initiated the modern interpretation of the properties of bodies in terms of the motions of their constituent particles. This was followed in the early 1800's by the employment of the idea of a discrete structure to bring system into the problems of chemical combination, and as a consequence, the evolution of the concept of the molecule, or group of tightly bound atoms, as the unit effective in the chemical combinations of the elements. This advance was due principally to Dalton and Avogadro. Finally, it was barely a century ago, after the establishment of the first law of thermodynamics, that this idea of the molecular structure of matter began to develop into a considerable body of physical doctrine, which started

1. Presidential address before the B.A.A.S., 1916.

with the work of Joule and Clausius in the 1850's and was perfected through the achievements of Maxwell and Boltzmann. Thus the real history of the atomic idea covers less than two and a half centuries in contrast with the twenty-five hundred years since the first conception of its fundamental postulate.

The modern theory of the properties of bodies as dependent on the motions of their atoms or molecules is founded on a combination of the principles of *mechanics* with those of *probability*. Both of these branches of science, at least in a quantitative form, are only some three hundred years old, although like the atomic idea some of the concepts of mechanics date back to Greco-Roman times and some notion of probability must have been extant as long as games of chance have existed. Now the principles of Newtonian mechanics, as developed in the seventeenth century by Galileo, Huygens, and Newton and generalized since then principally by d'Alembert, Lagrange, and Hamilton, determine the future motion of any body whenever the motion at any given time is known. But when we come to apply these principles to the motions of an enormous number of particles—only a little less than half a sextillion in a cubic inch of air under normal conditions—it becomes impossible for us with our relatively gross sense perceptions to follow the motions of the individual molecules, and thus it is only possible to deal with the average of such motions, which alone can produce the effects to which our sense perceptions can respond. In other words, we are forced to deal with the *statistical* relations in an enormous "population" of individuals, each subject to the laws of mechanics; we have to determine their most probable behavior and compare the calculated results with the properties of bodies as actually observed. Thus arose a new science which may be called *molecular mechanics*.

However, in the earlier stages of the development of the modern kinetic theory of matter the essentially statistical nature of the problem was not appreciated. The basic assumptions were that the molecules are hard elastic spheres identical in size and mass for a given substance and differing only in those respects for different substances; that the molecules of all bodies at temperatures above the absolute zero are in continual motion with the same speed (at a given temperature) although moving in all possible directions;

that in a solid body the molecular excursions are confined to very small distances about their original positions; that in liquid bodies there is no force tending to return a molecule to its original position, although its excursions are never sufficiently great to take it out of the influence of its neighbors; and that in a vapor (gas) its excursions are so great that its motion is entirely free except for the very short intervals occupied by encounters with other molecules or the walls of the containing vessel. With these simple assumptions it was a comparatively easy matter to picture the process of the melting of a solid as taking place at a speed great enough to overcome the forces tending to return the molecules to their original positions, and the process of the boiling of a liquid as occurring similarly at a speed sufficient to remove the molecules from the force fields of their neighbors. Further, it was not difficult to get a precise representation of the pressure exerted by a gas on the walls of the containing vessel, and indeed of the general law connecting the temperature, volume, and pressure of an "ideal" gas.

But although the picture thus obtained sufficed to explain the simpler properties of matter, it was faulty in several respects. Thus the ratio of the kinetic energy of a gas consisting of elastic spherical molecules heated at constant pressure to that which it possesses if heated at constant volume is found to be five thirds, which is the value as experimentally determined only in the case of monatomic vapors and gases (those whose molecules consist of a single atom); for all other vapors and gases the experimental value of this ratio is markedly smaller. Hence it can be seen that in general the conception of the molecule as an elastic sphere is inadequate; in all but monatomic gases the internal energy of the molecules due to the rotations or vibrations of its constituent atoms must be taken into account. A method of doing this was first worked out by Clausius in 1857.

It is further obvious that the assumption of a common speed for all the molecules (at a given temperature) would mean that none could escape from a solid before that speed had reached a value, as the temperature is increased, which would carry *all* of them into the liquid state. Thus the process of the melting of a solid would be a much more abrupt phenomenon than it is observed to be, and the phenomenon of sublimation would be wholly without an explanation. Similarly, the boiling of a liquid could not occur until the common molecular speed had reached a value that would suddenly leave them all free, and the phenomenon of evaporation below the boiling point could not be accounted for. Nor can the assumption of a common molecular speed correspond to the actual conditions as they must exist in a gas. Even if all the molecules had the same velocity originally, their encounters with each other and with the walls of the containing vessel would produce inequalities in velocity and result in a continually changing distribution of velocities among them. Since, as was remarked earlier, we are unable to follow the motions of the individual molecules, we are forced to statistical methods to determine what the distribution of velocities among the molecules may be. By an argument too mathematical in content to be given here this distribution may be shown to be governed by the same laws as those expressing the distribution of the magnitudes of the errors occurring in the repeated measurement of any physical quantity. That is, a few of the molecules will have very small velocities, a few will have very great velocities, and the greater number will possess intermediate velocities; for a comparison of such molecular systems the square root of the average of the squares of all the velocities in each system is the best index. This velocity of the mean square serves all the ends performed previously by the common speed in the explanation of the simpler phenomena, while the existence of velocities differing from this average provides a means of reconciling the more complicated ones with observed phenomena.

The recognition of the necessity of combining the methods of statistics with those of dynamics in order to arrive at a valid kinetic theory of gases, that is, the foundation of what we have called molecular mechanics, we owe to Maxwell. The velocity distribution described above first published by him in 1859, is known as a Maxwellian distribution. Much of the subsequent development of molecular mechanics centers around the matter of the satisfactory derivation of the law expressing this distribution. The original proof assumed that the component velocities were independent, which would seem to require demonstration. Further, Maxwell's derivation contemplated only simple particles and thus could be valid only for monatomic gases.

The first of the numerous attempts which have been made to put the Maxwellian distribution upon a firmer logical basis was made by Ludwig Boltzmann. He extended the application to include polyatomic molecules, confirmed the result that the distribution was unaffected by molecular collisions, and showed further that any assumed initial distribution tended to approach the Maxwellian under the influence of these encounters. In the course of his work Boltzmann discovered a certain function of the component velocities which could never decrease and which is thus analogous to entropy. In terms of this discovery the concept of entropy is to be interpreted as meaning that very large aggregates of molecules tend to pass from states of smaller to those of larger probability. But while this work of Boltzmann contributed significantly to the belief in the essential correctness of the Maxwellian distribution, it did not originally do as much for its logical foundation. However, later development of Boltzmann's gave an entirely new slant on the problem. Up to this time attention had been centered on the statistics of the individual particles constituting a system of particles. In this later work Boltzmann introduced the idea of studying the statistics of the whole system of particles as a unit and focused attention on the changes in configuration and velocity which succeed one another in a given system in the course of time. This point of view has dominated the subsequent development of the subject and is that adopted by Gibbs in his work.

Gibbs recognized that this point of view made possible the creation of a science of statistical mechanics which could be independent of all considerations of molecular structure and dependent solely on the laws of mechanics and of statistics. The broad basis thus afforded was kindred to his character and habits of thought as we have seen them revealed in other connections. In the preface to his book, *Elementary Principles in Statistical Mechanics*,[2] these mental characteristics appear so plainly that the following rather extensive quotations from it are valuable for the light they throw upon the man as well as for showing his attitude toward these particular problems.

2. Yale Bicentennial Publications (New York, Charles Scribner's Sons, 1902). *Collected Works*, II, viii–x.

The laws of thermodynamics, as empirically determined, express the approximate and probable behavior of systems of a great number of particles, or, more precisely, they express the laws of mechanics for such systems as they appear to beings who have not the fineness of perception to enable them to appreciate quantities of the order of magnitude of those which relate to single particles, and who cannot repeat their experiments often enough to obtain any but most probable results. The laws of statistical mechanics apply to conservative systems of any number of degrees of freedom, and are exact. This does not make them more difficult to establish than the approximate laws for systems of a great many degrees of freedom, or for limited classes of such systems. The reverse is rather the case, for our attention is not diverted from what is essential by the peculiarities of the system considered, and we are not obliged to satisfy ourselves that the effect of the quantities and circumstances neglected will be negligible in the result. The laws of thermodynamics may be easily obtained from the principles of statistical mechanics, of which they are the incomplete expression, but they make a somewhat blind guide in our search for those laws. This is perhaps the principal cause of the slow progress of rational thermodynamics, as contrasted with the rapid deduction of the consequences of its laws as empirically established. To this must be added that the rational foundation of thermodynamics lay in a branch of mechanics of which the fundamental notions and principles, and the characteristic operations, were alike unfamiliar to students of mechanics.

We may therefore confidently believe that nothing will more conduce to the clear apprehension of the relation of thermodynamics to rational mechanics, and to the interpretation of observed phenomena with reference to their evidence respecting the molecular constitution of bodies, than the study of the fundamental notions and principles of that department of mechanics to which thermodynamics is especially related.

Moreover, we avoid the gravest difficulties when, giving up the attempt to frame hypotheses concerning the constitution of material bodies, we pursue statistical inquiries as a branch of rational mechanics. In the present state of science, it seems hardly possible to frame a dynamic theory of molecular action which shall embrace the phenomena of thermodynamics, of radiation, and of the electrical manifestations which accompany the union of atoms. Yet any theory is obviously inadequate which does not take account of all these phenomena. Even if we confine our attention to the phenomena distinctively thermodynamic, we do not escape difficulties in as simple a matter as the number of degrees of freedom of a diatomic gas. It is well known that while theory would assign to the gas six degrees of freedom per molecule, in our experiments on specific heat we cannot account for more than five. Certainly, one is building on an insecure foundation, who rests his work on hypotheses concerning the constitution of matter.

Difficulties of this kind have deterred the author from attempting to explain the mysteries of nature, and have forced him to be contented with the more modest aim of deducing some of the more obvious propositions relating to the statistical branch of mechanics. Here, there can be no mistake in regard to the agreement of the hypotheses with the facts of nature, for nothing is assumed in that respect. The only error into which one can fall, is the want of agreement between the premises and the conclusions, and this, with care, one may hope, in the main, to avoid.

That Gibbs succeeded in his task, and in particular in fulfilling the hope expressed in the last sentence, there is no longer any doubt. No work of modern times has undergone a more searching criticism. At times certain of his conclusions have been questioned, even by so distinguished and competent a critic as Max Planck, the originator of the quantum hypothesis. But further examination in every case has confirmed the correctness of Gibbs' results. The form which he gave to the science of statistical mechanics has been found adequate to satisfy the demands of discoveries made since his time, even those involved in the acceptance of the reality of the quantum of action. With these modern additions, Gibbs' structure is found to embrace that larger theory which he characterized in the third paragraph quoted above as "hardly possible." On the other hand, the form given to the statistical theory by his distinguished predecessors, Maxwell and Boltzmann, has been shown to be incompetent to include these modern developments. The *Elementary Principles in Statistical Mechanics* was a fitting capstone to Gibbs' scientific career and a worthy companion to the "Equilibrium of Heterogeneous Substances."

It would be impossible to present in simple language any adequate account of Gibbs' achievements in this field. It must suffice to indicate briefly the main points in which his ideas have served to give permanent form and content to this new branch of mechanics. The fundamental notions he employed are all expressed in terms of a concept which he termed the "phase" of a mechanical system. By this term is meant the condition of the system as specified by its configuration and its velocity jointly. If we consider a very great number of such systems—denoted by Gibbs as an "ensemble" of systems—all identical in nature but differing in phase, they may be conceived as constituting what he called an "extension-in-phase" or as occupying what may be called alternatively a certain "phase-space." The distribution of the systems in phase within an ensemble is then specified by a quantity called the "density-in-phase" of the systems. If this density is to be considered as a continuous function of the coordinates defining the configurations and velocities (as is necessary in order to obtain integrated relations), the number of systems in an ensemble would strictly have to be infinitely great, although by increasing the number of systems sufficiently the approximation to a continuous distribution may be taken as practically adequate. But this logical difficulty may be avoided entirely by using the *relative* number of the mechanical systems within a given phase-space. This leads to the notion of the "probability" that an otherwise unspecified system will be found within a given element of the phase-space. In addition to these, two other basic notions were introduced by Gibbs. These, in analogy with that of extension-in-phase, he termed the "extension-in-configuration" and the "extension-in-velocity." They are simply factors or components of the phase-space.

Next, the motion of each of the mechanical systems considered is assumed to be given by Hamilton's form of the fundamental equations of motion. Then by a calculation of the number of systems lying within infinitesimal limits of phase there follows the basic equation of the classical statistical mechanics (Liouville's equation). From this Gibbs deduces for the case of statistical equilibrium his famous conservation principle. This may be stated variously in terms of the several quantities named above as the principle of conservation of density-in-phase, of extension-in-phase, of probability-of-phase, of extension-in-configuration, or of extension-in-velocity. It asserts that for equilibrium to subsist the quantity in terms of which it is expressed must remain constant in time. On this principle in one or more of its various forms is based the whole of Gibbs' development of statistical mechanics.

It should be noted that as early as 1884—eighteen years before the appearance of his book—Gibbs had read a paper before the American Association for the Advancement of Science in which he gave a derivation of one form of this fundamental equation, and an abstract was published in the *Proceedings* of that body.[3] The interest in this fact lies in the evidence it affords of the long period of time during which Gibbs was developing and sifting his ideas on the subject before his book was finally published in 1902. In his biennial lecture courses on "dynamics and thermodynamics" during this interval he apparently tried out several methods of presentation. The care which he took in the matter of the definition of the fundamental notions and the pains to which he went in order to secure the most logical development of the subject are also strikingly shown in the fragmentary notes recently found among his papers which were referred to in Chapter VII. Bumstead has commented in his biographical notice on the fact that Gibbs' chief limitation as a teacher was that his students were given a view only of his completed work and thus missed the advantage of seeing his great structures in the process of building. This is in large measure true. But here in these notes it is now possible to see something of the work of construction, of the painstaking planning, and of the scaffolding with which it was erected.

In these notes he argues with himself such matters as the best points for the introduction of the notions of extension-in-configuration and extension-in-velocity and whether these extensions should be defined independently of the coordinates "either physically or by the methods of multiple algebra." This last matter, which involves an approach to the fundamental equation from the standpoint of the Grassmann point analysis, I have referred to in Chapter VII; and although Gibbs decided against the use of this method of approach for the purposes of his book, it is clear from these notes that it had a great attraction for him and that he reached his adverse decision only because he did not want to obscure the physical argument by the use of mathematical methods which might be unfamiliar to many. As stated before, it seems probable that he was reserving this material for separate publication.

3. XXXIII (1884), 57, 58.

These matters of the basic notions, the fundamental equation and the principle of conservation, comprehend little, aside from the nomenclature and the method and precision of presentation, that was new or novel in content. Beginning with chapter iv, however, Gibbs began to break new ground with the concept of the "canonical" distribution in phase within an ensemble. This is defined as one in which the index (i.e., the logarithm) of the probability of phase is a linear function of the energy. It is interesting to note that he gives as the reason for this choice among all the possible distributions that it is the *simplest* conceivable. In his letter of acceptance of the Rumford Medal he had stated: "One of the principal objects of theoretical research in any department of knowledge is to find the point of view from which the subject appears in its greatest simplicity." And in none of his work has his devotion to this principle been more conspicuously justified. For it is in terms of the canonical distribution that the analytical development proves not only to be the most manageable but also that which yields the closest analogy between the behavior of the mechanical systems so specified and the thermodynamic properties of bodies as revealed by experiment.

It is the average value for the change in energy of the mechanical systems in a canonical ensemble expressed in terms of the changes in the average index of probability and of those of the coordinates of bodies external to the ensemble upon which it may exert forces that constitutes an equation of the same form as that which I have termed the "prime" equation in the thermodynamics of homogeneous substances.[4] From a comparison of these two equations it appears that if the average of the energy of the mechanical systems in a canonical ensemble is taken as the analogue of the intrinsic energy of a thermodynamic body, then the average index of probability (with its sign reversed) is the analogue of the entropy of the body; that a quantity which Gibbs termed the *modulus* of the distribution is analogous to the temperature of the body; and that the average of the forces exerted by the ensemble on external systems corresponds to the forces with which the thermodynamic body acts on its surroundings.

In order to determine the conditions under which these analo-

4. See p. 70.

gies can be considered valid it is necessary to investigate the properties of the statistical averages involved, to evaluate the deviations of the individual values of each quantity from its average value, and to determine their maximum and minimum properties. It is also of importance to see if distributions other than the canonical can lead to similar analogies. To these ends Gibbs directed a most exhaustive analysis and developed many theorems for its implementation. Without going into any of the details of this analysis the chief results may be stated briefly as follows:

First, another distribution which Gibbs called the microcanonical—one in which each of the mechanical systems possesses the same energy—also leads to an equation analogous to the prime equation of thermodynamics. In this distribution he showed that either the logarithm of the extension-in-phase or the logarithm of the rate of change of the extension-in-phase with the energy can be regarded as the analogue of entropy, and that the rate of change of the energy with the entropy (as thus defined) is the analogue of temperature. He showed further that when the number of degrees of freedom is made very large the two definitions of entropy for the microcanonical distribution coincide with each other and with that for the canonical distribution.

Next, he shows that for all the statistical quantities considered the deviations of the individual from the average values are of the same order of magnitude as the reciprocal of the number of degrees of freedom, and hence that when this is very great the differences between the individual and the average values would be imperceptible to human observation. Gibbs further showed "that when systems of different ensembles are brought into conditions analogous to thermal contact, the average result is the passage of energy from the ensemble of the greater modulus to that of the less, or in case of equal moduli, that we have a condition of statistical equilibrium in regard to the distribution of energy." He also demonstrated theorems relating to the index of probability which are analogous to those of Carnot's cycle and to the tendency of entropy to increase. All of these results cannot be summarized better than in his own words: [5]

We have thus precisely defined quantities, and rigorously demonstrated propositions, which hold for any number of degrees of freedom, and

5. *Collected Works*, II, Pt. 1, 169.

which, when the number of degrees of freedom (n) is enormously great, would appear to human faculties as the quantities and propositions of empirical thermodynamics.

Gibbs then proceeds to a careful and exhaustive consideration of the merits of the analogues yielded by the canonical and the microcanonical distributions. It would be impractical to go into the subtleties of this famous discussion. As before, the final result cannot be stated more clearly or more succinctly than in his own words: [6]

It would seem, therefore, that a canonical ensemble of phases is what best represents, with the precision necessary for exact mathematical reasoning, the notion of a body with a given temperature, if we conceive of the temperature as the state produced by such processes as we actually use in physics to produce a given temperature.

This concept of the canonical distribution and the recognition of its superiority for rational thermodynamics mark one of the high points among Gibbs' achievements. Although in a sense it merely furnishes another formulation of the principles of statistical mechanics, it is one which in virtue of its greater simplicity, its mathematical elegance, and its adaptability to the demands of later discoveries has come to supersede the earlier formulations of Maxwell and Boltzmann. In particular, Gibbs' approach to the statistical definition of entropy is more general and not open to the objections that can be urged against that of Boltzmann, which depends on the calculation of the permutations which are possible for any pair of molecules. The final result when the number of degrees of freedom is indefinitely increased is the same from either point of view, but Gibbs' development in which this is attained as the limiting case of an exact relation valid for any number of degrees of freedom has a more solid logical foundation than Boltzmann's, which is only valid in the limit. In addition, the Gibbsian approach possesses the advantage, stressed in the quotation above from his preface, of requiring no assumptions as to the structure of matter; it only presupposes ensembles of systems subject to the laws of mechanics.

The crowning achievement of the *Statistical Mechanics* was, however, reserved fittingly for the final chapter, which is concerned with the statistical equilibrium of ensembles which are

6. *Collected Works*, II, Pt. 1, 183.

supposed to be composed of different kinds of particles (molecules). Gibbs remarks in the preface to the book: "This supposition would naturally have been introduced earlier, if our object had been simply the expression of the laws of nature. It seemed desirable, however, to separate sharply the purely thermodynamic laws from those special modifications which belong rather to the theory of the properties of matter." In this chapter we find the culmination of the idea of the discrete structure of matter as determined by the mathematical theory, the foundations of which Gibbs had so carefully revised and extended throughout the book. In it he deduces the statistical analogue of that great and fundamental generalization of the prime equation of thermodynamics [7] with which he had enriched science a quarter of a century previously and on which his fame rests so securely.

Here again it is not feasible to follow all the subtleties of the argument. It is concerned with "grand ensembles"—those which can differ not only in phase but also in the nature of the constituent particles—and with the relations of these to the previously considered ensembles which thus become "petit ensembles"—those which can differ only in phase. It deals with the methods to be used in counting the number of different phases and the question as to whether interchange of place between particles of the same nature can be considered to constitute separately enumerable phases. He calls a computation which denies the status of a separate phase to displaced particles which cannot be otherwise identified one based on a *generic* definition of phase; and one which assigns a distinct phase to every position of a particle, regardless of the possibility of identification, one based on a *specific* definition of phase. He then proceeds to demonstrate with the same rigorous methods previously developed that the most precise analogy to the thermodynamically defined temperature, entropy, and chemical potential is to be found in the statistical equilibrium of a grand ensemble, canonically distributed with the generic definition of phase. He closes the discussion with a reversion to the old problem of the diffusion of a gas into itself and shows that the difference between this case and that of the interdiffusion of two different gases is completely explained by the adoption of the generic method of

7. See p. 77.

counting phases. Thus the celebrated "Gibbs paradox" of 1876, to which he had then furnished an empirical solution, received in the end a logical theoretical explanation.

The result of the classical statistical mechanics over which the most controversy has developed is that of the "equipartition" of energy among the degrees of freedom. This result is a consequence of the assumption that energy is a continuous and not a discretely constituted magnitude and that therefore its average value can be determined by a process of integration. Soon after the turn of the century with the coming of experimental command over a wider temperature range—particularly toward the absolute zero—and with the demonstration of the complex electronic structure of the atom combined with the failure of attempts to explain the phenomena of radiation from the classical viewpoint, it became increasingly evident that there was something seriously wrong with that viewpoint. Even before the source of the trouble was traced to the postulate of the continuity of energy and its replacement by the quantum hypothesis, there had been serious questioning of the equipartition result of the classical theory. This was voiced most cogently by Lord Kelvin in a celebrated paper entitled "Nineteenth Century Clouds over the Dynamical Theory of Heat and Light," first presented before the Royal Institution in April, 1900. In this paper he discusses two clouds—the "Relative Motion of Ether and Ponderable Matter," and the "Maxwell-Boltzmann Equipartition." Both clouds were destined to be soon dispersed, the first with the advent of Einsteinian relativity and the second with the consequences of the quantum developments. But although Kelvin's arguments now have little force, his correspondence with Gibbs on the matter shows the contrasting mental attitudes of these two eminent men and summarizes their positions on the equipartition matter so clearly that a few words about it may not be inappropriate.

Kelvin took an experimental attitude toward the equipartition problem, and sought to test its validity through repeated trials of lotteries and by ingeniously constructed problems such as that of the "caged atom." Gibbs' attitude, on the other hand, is shown most strikingly in his solution of this problem which has been preserved in the draft of a letter to Kelvin.[8] After giving the correct mathematical solution he remarks in closing, "Since the integrals are manageable, we are not obliged to have recourse to trials. I think however that this might easily be verified by lotteries such as you have used." In reply to this letter Kelvin neither attempts to refute the argument nor admits its validity but remarks amusingly:

I think you would find it interesting to actually go through lottery trials such as those I made, with modifications which would naturally occur to anyone retrying the subject. If you put it into the hands of some of your young students I think it may be incidentally beneficial to them; especially to any who may be likely to become millionaires, and may not carry away enough from Yale, if that be possible, to preserve them throughout life from the want of occupation of time and thought which leads to the incredible choice of the gaming tables of Monte Carlo or Aix-les-Bains.

Kelvin's attitude was thus entirely experimental and destructive. He was not concerned with the logical foundations of the theory but only with its conclusions, and he concentrated solely on the demonstration of its failures, which sometimes—as in this case of the caged atom—turned out not to be failures at all. On the other hand, Gibbs' treatment of the problem, based on a logical theory, was constructive, complete, and independent of any need for experimental justification. This incident contrasts the experimental with the theoretical approach and well illustrates Gibbs' power of abstract reasoning from the fewest possible basic assumptions.

On the quantum hypothesis the average energy is obtained by a process of summation of the discrete bundles of energy visualized by its fundamental assumption. This summation process takes the place of the integration process appropriate to the fundamental assumption of the classical theory. Although this step was not taken by Gibbs, it is nevertheless one of the greatest tributes to his intuition and sagacity that his canonical distribution permits of evaluation in terms of either the older or the newer ideas of the structure of energy; and that when it is so evaluated in terms of the quantum idea, and the results are interpreted in the light of

8. In the "Scientific Correspondence."

his conception of the generic definition of phase, it leads directly and naturally into the modern world of new sorts of statistics and of wave mechanics. Thus the *Elementary Principles in Statistical Mechanics* forms a sort of bridge between two eras in physical thought, a structure well anchored on the classical side and forming the natural gateway leading to a new world of ideas. This is not the place, however, to go into the matter of the more recent developments in detail. For those who may be interested in following the application of Gibbs' methods to the evolution of the Einstein-Bose and the Fermi-Dirac statistics and of quantum wave mechanics, an adequate account will be found in Articles U and V by Professor Paul S. Epstein in *A Commentary*, Volume II.

As has been intimated above, this last work of Gibbs is not easy to read; and it did not immediately reach its full stature in the minds of men. Even for the professed statistician the novelties in the point of view and the precisely compressed style offered formidable difficulties; while for the run-of-the-mine physicist the subtleties which were its strength seemed at first rather far removed from reality. The first published critique of the book [9] came from S. H. Burbury who, judging from the eight letters in the "Scientific Correspondence" as well as from his published article, never quite comprehended the spirit and implications of Gibbs' argument. He was so entrenched in the prepossessions of the microcanonical point of view that he was never able to grasp the larger vision of the canonical. His criticisms were adequately met by Bumstead's reply.[10] Further critiques in various continental publications by Planck, Ornstein, Lorentz, and others in the first decade after the appearance of the book, while not all showing entire agreement with Gibbs' point of view, yet made it manifest that the weight of scientific opinion was tending in his direction. These early debates culminated in a summation by P. and T. Ehrenfest [11] which served to clarify the issues. Since then there has been growing agreement with Gibbs' conclusions. With the advent of wave mechanics and the newer quantum theory it has become obvious

9. *Phil. Mag.* (August, 1903).
10. *Ibid.* (January, 1904).
11. *Enc. der math. Wis.*, IV, 4, 32.

that only from the standpoint of these developments is it possible to appreciate fully the magnitude of Gibbs' contribution to the rationalization of the concept of entropy. While the discovery since his death of certain mathematical tools (notably the Lebesgue's integrals) has made possible a further refinement of rigor in the derivation of the conservation principle, the fertility and power of Gibbs' achievement have but grown with time.

It has rarely been given to a man to penetrate so far in advance of his contemporaries twice in a lifetime. If the "Equilibrium of Heterogeneous Substances" was ahead of its time, so was the *Statistical Mechanics,* and by about the same interval. While the latter work cannot be said to have been neglected as the former was to some extent, yet for an equally long time it was not understood and appreciated. With their coming into their own these two works, so complementary in their nature, so penetrating in their insight into the inmost secrets of nature, and each set forth with meticulous logic, will endure as two of the greatest monuments of the human mind.

XI

Professor of Mathematical Physics: the Teacher

O F human relationships that of teacher and pupil is at once the most universal and one of the most difficult to evaluate. We all have to learn and, consciously or unconsciously, to teach. This is a fundamental fact of life and a condition of progress. But success in the educational process is a complicated function of the qualities of both the teacher and the taught as well as of the nature of the subject matter involved. Hence it is not always easy to arrive at a just apportionment between the parties to the relationship of the credit for the results achieved. This is as true in the field of formal education as it is in the more informal schools of the family and society.

Moreover, such an evaluation becomes increasingly difficult as the educational process becomes concerned with the more abstract and recondite developments of human thought. In the earlier stages of formal education, where almost all the fields of knowledge are *terrae incognitae* to the pupil, the function of the teacher is largely confined to the inculcation of facts and standardized techniques; the "textbook" is the principal tool of instruction, and memory drill the chief classroom exercise. In the later stages and certainly at the graduate level the objectives of the teacher are or should be the arousing of interest in the methods of thought and the presentation of a true picture of his subject in the scheme of knowledge. In the pursuance of these purposes the textbook becomes several reference works, the memory drill moves from the classroom to the student's study, the "recitation" becomes a lecture and a discussion. In addition, at the graduate level the intellectual maturity of the pupil is closer to that of the teacher; his habits of thought have been more or less conditioned by his previous educational experience; his conception of the objectives of the instruction in any particular realm of knowledge and of the uses to which it may be put may or may not be sympathetic with those of the teacher; his mental aptitudes and attitudes may create difficulties unappreciated by either the teacher or the pupil.

Thus assessing the success of a teacher such as Willard Gibbs becomes a problem of evaluating not only *his* qualities but also those of his pupils and their preparation for and attitude toward their graduate work. In the course of the thirty-two years of his teaching somewhat less than one hundred students attended Gibbs' courses.[1] They were all mature students whose habits of thought had been formed in a variety of environments, whose objectives in undertaking graduate study were diverse, and whose interest in and fitness for mathematics and physics had for the most part undergone only the conventional screening of the average American undergraduate curriculum, although a few came with more advanced preparation. Some of these pupils came to Gibbs' courses with an inherent love of science for itself, others were motivated chiefly by the object of acquiring the tools with which to earn a living. Some were destined to careers in research, others (the majority) to teaching in college or preparatory school, a few to applied physics in government or industrial posts, and

1. It is impossible to give an exact number, owing to the absence of any graduate school records prior to 1896, the year after Professor Andrew W. Phillips became dean. After that date the records show that 63 attended one or more of the courses; 36 of these attained the doctorate in astronomy, chemistry, economics, mathematics, or physics. For the earlier period it is possible to form a rough estimate of the number of Gibbs' students from the pamphlet, *Doctors of Philosophy of Yale University 1861–1927* (Yale University, 1927), together with the reports covering the years 1873–85 by the secretary of the Corporation, Professor Franklin B. Dexter, which gives among other things the number of students and the number of hours per week taught by each instructor. Judging from the titles of the dissertations given in the first of these documents there were some 27 of them with which it is reasonable to suppose that Gibbs was more or less concerned, and the number prior to 1885 checks as well as could be expected with the numbers given in the Dexter reports. As to the number of those who in this earlier period (before 1896) may have attended some of Gibbs' lectures and who did not go on to a degree, complete information is lacking. However, I myself have personal knowledge of one such, Hastings in his "Josiah Willard Gibbs" mentions another, Irving Fisher in his contribution to "P.R.I." names a third, and a fourth has been called to my attention by the late Dean Charles H. Warren of the Sheffield Scientific School. Thus the best estimate of the total number is 94. This may be low by two or three, but the total almost certainly was less than 100.

scarcely any to careers in which mathematics or physics have had no part. In brief, Gibbs' students as a group show such a variety in their preparation for his work, such differences in their outlook on life, and such a range of talents that unanimity of opinion on the merits of their teacher can scarcely be expected. Among them are to be found some who benefited little by their contact with him and who in consequence rated him a poor teacher; but there were others, and I believe they constitute the majority, who considered him among the best if not at the top among their instructors. Only a handful of these students still survive, and it is fortunate that at this late date we have from some of these firsthand opinions and judgments of Gibbs' ability as a teacher.

These are to be found in the "Personal Recollections and Impressions," to which frequent reference has been made in these pages. These estimates exhibit a rather remarkable unanimity as to the difficulty experienced by the writers in following the lectures, owing mainly to the generality of treatment and to the meticulous precision with which the arguments were clothed. Most of them stress the effort on their own part which they found necessary in order to reach an adequate understanding of the subject matter under discussion. Several emphasize that they frequently found it imperative to interrupt a lecture to clear up a difficulty or to go to Gibbs outside of the lecture period for a fuller explanation. They are all agreed however that such interruptions or outside consultations were uniformly rewarding and successful in their purpose.[2]

This necessity for active participation on the part of the student, far from being evidence of poor teaching, seems to me to lie close to the heart of good graduate as distinguished from undergraduate instruction. The days of "spoon feeding" should by then have been passed; and the idea that the concepts and methods which have been won for the race by the most exacting of mental processes can be passed on by word of mouth alone is as fallacious as it seems to be prevalent. Physics is not a subject which can be mastered by everyone. The man in the street may appreciate some of its results, but for real understanding of them there is required an innate mathematical ability not possessed by every-

2. See especially the contributions of H. L. Bronson and O. C. Lester in "P.R.I."

one and a long and arduous training in exact thinking. Thus the fact that concepts intrinsically abstruse or novel (to the student) were not adequately grasped by a class at a first hearing is not evidence of imperfect presentation or of poor teaching but rather of the nature of the ideas and of the mentality or the previous training of the listeners.

Nevertheless it is true that Gibbs, more than most teachers, seemed indifferent to the degree of his pupils' preparedness to follow his work. He is said once to have remarked that he had never had more than half a dozen students who were properly so prepared, and this is probably not far from the truth. But this lack of preparation he apparently regarded as a handicap to be overcome by the student and not a matter to affect the pace or the content of his lectures. I shall never forget my own dismay when I found, in the first course of his which I attended, constant use being made of the ideas of generalized coordinates and the calculus of variations, both topics of which my undergraduate preparation had left me in blissful ignorance. But the effort I was thus forced to make in order to catch up with his starting point was a valuable factor in my education. To those who, conditioned by the spoon-feeding methods prevalent in undergraduate instruction, or who, from essential if unrecognized lack of interest in the true inwardness of natural phenomena or for any other reason, did not or could not make the requisite effort on their own behalf Gibbs would make no overtures of help, and they naturally found him a poor teacher. On the other hand a well-prepared student, or one sufficiently unashamed of his ignorance to overcome a natural shyness to ask for help from such a master and who would make a determined effort to overcome his handicaps, received friendly and extraordinarily effective aid in the resolution of his difficulties. Such students found Gibbs a superlative teacher. After all, the essential point in graduate work is the training of the student to help himself, to teach him to stand on his own feet; and Gibbs' calm assumption that the student and not the teacher was the party primarily responsible for its accomplishment was an effective if somewhat unorthodox method of securing the result.

But if he threw the responsibility for learning upon the student, he was most conscientious in testing its accomplishment. The examinations he set at the conclusion of a course were usually exhaustively comprehensive of the subject matter covered, and answering the questions properly in their entirety would have taken days instead of the allotted hours. I do not remember any of the better students of my time who would confess to having answered all the questions on these examinations, although I recollect one individual who boasted of so doing. I have recently found from the records in the dean's office that this student's work for that course is recorded as "unsatisfactory"! But I do not think that Gibbs in forming his judgment of the performance of a student placed as much reliance on the final examination as he did on the more informal contacts of the classroom. From the solutions of the problems proposed in the course of the lectures (which were always returned meticulously corrected), and from frequent discussions on various points raised in them, he was able to form estimates of the quality of his students and of the degree to which they were assimilating the ideas presented, which in my observation carried more weight with him than did the results of the final examination. At any rate, the records of the dean's office, when compared with achievements in later life, show that he made few if any mistakes in his estimates of student performance.

In my own experience I remember him as the teacher with the greatest flexibility of method and the least addiction to fixed shibboleths of presentation of all those under whom I studied. In the development of a topic he would sometimes proceed from the general to the particular and sometimes in the reverse direction (more often the former), and at other times he would suggest the generalization of the particular or the particularization of the general as a problem for the ingenuity of the student. He would occasionally stop in what seemed to most of us the middle of a demonstration and ask if the proposition were proved. If we looked dumb (as was usually the case) he would proceed to complete the formal derivation of the result and then descant on what a "proof" really was or what the relation was of "understanding" to "proof." He was fertile in suggesting illustrations and analogies and always careful to point out their limitations.

He was particularly apt in devising what might be called sum-
marizing mnemonics. One of these which has been of the greatest value both to me and to the generations of students to whom
I have passed it on linked together the seven quantities enter-
ing into magnetic theory in an H-shaped figure, the three magnitudes in each of the vertical arms being related to each other by
operations of differentiation (downward) or of integration (up-
ward), while the connection between the two sets was indicated
along the horizontal arm by the fundamental relation connecting the intensity of magnetization, the magnetic induction, and
the magnetic force. Such simple but very effective aids to the
memory were outstanding features of his lectures.

The methods and manner of presentation of any given subject were so varied from year to year as to make the repetition of
his courses highly valuable to most students and a common practice among them. Sometimes the variation consisted merely in
changing the order in which the topics were taken up but at
others there were more radical changes. Thus when I took the
course in electricity and magnetism in the academic year 1895–96
we followed Maxwell's *Treatise* closely, with assigned readings
from the text followed by discussion and translation into the
Gibbsian vector notations. When I repeated the course in 1897–98
no text was used, the lectures employed the compact vector notations ab initio, and the treatment of electrostatics and magneto-
statics was much curtailed compared with that of electromagnet-
ism and electrodynamics. Similarly with the course on the
electromagnetic theory of light: in some years he prefaced the
course with an extensive account of vector harmonic motion before proceeding to phenomenological matters, while in others he
developed the vector methods piecemeal as they became necessary to the description of the phenomena. In the more severely
mathematical courses on vector analysis, multiple algebra, and
dynamics and thermodynamics (statistical mechanics) there was
naturally less variation from year to year in the order of presentation of the topics covered, although there might be considerable
change in the relative emphasis placed on them and in the illustrations used. In spite of the fact that the course on thermodynamics and the properties of matter was largely an exposition

of his great memoir "On the Equilibrium of Heterogeneous Substances," he never to my knowledge used that as a text or referred directly to it. This course was varied on its different repetitions mostly in the amount of time devoted to the derivation of the first and second laws and in the emphasis placed on the various applications of the equilibrium conditions. In 1895–96 when I took the course little time was devoted to the phase rule (possibly because there were no chemists in the class that year) and the major emphasis was placed on the problems of gaseous equilibrium and of capillarity.

This variation in the structure of his courses was typical of the man and of the independence and virility of his thinking. In his lectures he did not expound the work of others but interpreted nature. As his interest focused on one or another of the aspects of a subject his exposition would be altered to bring that aspect into a better perspective. Thus his interest in Lord Kelvin's problems on the propagation of electrostatic force and of osmosis had immediate influence on the form and content of his presentation of germane topics in electricity and magnetism and in thermodynamics. In the light of the fragmentary notes recently found among his papers further credibility is afforded for the assumption made in the previous chapter that some of the variations which he introduced in the presentation of his work on statistical mechanics in different years were in the nature of experiments to determine the best form for ultimate publication. But whatever may have been the predisposing causes of these continual changes in the form and the content of his courses, the very fact that they never became stereotyped is evidence of the living, growing nature of his concepts of things physical and of his independence of the conventional in their portrayal.

He would sometimes abruptly alter or interpolate a point of view in the midst of a lecture with an effect like that produced by a sudden change of lighting on a familiar scene. Contrasts might be sharpened or softened, relations seen from an angle that made them seem novel, or the whole picture changed in the scale of its setting. Such sudden inspirations were always prefaced by one of his few mannerisms. He would rock gently back and forth on his feet, partially supported by a pointer held against the floor in both hands clasped behind his back, contemplating what he had just written on the blackboard. After a few moments he would rouse from this mood, which I can only describe as one of alert abstraction, with the words, "Or, one may say . . . ," and then would follow the metamorphosis, sometimes simple, sometimes spectacular, but always illuminating.

Another aspect of Gibbs' quality as a teacher was an uncanny ability to diagnose quickly the exact source of a student's difficulty, and the faculty for then leading him to discover the solution for himself. I never had a teacher who could so quickly and so accurately get to the bottom of what was troubling me as could Gibbs. Whether my difficulty arose from deficiencies in my preparation, from the strangeness to me of a new concept, or merely from a stupid misunderstanding of some point in the lectures, I never went to him for help in vain or came away from the interview without a clarification both of the matter in question and of my own mental processes. It is my belief that it is in the lack of such ability to grasp the difficulties as they appear to the student that many of the failures of teachers are to be found; and it may be because of Gibbs' success in this essential of good teaching, both in my own case and in that of several of his other students such as those recorded in the "Personal Recollections and Impressions," that my memories of his teaching have remained so vivid.[3] Whatever the cause, Gibbs remains in my memory as the greatest teacher as well as the greatest mind with which I ever came in contact. His ability to penetrate surface appearances to the essential elements of phenomena, the comprehensiveness of his outlook on nature, his remarkable physical intuition, the logical severity of his reasoning, his avoidance of special hypotheses, the flexibility and diversity of his methods of attacking a problem, his tolerance, his utter sincerity and simplicity—all stand out in my recollections of his lectures as plainly as they appear in his published work. I remember clearly my sensations when I first realized the convincing completeness of his derivation of the criteria of thermochemical equilibria; when I first perceived the comprehensiveness and power of his great

3. See especially a similar vivid recollection of this aspect of his teaching ability testified to by Miss Van Name in her contribution to "P.R.I."

contribution in the idea of the partial or chemical potential; when I sensed the importance of the new concepts he introduced in statistical mechanics. I do not mean to imply that as a student I achieved a just evaluation of Gibbs' greatness in these or other respects, but I do remember my intellectual excitement at my first partial and immature apprehensions of their significance. The horizons then opened to my view have taken on depth and detail as the years have passed, but the memory of my first glimpses of them is one of the most treasured of my recollections of my great teacher.

There were remarkably few students who wrote their dissertations under Gibbs' direction, although there were probably a considerably larger number who discussed with him some of the matters arising in the course of such work being done primarily under other teachers. For the whole period covered by his teaching there were 63 students who took at least one of his courses and who later received the doctor's degree: 6 in astronomy, 2 in chemistry, 6 in economics, 22 in mathematics, 1 in philosophy, and 26 in physics. While the work of all of these may be presumed to have been influenced to some extent by the courses they may have taken with Gibbs, it is very difficult to say how many of them owed their chief inspiration to him. For the earlier portion of the period there is nothing to go by except the subjects of the dissertations. On the basis of such knowledge as I possess of the subjects in which Gibbs took a sufficiently active interest to have acted as a sponsor, I should say that only two of these theses in mathematics and three of those in physics can be ascribed to his direction. For the period covered by my own recollection (from 1894 on) there were but one thesis in mathematics and only seven in physics written by the forty-two who attended the courses and who subsequently earned the degree which can be similarly ascribed. Thus it would seem that in the whole period of his teaching there were but a baker's dozen of dissertations which can be said to owe their inspiration to Gibbs.

I have personal knowledge as to the degree of supervision exercised by Gibbs or as to the amount of help the authors received from him in the case of only three of the theses written during my time. These were those submitted by Henry A. Bumstead, George P. Starkweather, and myself. From recollections of talks with both Bumstead and Starkweather as well as from my own experience it is plain that Gibbs, in this phase of graduate instruction as in his lectures, left the responsibility largely on the shoulders of the student. In none of these three cases did he even take the initiative in suggesting the subject for the thesis; in each case the student, intrigued by some point or phase of Gibbs' lectures, went to him to ask if a further development or investigation of the point which had caught his attention would be considered a suitable subject for a thesis. Even when the subject had been approved Gibbs did little or nothing in the actual direction of the work, although he was most helpful in bibliographical suggestions and in discussion of the results obtained. Indeed he seemed to take a pride that these results were due to the student's initiative and not to his own leading. I remember very well an occasion in May of 1897 when Bumstead and I were conferring on some undergraduate laboratory affairs. Gibbs appeared unexpectedly with Bumstead's thesis in his hand, and I was privileged to listen to a brilliant discussion on some points in the history of electrodynamics, in the course of which Gibbs expressed his especial gratification that Bumstead had come to certain conclusions without any suggestion or leading from himself. In the case of my own thesis it was not until after the experimental work had been completed that Gibbs' discussion of the results which I had obtained gave me any intimation that he was satisfied with my work or concurred in the rather unexpected conclusions at which I had arrived, guided solely by the experimental facts and without any specific hints from him.

But if he assumed less responsibility for the actual prosecution of the work for the degree than did many teachers then or now, Gibbs took the greatest pains to make certain that the completed work on any dissertation on which he was a referee was worthy of the doctorate. The incident related by Wilson in his Gibbs lecture before the American Mathematical Society [4] is but one illustration of the care he would take in this respect. It seems that

4. *Scientific Monthly* (March, 1931).

Gibbs had been named a referee on a thesis involving the theory of algebraic numbers, a subject to which he had paid scant attention since his student days in Germany. Wilson reports that he ran across Gibbs one day in the library surrounded by books on number theory, and remarked that he had not realized Gibbs was familiar with the subject. Gibbs replied that he was not but that he thought with the aid of some books he might be able to come to a decision on the acceptability of the thesis. Other similar instances have been told me by more than one of his colleagues, and one I have only recently come across: in going through his papers, I found some sheets of computations checking the results that I had given in my own thesis!

The conscientious manner in which he performed this duty was characteristic of the way in which he met all his academic obligations. Although he never had in any year more than an occasional student coming under the jurisdiction of the college faculty, and then always one of a caliber requiring no faculty action except the award of honors, he was nevertheless a very regular attendant at faculty meetings. It was in connection with his infrequent participation in the discussions at these meetings that those of his colleagues not on the mathematical or physical faculties gained the greater part of their knowledge of him. There is ample evidence that his comments on such occasions were pithy and to the point; but because he always approached every problem, whether of science or of the ordinary affairs of life, from an original and frequently an unconventional point of view, some of his contributions to these discussions were not always appreciated in a sense he intended. Thus his injection of the thought, "mathematics is a language," into a discussion of the revision of the language requirements for the bachelor's degree was in some quarters regarded as an irrelevance; whereas for Gibbs it meant that if language is a means of expressing thought then mathematics is obviously in the same category in the educational scheme as Greek or Latin or German or French, and logically the claims of no one of them can be ignored in planning a balanced course of study.

An incident related by Irving Fisher [5] of Gibbs' comments in one

5. In "P.R.I."

faculty meeting on a proposal to report student grades only to sixteenths of the highest grade is a good illustration of his unconventional approach to a practical problem. All of us who have been teachers have been faced with the problem of averaging a student's marks; and some, with a naïve faith in the virtues of a mathematical average, have carried the process to an absurd limit—on the scale then in use at Yale to the point of reporting grades to one four-hundredth of the highest grade. But in the proposal to ban such a fine scale in favor of a coarser one there lurked a catch not immediately obvious to the nonmathematical mind, if the scheme were carried through with the same blind adherence to rule as had sometimes been exhibited in using the fine scale. The catch is that a strict adherence to the new rule might nullify any attempt on the part of the student to raise his grade if subsequent marks were insufficient to raise the average to the next sixteenth, thus leaving his grade unchanged. Conversely, subsequent low marks might be insufficient to lower his grade. Thus Gibbs' dry and precise setting forth of a dilemma which would not occur to many of his colleagues (and which according to Fisher convulsed the faculty with laughter) was in effect a powerful plea for the exercise of common sense and against tying the instructor's hands by any rule which might lead to absurd results. In this incident we see the working of a mind as effective in mundane affairs as it was in the abstruse realms of mathematical physics.

Another aspect of Gibbs as a teacher was his kindly and sympathetic reception of students who went to him for advice. This is evidenced in the "Personal Recollections and Impressions" by several of his students, the incident related by Professor Arthur S. Gale [6] being particularly illuminating. Gale, who had specialized in both mathematics and physics during his undergraduate course, had by his senior year come to lean strongly toward mathematics as a profession. So, when toward the end of that year he was offered by Professor Arthur W. Wright a nomination to the Sloane Fellowship in physics (which carried with it one of the largest stipends of any in the university), with the necessity

6. Fayerweather Professor of Mathematics, Emeritus, University of Rochester.

for a decision within a few hours, he was presented with a formidable dilemma. After brief interviews with Professor Wright and with Professor Andrew W. Phillips of the mathematical faculty and dean of the Graduate School, Gale says,

I returned to the Sloane Laboratory to see Gibbs, whose reception of me was kindly and friendly. I stated my dilemma and told him some of the things Wright and Phillips had said. He listened attentively. When I had finished he looked me straight in the eye, his blue eyes twinkling amazingly, and immediately replied, "Perhaps I can give you better advice than either of these other gentlemen as I am, as it were, on the fence between mathematics and physics, and my advice to you is to choose the field in which you will find the greater happiness." We exchanged a few remarks and I withdrew.

These three conversations occupied not more than forty minutes. "Buffalo" Wright had offered me a near certainty. "Andy" Phillips had stated his "opinion" as to the aid I might expect if I decided to study mathematics. Neither, wise men that they were, attempted to influence my decision. Nor did Willard Gibbs. Instead he brought into sharp focus a fundamental principle that I should not overlook in making a decision. Much later, during nearly a score of years of administrative work with undergraduates, I found many opportunities to relate the incident and to pass on to others the advice Gibbs gave me.

In recent years I have sometimes wondered how a senior would dare to take a personal problem to a scientist with the tremendous reputation Gibbs had acquired. I can only say that at the time it seemed to be the obvious and the natural thing to do. I needed advice, and I knew that he could help me, not alone because he was a great scientist, but because I felt that he was a kindly, sympathetic, and understanding man. When I entered his office unexpectedly he immediately gave me his full attention while his smile conveyed a cordial welcome. When he spoke, I knew at once that a wise man had brushed aside everything of secondary importance and had penetrated directly to the heart of my problem.

This incident is revealing in several ways. It pictures a man of unaffected courtesy who received a student as he would a colleague. It discloses a quiet sense of humor. It shows a man who was sure of himself and had confidence in his judgments. Above all, his attitude and the advice he gave were those of a man who had practiced the advice for himself and who knew that the "greater happiness" did not come as a gift or by chance but as the result of the conscious adjustment of personality to environment. That Gibbs was pre-eminently a happy man is a fact that has been insufficiently emphasized by his previous biographers, although it is one to which there are many witnesses. It is a characteristic which stands out in my own memories of him. It is implicit in all the accounts of his family and student relationships as recorded in the "Personal Recollections and Impressions." All that we know of him from faculty friends and neighbors emphasizes this trait. The late Miss Josephine Newton, daughter of Gibbs' colleague and intimate friend Hubert A. Newton, is quoted [7] as saying that he was "the happiest man" she ever knew. Another account of Miss Newton's impressions of Gibbs by Miss Margaret Whitney makes the same point in more detail and in confirmation of her own recollections.[8]

The fact that Gibbs was so fundamentally a happy man and that he consistently throughout his life "pursued" happiness successfully seems to me to be an important key to the understanding of his character. Much in his career that might otherwise be puzzling becomes plain in the light of the fact that he consciously made the "greater happiness" the touchstone for his decisions. It explains why he was content to serve Yale for ten years without salary; it rationalizes his refusal of the posts at Bowdoin and Johns Hopkins; it gives the clue to his choice of a life of limited social contacts. And it also furnishes, I think, the real explanation of his attitude of apparent indifference to the preparation of his students to undertake his courses and of the limited supervision of their dissertations. For he knew that his own competence and highest intellectual satisfactions, his "greater happiness," lay in the exploration and exposition of the more abstruse phases of natural phenomena, and that that of the students could only be realized by overcoming the difficulties in the understanding of such matters by their own efforts. Thus his relations with his students were not dictated by indifference or selfishness but were the result of the conviction that in the fulfillment of intellectual satisfactions lies the key to success in the life of the spirit.

But the attitude of detachment from the work of his students,

7. See the contribution of Miss Van Name in "P.R.I.," quoted more fully in the following chapter.
8. "One of the Prophets."

together with his own solitary habit of working, was undoubtedly responsible for the fact that Gibbs founded no "school" or group of students developing his ideas and exploiting his discoveries. It has been lamented that Yale chemists took such a negligible part in developing the physical chemistry which Gibbs had founded; and indeed their failure to seize the opportunity open to them from the late seventies onward does in perspective seem somewhat strange and regrettable. There were several causes for this failure to follow up Gibbs' discoveries with experimental work, such as the conservative atmosphere of the college and the novelty of the content and form of presentation in the great monograph; but some share of the blame, if blame there is, must be ascribed to Gibbs himself. His conception of his obligations to his students was very definite and conscientiously lived up to; and it contemplated no responsibility for their preparation for his work or for the later use they might make of it. Thus he was both by temperament and as a matter of principle unfitted to found a school. Some may regard this as unfortunate, but I am very certain that if he had dissipated his energies in a more elementary exposition of physics or in a more active and zealous propagandizing of his discoveries his contributions to our knowledge would have been seriously curtailed and his position in the history of science would have become a much more commonplace one.

A final example of Gibbs' quality as a teacher is afforded in a draft reply to one of a series of some twenty-two letters which he received from an elderly retired clergyman from the Middle West. This correspondence, only recently discovered among his papers, gives a glimpse of a side of Gibbs' character not revealed as clearly elsewhere. The point at issue was the Laplace correction to the Newtonian expression for the velocity of sound in a gas, a correction which the reverend gentleman could not be made to understand or accept. Gibbs' position speaks for itself in the following excerpts:

I have nothing more to add on the mathematical side of the question since I understand that your mind is no longer open to argument. As an excuse for having carried a profitless correspondence so far, I will only remind you that you represented yourself as a "searcher after truth," & that you begged for a "hint of the decisive evidence," &c. Do not understand me as finding any fault with your present position. When a man is in possession of the truth it would be in the highest degree illogical to search after it. . . .

Still since after much vacillation you seem to have settled down to the opinion that my letters are characterized by ledgerdemain and wriggling, I can only say that nothing has been further from my purpose than any indirection. I have sought to state the matter in as direct and straightforward a manner as possible, to avoid everything that could confuse judgment. I have left your charges against me (as well as other physicists) unanswered whenever they seemed to me to be immaterial, and only concerned myself to call you back from every digression.

In your last letter you speak of my "pluck" and "patience." I do not see the point of the word "pluck." It requires no pluck to stand by a simple proportion which expresses nothing but Newton's second law of motion. That is all the ground I care to defend, for from that alone follows the result with the merciless rigor of algebra. All the other questions, whether physicists in general & myself in particular are a pack of fools, I have allowed you to decide for yourself with perhaps a pusillanimous indifference. Even with your misstatements of my position, I have not concerned myself, only trying to set before you the simplest mechanical statement of the case. I may have been pusillanimous in declining many provocations to discussion, but I have certainly shown no pluck.

The patience which you attribute to me I will not disclaim. Perhaps you will appreciate it better if I tell you that by some irony of fate I have received two of your letters at the same time with other letters (say 6 pages long of German handwriting) from a man who disbelieves in the ratio which has been found for the circumference to the diameter of the circle, and claims that the true ratio is 3.125. You may imagine it was no easy matter to answer these letters which were not by any means the first I had received from him on the subject.

Every college professor of any prominence has probably experienced the importunities and impertinences of such cranks, but few I venture to think have endured the persecution with a more imperturbable calm or a more courteous insistence on holding the discussion to an impersonal plane. Behind the mild sarcasm of this letter (which apparently went entirely over the head of his correspondent) there is to be seen much of the clarity and serenity of Gibbs' philosophy.

XII

The Last Years

GIBBS in his later years was a man of striking appearance. A little over medium height, with a good figure, he carried himself well and walked rather rapidly and with a purposeful stride. He was always neatly dressed, usually wore a soft felt hat on the street, and never exhibited any of the physical mannerisms or eccentricities sometimes thought to be inseparable from genius. His hair and full beard were gray and his complexion clear and ruddy—almost florid. His eyes were blue and could twinkle amazingly on occasion. His forehead was high, his nose well formed and of a good length, and his mouth capable of a very sweet and intimate smile. In repose his expression was rather grave and abstracted, but how it could light up and become animated in greeting a friend or in pointing up a humorous turn to a discussion! His countenance was very mobile in conversation, every thought revealing itself in his changing expression. His manner was cordial without being effusive and conveyed clearly the innate simplicity and sincerity of his nature.

The best likeness of him is in my opinion that shown in a photograph taken in the early nineties and reproduced as the frontispiece of this book. The photoengraving, used as a frontispiece to the *Scientific Papers* (and the *Collected Works*), was made from a photograph probably taken at nearly the same time and, while generally satisfactory, gives an impression of a greater severity than I remember and does not suggest his blondness so well as does the earlier picture. It was from the photoengraving that the portrait by Miss Leslie Emmet, which hangs in the Graduate Club in New Haven (see plate facing p. 87), was done. This is in my opinion an improvement on the engraving, although it makes his complexion too sallow. The same engraving was used by Lee Lawrie in designing the bronze portrait tablet which is mounted on the wall of the main stairway of the Sloane Laboratory, a photograph of which is shown opposite p. 87.[1] From these various likenesses it is possible, I think, for one who never saw Gibbs to gain some idea of the nobility of his appearance, the dignity of his bearing, the directness and penetration of his glance, and the absence of all pomposity or self-consciousness. They all portray the gentleman and scholar much as he appeared in life.

The honors which came to him in these later years were many and varied. In 1885 he was elected a corresponding member of the British Association for the Advancement of Science and a vice-president of the American Association for the Advancement of Science. In 1886 he was named a foreign member of the Dutch Society of Sciences (Haarlem). The year 1889 saw him elected a correspondent (in the mathematical class) of the Royal Society of Sciences (Göttingen). In 1891 he was made an honorary member of the Cambridge Philosophical Society (England) and of the Royal Institution of Great Britain, in 1892 of the London Mathematical Society and of the Manchester Literary and Philosophical Society. That same year he was elected an associate of the Royal Academy of Amsterdam (section of mathematics and physics). In 1893 he was awarded the honorary degree of doctor of philosophy by the University of Erlangen (Germany) and that of doctor of laws by Williams College in this country. In 1895 he was elected a member of the American Philosophical Society of Philadelphia, and the following year he received the honorary degree of doctor of laws from Princeton University on the occasion of the celebration of its Sesquicentennial. In 1897 he was elected a foreign associate of the Royal Society of London. In 1900 he was elected a corresponding member of the Royal Prussian Academy of Sciences (Berlin) and of the French Institute, as well as a non-resident member of the Washington Academy of Sciences (D. C.). He received the Copley Medal of the Royal Society of London

1. It should be mentioned perhaps that neither Miss Emmet nor Mr. Lawrie had ever seen Gibbs. It is also of interest to note that the painting was financed by an anonymous Yale graduate who until he was approached on the matter had never heard of Gibbs; and that the sculpture was initiated by a gift for a memorial to him by Professor Walther Nernst of Göttingen, who had never met Gibbs and only knew him through his writings.

in 1901 which, in the days before the establishment of the Nobel prizes,[2] was generally regarded as the highest honor open to a man of science. In 1902 he was elected a corresponding member of the Royal Bavarian Academy of Sciences and was awarded the degree of doctor of mathematics by the University of Christiania (Norway).

This long and impressive list of degrees, awards, and honorary memberships suggests several reflections. In the first place this list, together with the earlier recognition detailed in Chapter VI, answers authoritatively and completely the allegations that Gibbs was for long unappreciated and that he was "a prophet not without honor save in his own country." It is true that Gibbs' name never became one to conjure with to the man in the street as is that of Einstein today, that he remained unknown to the average graduate of his own university, and that his real greatness was not appreciated outside of a small circle of his colleagues at Yale and among the leaders of scientific thought. But there is no question that he received in his lifetime a generous and cordial recognition from those qualified to judge of his achievements. It was moreover the only sort of recognition which Gibbs himself desired. Stories like that told by Sir J. J. Thomson [3] are amusing but reflect a condition of things that did not worry Gibbs at all. Thomson says:

I had myself personal experience of how little his work was known in his own country. When a new University was founded in 1887 the newly elected President came over to Europe to find Professors. He came to Cambridge and asked me if I could tell him of anyone who would make a good Professor of Molecular Physics. I said, "You need not come to England for that; the best man you could get is an American, Willard Gibbs." "Oh," he said, "you mean Wolcott Gibbs," mentioning a prominent American chemist. "No, I don't," I said, "I mean Willard Gibbs," and I told him something about Gibbs' work. He sat thinking for a min-

2. The first Nobel awards were made in 1901, that in physics going to Röntgen for his discovery of the X rays. For a popular account of the history of these awards, including lists of recipients and also of the notable omissions, see an article in the *Scientific American, 181,* No. 6 (December, 1949), 11, by George W. Gray. Among the outstanding omissions is noted that of Gibbs, and it is pointed out that in the cases of no fewer than four of those who have received the award it was given for work based directly on applications of Gibbs' concepts.

3. *Recollections and Reflections* (New York, Macmillan, 1937), pp. 185–186.

ute or two and then said, "I'd like you to give me another name. Willard Gibbs cannot be a man of much personal magnetism or I should have heard of him."

From Gibbs' point of view the real point of the story would lie in the fact that he *was* known to Thomson who could understand his work; that he was unknown to the other (who was not a physicist or a chemist) would seem only natural and of no importance whatever. He had no desire for uncomprehending recognition or for popular acclaim.

But the list of honors cited also suggests certain things which afford some interesting sidelights on Gibbs' character. It will be noted for instance that he received no honors from the American Mathematical or Physical societies. In fact he did not become a member of the American Mathematical Society [4] until just before his death, and he never became a member of the American Physical Society at all. These facts are not to be interpreted as a lack of appreciation of Gibbs on the part of these societies but, on the contrary, were due to his own lack of interest in belonging to them. He was emphatically not a "joiner," and his point of view is shown clearly in a draft of a letter to Professor Thomas S. Fiske of Columbia University, dated February 6, 1891, recently found among his papers. In this draft he says:

I think there is room in this section of the country for a Mathematical Society of broader scope than any wh exists, perhaps one wh may be more or less national in character, & I have felt very favorably inclined toward the plan in wh you have kindly invited me to join. On consideration, however, especially of my confirmed absenteeism in the few societies to wh I belong, it seems hardly worth while for me to join in the undertaking, except to assure you of my best wishes for your success.

With a society of a considerable membership & income, a publication of some kind wd naturally follow. The amount of financial foundation wh would make it wise to commence, the scope of the Journal, & its relations to existing publications, are matters on wh the opinion of those

4. Although the notice of his election to this body is included with the diplomas and other documents of honorary awards to Gibbs in the Yale library, it is somewhat doubtful if this really represents an honorary award. Professor Wilson recollects that Professor Cole, then secretary of the American Mathematical Society, made repeated attempts to induce Gibbs to join the society, and it is not impossible that he was ultimately successful and that the document preserved at Yale is merely the routine notice of election following the payment of dues.

who have had some editorial experience wd be much more valuable than mine. The plan wh you particularly mention, that of historical & critical articles, seems one where there is quite an opening for a useful activity.

That he held similar views with respect to the formation of the American Physical Society is a matter of my own personal knowledge. I remember well the discussions among the members of the physics faculty at Yale during the spring of 1899 when the subject was being agitated. Gibbs' attitude was one of cordial approval of the movement, but his reaction to joining the new society himself was precisely that shown in the letter quoted above. He obviously felt that his own participation in such activities would so dissipate his energies as to hamper the development of the work he had most at heart. He never needed outside contacts for inspiration and plainly felt that they might prove embarrassing to his established habits of working.

Although the honors which he thus received during these last years must have been a source of much gratification, he never showed outwardly that they were matters of great consequence to him. His Princeton doctorate in 1896 is recorded in my rough lecture notes on the course on the electromagnetic theory of light as follows: "Cut Thurs. Oct. 22. Gibbs at Princeton getting L.L.D." He had made no announcement in the lecture on Monday of that week of his intention to omit the Thursday lecture and, as I remember it, we in the class were first informed of the cause of his absence by the Sloane Laboratory janitor when we appeared on Thursday morning expecting the usual lecture. My notes on the course on dynamics and thermodynamics show that on the next day, Friday the twenty-third, he lectured in that course as usual and with no reference to his absence of the previous day. If the granting of this degree had not happened to fall on the day of a lecture we in the class would not have known of it unless we had chanced to note it in the published accounts of the Princeton Sesquicentennial. To the best of my knowledge Gibbs never gave out a notice of any of the honors which he received. In fact I believe that most of them became known to the majority of his colleagues only when they were listed in his obituary notices.

Nor did these honors in any way affect his bearing with his friends or his mode of living. His courteous, cordial relations with all—students, colleagues, or acquaintances—remained unchanged, and no hint was given in conversation that his opinions should carry an increased emphasis deriving from his growing prestige in the world of science. His social life followed the same routine as before and as always, aside from the customary vacation trips to Vermont or the White Mountains, was centered almost exclusively in his home. The center of the faculty social life at that time—at least among the younger men—was in the Graduates Club, of which Gibbs was not a member, and hence we graduate students and younger instructors saw less of him outside of the classroom than was the case with others of our teachers who frequented the club.[5] But evidence of the unchanged serenity and geniality of his social relationships is not wanting. These characteristics are emphasized in Hastings' biographical memoir and stand out in the contributions of Gibbs' niece and nephews to the "Personal Recollections and Impressions." I cannot portray this side of his character and the general atmosphere of the family life better than it is done in the following excerpts from these recollections.

Thus Professor Ralph Gibbs Van Name says:

Willard Gibbs took an active part in the life of the family group, and no doubt found much satisfaction in doing so, for he held us all in great affection. Not only was he ready at all times to give careful consideration to all kinds of problems affecting the household, but he cheerfully assumed a generous share of the household tasks, such as the regulation of the furnace, trimming of the oil lamps, exercising of the family horse, locking up at night, etc. . . .

Towards us children Uncle Willard was all kindness and generosity. He liked to give us pleasure by taking us to see unusual and interesting events, and to visit attractive localities in the neighborhood of New Haven. He took great interest in our activities, appreciated our good qualities, and was tolerant of our faults. . . .

5. In my contribution to "P.R.I." I have stated that I recollected one occasion on which Gibbs was present at the club. I have since then become convinced that my memory was at fault in placing him among the group at the time of the incident which I related and as to which my recollection that it occurred at an autumn meeting of the National Academy in New Haven is quite clear. As the last of these autumn meetings in New Haven during Gibbs' lifetime was in November, 1898, and as at that time the place at which my memory clearly establishes the incident was not in existence, I am forced to the conclusion that I have confused two occasions when the same topic was under discussion. It remains true that Gibbs' attitude is fairly represented in the incident as described.

Within the family circle my uncle's advice was sought on a wide variety of subjects, for we all had great confidence in his judgment. Unless the matter was already familiar to him he would seldom give an immediate opinion. He would first take pains to be sure of the facts, and would then often ponder a few minutes before giving his views. But although his procedure was deliberate, the opinion was usually forthcoming in a comparatively short time, and one received the impression of a mind which functioned with truly remarkable speed and certainty.

And Dr. Willard Gibbs Van Name writes:

As a companion he was able to talk interestingly on a great variety of subjects and usually had no lack of ideas on them. He had a keen sense of humor and enjoyed a joke; he appreciated good music and a good theatrical performance but did not attend such events very often. . . . Willard Gibbs' accomplishments were not by any means all of an intellectual or sedentary character. He had a great deal of mechanical ability and understanding of the various types of machinery then in use, including electrical ones, which were of course not as many as today, and he was always ready to talk about and explain their workings. . . .

My uncle was a great lover of nature and was always fond of taking walks, often quite long ones, . . . and during the last dozen years or more of his life this became his exclusive method of getting exercise. As the city grew and the rural areas receded, he would take a trolley car to some point outside the city and start his walk from there. That he generally had to take these walks by himself was not due to lack of sociability but to his being too good a pedestrian for his friends to keep up with him. Walking alone in this way his mind was not usually far from the subjects of his studies, and it is not unlikely that some of his important ideas developed in the course of them.

Though he never had a scientific interest in natural history or botany he was familiar with the common native trees and the more conspicuous wildflowers and knew many of their characters and peculiarities. I acquired much of my first knowledge of some of them from him on walks that I took with him.

To complete this composite family portrait I quote from the recollections of Gibbs' niece, Miss Theodora Van Name.

If I were asked what was Willard Gibbs' most striking characteristic, I should unhesitatingly reply, "his serenity." His calm equanimity was seldom ruffled. This opinion is confirmed by Miss Josephine Newton, daughter of Professor H. A. Newton, colleague and intimate friend of my uncle's, and a near neighbor of ours.[6] Miss Newton's recollection of Willard Gibbs goes back even farther in time than mine does and it extended over a long period of years. When I asked her recently for her impression of my uncle, she replied that she had always considered him as "the happiest man" she ever knew. This cheerfulness was, I think, due partly to an excellent sense of proportion which enabled him to estimate things at their true value, and partly to the uniformly good digestion which he enjoyed.

He was a man of quiet determination who knew what he wanted to do in life, and went ahead and did it, without faltering or hesitation . . .

His most noticeable mental attribute was the power of intense concentration, a faculty which he possessed in a superlative degree.

My uncle was well-read; was familiar with the standard authors in prose and poetry, and could quote from Shakespeare, Milton, Dickens, Thackeray, Jane Austen, etc. . . .

Despite his quiet manner, my uncle had a keen sense of humor, and a love of fun. He was fond of laughing and joking with intimate friends, such as Professor "Andy" Phillips. During the last decade of his life he passed his summer vacations in company with this friend, Professor Andrew W. Phillips, at various mountain resorts, usually in the White Mountains or in Vermont. As a typical vacation I well remember the summer of 1893, which I spent with him and his unmarried sister, my Aunt Anna, in Greensboro, Vermont. My uncle entered freely into the life of the small group (consisting chiefly of college professors and their families) in the boarding house half-way up the hill. Once, after riding in a hay wagon to attend a circus in a nearby village [during which a thundershower was experienced], we all composed "poems," and collected them in a booklet for our host, Professor Arnold Guyot Cameron.[7] My uncle's contribution in pseudo-classic style was easily the best of the group of verses. Professor Cameron has kindly sent me a copy of these hastily-scribbled lines, which I include here as showing my distinguished uncle in his lighter vein.

The Storm

When Iris skipping on her airy bow
Saw a fair rival on the rope below;
And Hermes pirouetting in the air

6. Miss Newton has died since this was written.

7. Professor Cameron was at that time an assistant professor in French in the Sheffield Scientific School. Just before his recent death he presented the original manuscript of the poem to Miss Van Name. It is now deposited with the Gibbs papers in the Yale library.

Saw mortals greater wonders do and dare,
And Phoebus resting with his smoking team,
Where evening's shades absorb his fiery beam,
Saw Forepaugh's jockeys on the plain afar
Curb the proud steeds, and wheel the thundering car,
With one accord to father Jove they cried
"Avenge our insults, humble mortal pride."
"Your plaints are heard," replied the voice sublime,
"And Aeol's minions shall avenge the crime."
Forth from the windy caves the Boreal Blast,
The turgid Typhoon, and the Simoon passed.
Twixt North and South and East and West winds pressed,
The tortured rain-clouds did their level best;
But as the prodigal, beset by duns,
With doubtful hands his various pockets turns,
Some noisy nickels rattle to the floor,
The scanty remnants of his golden store,
The spendthrift rain-clouds found it was no go,
The stock of water in the sky was low.
In vain the cloudlets gave their little all,
The pattering raindrops quickly ceased to fall.
While up the steepy hill of Hardwick Street
The patient horses dragged their weary feet,
Our jolly party nestling in the hay,
With jest and song whiled many an hour away,
And quiet Luna with her face serene
Smiled from on high upon the varied scene.

The impression one gains from these accounts is strikingly reminiscent of that presented by Miss Margaret Whitney and Mr. Newell Martin of a date two decades earlier. In the interval the unknown college professor had become known and recognized as one of the great physical philosophers of all time, and yet he still showed to his family and friends the same modest bearing, the same kindly interest in their concerns, the same cordial friendliness of demeanor, the same lack of any trace of a consciousness of superiority.

That Gibbs could indulge in scientific as well as in "poetical" diversion is shown in two of the informal talks he gave before the Mathematical Club in the early nineties. These were the times when the first experiments which ultimately resulted in giving us the modern motion picture were exciting some scientific interest. These early efforts to portray motion had shown that the artist's representation of a moving horse, both in painting and sculpture, was in general an impossible one. When the art of "stopping" the motion photographically had become sufficiently advanced to permit the examination of successive exposures taken at intervals of time less than that of the "persistence of vision" of the eye, these mistakes became particularly evident. With his interest in horses, as an accomplished rider, and his firsthand observation of their paces Gibbs was led to present before the Mathematical Club the paper to which Irving Fisher refers in his contribution to the "Personal Recollections and Impressions." [8] This talk was given shortly before my time, but I remember the amused comments of some of those who had heard it as to the thoroughness with which Gibbs had covered all the known paces to which a horse could be trained.

In addition to this paper on "The Paces of the Horse" he gave another a little later which had a similar inspiration in the early development of the motion picture. In the London *Nature,* as I remember it, there had been reproduced about this time a series of successive stills taken of a falling cat. The original movie had been made, I believe, by a French experimenter. Gibbs' talk, which was given on December 4, 1894, was entitled "On Motions by Which Falling Animals May Be Able to Fall on Their Feet," and I remember clearly the amusement, tempered by admiration of his analytical skill, with which the audience received the explanation of how it was possible for a cat, by appropriate manipulation of its "moment of momentum," to fall upon its feet. This application of physical principles to an everyday if somewhat obscure phenomenon made a great impression on me. I have been unable to find any reference to it among his notes which have survived, although the earlier talk with the title "Theory of Paces" is listed on one of a number of sheets containing notations as to courses, textbooks, subjects for study, and subjects for papers.

8. According to the "Yale University Bulletin" (a weekly announcement of university events), Gibbs gave this talk on January 17, 1893, with the title, "The Paces of the Horse"; and according to the records of the Connecticut Academy, on the following evening he presented a paper entitled "The Slower Gaits of Quadrupeds."

Another aspect of Gibbs' abilities which has been largely forgotten in the light of his great achievements in theoretical physics is his penetrating insight into experimental problems. That this was recognized however by some of his contemporaries is shown by their queries in several of the letters in the "Scientific Correspondence," such as those in the Michelson letter quoted in Chapter IX. Hastings, in his biographical memoir, cites the two inventions (the railway car brake and the improved Watt governor) as proof that Gibbs "possessed all the mental qualifications for a successful experimenter," and states that no one of his intimates doubted his capacity for experimental research if he had ever found it necessary for the furtherance of his theoretical studies. A further confirmation of this opinion is to be found in the proposal of an experimental research program having to do with van der Waals' "theory of corresponding states," which he sent to the late Professor Carl Barus of Brown University in 1897. This was later (1906) published in the *American Journal of Science* by Professor Barus under the title "Certain Suggestions by J. Willard Gibbs on Geophysical Research."

No one who followed his lectures and heard his often amazingly ingenious asides in explanation of the physical significance of some abstruse theoretical or mathematical development can doubt that in other circumstances Gibbs might have shone as an experimenter of more than average competence. The reason given by Hastings for the negligible amount of experimental work actually performed by Gibbs is probably valid. He attributes it to the fact that the experimental activity of the period of Gibbs' labors was so great as to furnish all of the data needed for his theoretical studies. But in any case no experimental work that he might have done could have had such significance for later experimental developments or potentiality in molding the future course of scientific thought as his genius in the abstract realms of theory.

Gibbs' academic activities during these last years followed in much the same groove as they had for the past quarter-century. His classes averaged a little larger in size than they had before, but the lectures covered the same list of subjects. Owing to difficulties in fitting the schedules of those students who were also giving part-time instruction in the college or the scientific school, he would more frequently than formerly arrange for a repetition of his lectures to suit their convenience or even give a course not scheduled for that year if that was the only way in which a student could get it. One case of such a voluntary addition to his teaching load is told by Professor Oliver C. Lester in the "Personal Recollections and Impressions." Lester had taken all but one of Gibbs' courses, and with regard to that one he says:

The course in Electromagnetic Theory was to be omitted during what I thought would be my last year at Yale. One day after a lecture I mentioned my regret at this situation and he at once said that no matter if it was so scheduled, he would be very glad to give that course next year. When I raised the point of the imposition on his time in giving a whole course, a year's work, for the benefit (as it appeared at the time) of just one student, he replied that it would be no imposition at all; that he did not often have a student in that course and that he would be glad to do it.

Such a rearrangement of schedules is but another instance of Gibbs' flexibility of method in instruction; and the cheerful taking on of an added load is only an added example of a real interest in his students. I know of at least two other cases in which he made similar arrangements for the benefit of a student at the expense of his own convenience.

As Gibbs had been the founder of the Mathematical Club at Yale in 1877 and one of its active members throughout the following years, so he was foremost among the founders and supporters of the Physics Club organized in 1899. If my memory serves me aright he never gave a paper before the club (except at a joint meeting with the Mathematical Club) but he was a regular attendant at the meetings and an acute and helpful participant in the discussions following the formal papers. In January, 1903, a dinner was given to celebrate the twenty-fifth anniversary of the founding of the Mathematical Club and members of the other discussion clubs were invited. It was a rather formal affair with a printed program containing rhymed introductions of the speakers by the toastmaster, Professor Phillips. Gibbs was the second on the list and his subject was "Values." It treated the ideals which in his opinion should actuate the scientific investigator, and was a carefully thought out and beautifully expressed address. Professor Lester in the "Personal Recollections and Impressions" recalls an earlier occasion where Gibbs was not on the list of speakers but was tricked into an impromptu talk by Professor Pierpont. The latter in an address lauding the beauties of pure mathematics as a logical structure deliberately belittled applied mathematics. This brought Gibbs to his feet; and no one who was present ever forgot the cogency and perfect form of his extemporaneous exposition of the *raison d'être* of applied mathematics and of the satisfactions to be found in the use of one's mathematical ability in the solution of the problems set by nature.

The ability to expound interestingly the broad outlines and the philosophy of physics shown on these occasions causes regret that there did not arise more opportunities for the expression of his views on other matters of general scientific interest connected with the history or the future of physics. It is possible that we might have learned something of these views if his reply to a letter from Miss Alice Bache Gould dated May 15, 1897,[9] had survived. Miss Gould requested Gibbs' advice on possible subjects for a memorial award in honor of her father, the astronomer Benjamin Apthorp Gould, which she was thinking of establishing. She was concerned that the award should not be for any subject of ephemeral interest, and expressed some doubt of the existence in this country of a sufficient interest in applied mathematics to justify such an award, at least if it were made at reasonably frequent intervals. In Gibbs' reply we might have possessed some interesting thoughts on the future of research in the mathematical sciences in this country. Unfortunately I have been unable to find any trace of it.

Gibbs' social, like his physical, orbit had changed little with the years. Since the death of his sister Emily in 1864 there had been no losses by death either in the family or in the circle of his intimates. The household had been enlarged by the addition of his brother-in-law and the coming of the three children; and although the growth of the university had necessarily expanded his acquaint-

9. In the "Scientific Correspondence."

anceship, it would seem that there had been little change in the number of his intimate friends. But in the latter part of the nineties he suffered two severe losses. The first was the death of the teacher of his young manhood and his lifelong friend and confidant, Hubert Anson Newton, which occurred in the summer of 1896. The Newton home was on his path to the Sloane Laboratory, and Gibbs was in the habit of dropping in there either going to or coming from his office. The mind and character of Newton as revealed in Gibbs' account of him [10] were very like his own, and it is not surprising that they found much in common, aside from their scientific interests. Miss Margaret Whitney in "One of the Prophets" reports, on the authority of Newton's daughters: "Morning after morning they would spend time in eager discussion interposed with peals of laughter. The Newton family said they retreated into the fourth dimension and closed the door."

The death of this close friend left a gap in Gibbs' life that was never filled, but it is characteristic of both men that the survivor should carry on with no outward show of grief. The eloquent passage with which Gibbs closes his sketch of his friend is at the same time an expression of the highest ambition of the one and of the love of the other: ". . . and so long as astronomers, while they watch the return of the Leonids marking off the passage of the centuries, shall care to turn the earlier pages of this branch of astronomy, his name will have an honorable place in the history of the science." The second blow was the death of his older sister Anna. She was taken ill in 1895 and after a partial recovery finally died in 1898. She was never strong physically and was very shy and retiring by nature. She had not, as had her brother, inherited any scientific tendencies, but otherwise they shared similar tastes, enjoyed the same quiet pleasures, and had been most congenial and companionable from the days of their European sojourn onward. She was one who delighted in talking of past days and experiences, and much of what we know of the earlier family life and times is due to her.[11] She and Willard were constant companions on vacation trips where his ability and willingness to make friends and to enter into the community activities must have added much to her

10. *Am. Journ. Sci.* (May, 1897). *The Scientific Papers*, II, 268.
11. "P.R.I.," contribution of W. G. Van Name.

enjoyment of fresh environments, as indeed it did to all who met them on these occasions. Her death also left an unfilled gap in Willard's life, albeit of a different kind than that left by Newton. Both were relationships of deep affection, one rooted in family and everyday things, the other in his work and scientific interests. In both he had found relaxation and inspiration.

Whether it was from loneliness generated by the breaking of these two ties, or merely advancing years, or perhaps that the advent of the new physics—that of the X rays, the electron, and radio-activity—was producing in Gibbs an intellectual unrest, it appeared to me that from about 1898 on he was more preoccupied and abstracted in manner than formerly. He performed all of his duties with the same quiet efficiency as ever, was as cordial and friendly as before, but he seemed to me more grave about it all. My impression may be mistaken; after all I am going back more than fifty years in my memories and I may be reading something into them that is only a product of my own imagination. But I can only say for what it is worth that without any abatement of interest or enthusiasm Gibbs' outlook seems to me to have become from that time tinged with a soberness it did not possess before, and that it was partly at least connected with the newer trends in physics. I think that nearly all of the older physicists of the period, particularly those who had been brought up in the classical traditions of mathematical physics, were more or less disturbed by these newer developments. Signs of such a disturbance may be detected I believe in the later work of Kelvin and Rayleigh. In Gibbs' case this solicitude was frequently expressed in connection with the implications involved with respect to the electron. Here the increased number of degrees of freedom thus introduced, which in the classical theory had to share in the energy of the atoms and molecules of which they were constituents, was a matter that gave him considerable concern. Since, as he had pointed out in the passage from the preface to his *Statistical Mechanics* quoted in Chapter X, even the relatively small number of degrees of freedom demanded by the theory for a diatomic molecule exceeds the number which can be accounted for experimentally, the situation with the inclusion in the picture of an electronic structure for the atoms and molecules did seem to become almost hopeless—at least from the classical equipartition standpoint. I remember Gibbs remarking during a Physics Club discussion that the added complications introduced into the specific heat problem by the electron were such as to make him think that perhaps it was time he passed on! [12]

But at the same time it must be remembered that with the concepts of canonical distribution and of generic phases Gibbs had provided tools competent to deal with the problems arising from a radically altered conception of the nature of energy. It is therefore interesting to speculate on what Gibbs' attitude would have been on the question of the atomicity of energy had he lived longer. Although the idea of the "quantum of action" was given to the world in the year 1900, it had made but little progress toward acceptance by the time of Gibbs' death in the spring of 1903. Professor Wilson tells me that during his year in Paris (1902–03) he heard nothing of it, and as well as I can recollect little or no discussion of it took place in New Haven during the same period. So it is not surprising that no record of Gibbs' thought on the subject is to be found. But it seems to me that he would have welcomed the new concept for the possibility it offered of resolving the dilemma of the specific heats of polyatomic gases, if for no other reason. While this is only an inference on my part, it is one that others of his students do not find incredible. Thus Professor Wilson writes me: "One may hope that he would have picked up the new quantum theory, for he was concerned about the ratio of the specific heats and degrees of freedom and knew that somehow the excess degrees must be denied their energy." And Professor Bronson of Dalhousie University writes in the "Personal Recollections and Impressions": "I cannot help wondering whether he would have found anything upsetting in modern quantum ideas. I suspect that he would have found them quite natural."

There is a further hint of a tentative acceptance of a modern viewpoint on atomic and molecular structure in the conversation, dating from some time in the year 1900, reported by Dr. Joseph H. Hart in the same volume of reminiscences. He says:

I was sitting in his office talking about nothing in particular outside the courses I was taking, when he said "Mr. Hart, it is my firm conviction

12. Wilson recalls the same incident in his Gibbs lecture, *Scientific Monthly* (March, 1931).

that every little molecule or atom has a definite atmosphere about it very much like the earth's atmosphere about it (the earth). I suppose I have no real grounds for such a conviction, that is, no present scientific grounds, but such a concept would explain so many things that it seems a pity that it has not been developed." We talked about many other things, but that particular remark has stuck for forty-five years.

Thus it seems reasonable to infer that at least some of his concern as to the modern trends in physics was in process of dissipation in the opening years of the twentieth century. As to what his attitude would have been toward the second of the great generalizations of modern physics, which came some two years after his death—that of Einsteinian relativity—there is, so far as I am aware, not the slightest hint which can afford an answer. I have enlarged previously, in commenting on the Michelson correspondence, on the fact that Gibbs never expressed any opinion on the subject of the electrodynamics of moving media, and whether he would have welcomed Einstein's interpretation of the null result of the Michelson-Morley experiment is a question whose answer must remain a mystery.

But whatever question there may be as to the role Gibbs might have played in the further development of physics had he lived for say another ten years, it is certain that he would have continued to be constructively active. We know from the interview reported by Wilson,[13] which took place in June, 1902, and from the scattered and fragmentary notes left among his papers that he had a definite program for future work and that it involved extensions and further developments of his earlier work rather than the breaking of new ground. However, from the power, originality, and flexibility of his mind it would be foolhardy to deny that he might have penetrated into fresh fields or have anticipated the inclusion in his system of statistical mechanics of some of the results of the newer ideas, such as those of the quantum hypothesis, which it remained for others to accomplish much later. He had twice in his lifetime pioneered in the exploration of domains unseen or only dimly perceived by his contemporaries; and he possessed such unrivaled physical intuition and so impersonal and comprehensive an outlook that one hesitates to say he had come to the end of his creative

13. *Ibid.*

achievement. But as to what its content might have been it is futile and unnecessary to speculate further. The record of his actual accomplishment places him among the immortals.

Little more remains to be said than the bare recording of the events leading up to his death. The years 1900 and 1901 were dominated by his preoccupation with the preparation of the manuscript of *Statistical Mechanics* for the press. For the first time in his life he found it necessary to work regularly in his office during the evening hours. [14] It has been said by no less close a friend than Professor Phillips that it was the labor on this book that broke him down physically. But this does not seem plausible to me or to others who were in contact with him at the time. It is probably true that the strain of preparing the manuscript to meet a given date did tire him perceptibly, but from my own observation of him in 1902 and from the testimony of members of the family and of his students it would seem that he had entirely recovered his usual strength and spirits by the time the book had appeared. During this period in addition to his routine duties he was active as an intermediary between the university Corporation and certain distinguished scientists whom the university desired to honor with degrees on the occasion of the bicentennial celebration of the founding of Yale College. Letters regretting their inability to be present for this event from Lord Rayleigh and Henri Poincaré and one of acceptance from Lord Kelvin are preserved in the "Scientific Correspondence." Kelvin's degree was not conferred, however, at the time of the celebration but later at a special convocation.

In the fall of 1902 Gibbs was in correspondence with Longmans, Green and Company with regard to reprinting the "Equilibrium" monograph with additions. The proposal came first from the publishers, and after several exchanges of letters concerning the size of the proposed book (Gibbs estimated that the new material would run to some fifty pages) the final contract was signed on February 28, 1903.[15] At this time, just two months before his death, he had made but little progress toward completing the manuscript, although the subject headings were all blocked out as pub-

14. That he had previously been unaccustomed to work at night is testified to by W. G. Van Name in "P.R.I."
15. The signed contract has only recently been found among his papers.

lished in *The Scientific Papers* and the *Collected Works*. Some correspondence dating from this time has also been preserved relating to proposals for publishing translations of *Statistical Mechanics* into both French and German.

Meanwhile Gibbs went on with his usual duties and appointments with apparently no thought that the end was near. Although during these last years he had had some trouble from a bladder ailment, it did not seem to be serious; it made no interruptions to his work and was not the cause of his sudden death. He became ill before the close of the Easter recess in April, though with no symptoms to cause alarm. On Sunday, April 26, his physician told him that he was getting better and would soon be out again. But two days later he suddenly became worse and toward evening somewhat delirious. At eleven o'clock that night, Tuesday, April 28, 1903, he died. This totally unexpected termination to what seemed but a minor illness was diagnosed as due to an intestinal obstruction, although no autopsy was performed. Only his brother-in-law and older nephew were present at the end, his sister, younger nephew, and niece being abroad at the time. A simple funeral service was held two days later at the house at 121 High Street, and the interment was in the Grove Street Cemetery not two blocks distant, where the inscription on the stone marking the grave reads simply on one side:

JOSIAH WILLARD GIBBS

BORN FEB. 11, 1839, DIED APRIL 28, 1903

and on the other side:

PROFESSOR OF MATHEMATICAL PHYSICS

IN YALE UNIVERSITY, 1871–1903

A largely attended memorial meeting was held in the Sloane Laboratory later in May. The following account of this meeting is taken from the minutes of the Physics Club as recorded by Professor A. W. Wright.

Fortieth Meeting
Sloane Physical Laboratory, the large lecture-room, Tuesday evening, May 19, 1903.

Special Meeting of the Club, in conjunction with the Mathematical Club, the Chemical Club and the Engineering Club, held in honor of Professor J. W. Gibbs. Besides the members of the different clubs many of the officers and students of the University were present, as well as other friends of the deceased professor. Brief addresses were made by President Hadley, Ex-President Dwight, Professor Phillips, and by Professor J. J. Thomson, of Cambridge, England who was present. In appreciation of the work of Professor Gibbs in different fields of mathematical Physics addresses were made, by Professor Mixter, upon Chemical Physics; Professor P. F. Smith, upon Multiple Algebra; Professor H. A. Bumstead, upon the contributions to Thermodynamic Science; Dr. L. P. Wheeler, on Electro-magnetic Theory; and Professor J. Pierpont, some personal reminiscences.

The following minute, presented by Professor Phillips, was adopted:

Professor Gibbs founded the Mathematical Club in 1877, and contributed to it many papers on a variety of subjects in Mathematics and Mathematical Physics. His papers on Vector Analysis, with its applications to the Electro-magnetic Theory of Light, and to the Computation of Orbits, together with other important papers, were presented to this Club first of all. He was the Executive Officer of the Club for the first ten years of its existence, and was a constant attendant on its meetings until his last illness. He took a great interest in all of the proceedings of the Club, not only by presenting papers of his own, but his contributions to its discussions were a most valuable part of the proceedings.

He was also a member of the Physical Club from its foundation in 1899. There he was always present, and by his active part in the discussions, was very influential in maintaining a high standard for the work of the Club. His influence was also felt in other organizations with which he was less intimately connected, such as the Chemical Club and the Engineering Club, wherever their work derived its stimulus from the principles evolved by him in his researches.

To all those who were concerned in the work of these clubs he proved himself a helpful colleague and inspiring leader. To nearly all the members of the Mathematical and Physical Clubs, and to many of the members of the Chemical and Engineering Clubs, he had at some time stood in the relation of teacher, and to them the influence of his genius and originality was of incalculable value.

His pupils, in becoming teachers, have continued and extended his influence over the course of thought in the domain of the Mathematical and Physical Sciences.

His departure leaves with all his associates a sense of irreparable loss.

His work was unique, and while we cannot hope that his place will be made good, yet the results achieved by him in training others will perpetuate his activities, and his own scientific work is imperishable.

Arthur W. Wright ⎫
Andrew W. Phillips ⎬ Committee.
James Pierpont ⎭

The simplicity of these exercises and the sincerity of the tributes to the man and his achievements were all in accord with the character of Willard Gibbs and were much as he would have wished them to be: no fanfare, no academic procession, nothing but quiet words of appreciation from those who could understand something of his work and character and who would cherish his memory.

APPENDICES

APPENDIX I
Genealogical Chart

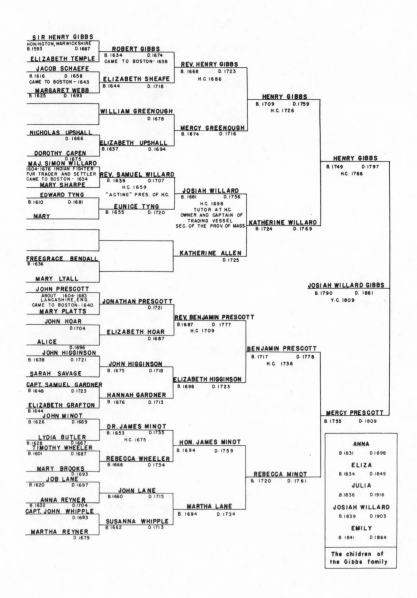

SIR HENRY GIBBS
HONINGTON, WARWICKSHIRE
B. 1593   D. 1667
ELIZABETH TEMPLE
JACOB SCHAEFE
B. 1616   D. 1658
CAME TO BOSTON - 1643
MARGARET WEBB
B. 1625   D. 1693

ROBERT GIBBS
B. 1634   D. 1674
CAME TO BOSTON - 1658
ELIZABETH SHEAFE
B. 1644   D. 1718

REV. HENRY GIBBS
B. 1668   D. 1723
H.C. 1686

HENRY GIBBS
B. 1709   D. 1759
H.C. 1726

WILLIAM GREENOUGH
D. 1678
NICHOLAS UPSHALL
D. 1666
DOROTHY CAPEN
D. 1675
MAJ. SIMON WILLARD
1604-1676 INDIAN FIGHTER
FUR TRADER AND SETTLER
CAME TO BOSTON - 1634
MARY SHARPE
EDWARD TYNG
B. 1610   D. 1681
MARY

ELIZABETH UPSHALL
B. 1637   D. 1694
REV. SAMUEL WILLARD
B. 1639   D. 1707
H.C. 1659
"ACTING" PRES. OF H.C.
EUNICE TYNG
B. 1655   D. 1720

MERCY GREENOUGH
B. 1674   D. 1716

JOSIAH WILLARD
B. 1681   D. 1756
H.C. 1698
TUTOR AT H.C.
OWNER AND CAPTAIN OF
TRADING VESSEL
SEC. OF THE PROV. OF MASS.

HENRY GIBBS
B. 1749   D. 1797
H.C. 1766

KATHERINE WILLARD
B. 1724   D. 1769

FREEGRACE BENDALL
B. 1636
MARY LYALL

KATHERINE ALLEN
D. 1725

JOSIAH WILLARD GIBBS
B. 1790   D. 1861
Y.C. 1809

JOHN PRESCOTT
ABOUT 1604-1683
LANCASHIRE, ENG.
CAME TO BOSTON - 1640
MARY PLATTS
JOHN HOAR
D. 1704
ALICE
D. 1696

JONATHAN PRESCOTT
D. 1721

ELIZABETH HOAR
D. 1687

REV. BENJAMIN PRESCOTT
B. 1687   D. 1777
H.C. 1709

BENJAMIN PRESCOTT
B. 1717   D. 1778
H.C. 1736

JOHN HIGGINSON
B. 1638   D. 1721
SARAH SAVAGE
CAPT. SAMUEL GARDNER
B. 1648   D. 1723
ELIZABETH GRAFTON
B. 1644

JOHN HIGGINSON
B. 1675   D. 1718

HANNAH GARDNER
B. 1676   D. 1713

ELIZABETH HIGGINSON
B. 1696   D. 1723

MERCY PRESCOTT
B. 1755   D. 1809

JOHN MINOT
B. 1626   D. 1669
LYDIA BUTLER
B. 1628   D. 1667
TIMOTHY WHEELER
B. 1601   D. 1687
MARY BROOKS
D. 1693

DR. JAMES MINOT
B. 1653   D. 1735
H.C. 1675

REBECCA WHEELER
B. 1666   D. 1734

HON. JAMES MINOT
B. 1694   D. 1759

REBECCA MINOT
B. 1720   D. 1761

JOB LANE
B. 1620   D. 1697
ANNA REYNER
B. 1632   D. 1704
CAPT. JOHN WHIPPLE
D. 1683
MARTHA REYNER
D. 1679

JOHN LANE
B. 1660   D. 1715

SUSANNA WHIPPLE
B. 1662   D. 1713

MARTHA LANE
B. 1694   D. 1734

ANNA
B. 1831   D. 1898

ELIZA
B. 1834   D. 1849

JULIA
B. 1836   D. 1916

JOSIAH WILLARD
B. 1839   D. 1903

EMILY
B. 1841   D. 1864

The children of
the Gibbs family

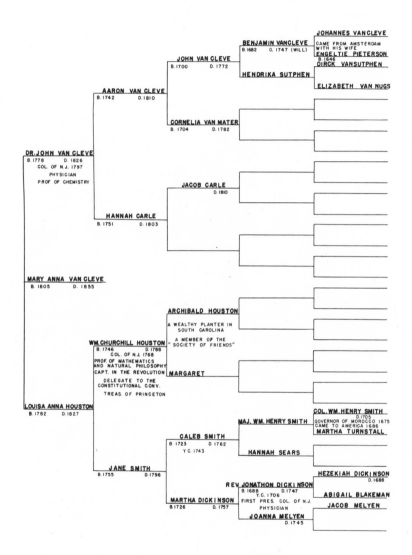

JOHANNES VANCLEVE
CAME FROM AMSTERDAM
WITH HIS WIFE
ENGELTIE PIETERSON
B. 1646
DIRCK VANSUTPHEN

ELIZABETH VAN NUGS

BENJAMIN VANCLEVE
B. 1682   D. 1747 (WILL)

HENDRIKA SUTPHEN

JOHN VAN CLEVE
B. 1700   D. 1772

CORNELIA VAN MATER
B. 1704   D. 1782

AARON VAN CLEVE
B. 1742   D. 1810

JACOB CARLE
D. 1810

HANNAH CARLE
B. 1751   D. 1803

DR. JOHN VAN CLEVE
B. 1778   D. 1826
COL. OF N.J. 1797
PHYSICIAN
PROF OF CHEMISTRY

MARY ANNA VAN CLEVE
B. 1805   D. 1855

ARCHIBALD HOUSTON
A WEALTHY PLANTER IN
SOUTH CAROLINA
A MEMBER OF THE
"SOCIETY OF FRIENDS"

MARGARET

WM. CHURCHILL HOUSTON
B. 1746   D. 1788
COL. OF N.J. 1768
PROF OF MATHEMATICS
AND NATURAL PHILOSOPHY
CAPT. IN THE REVOLUTION
DELEGATE TO THE
CONSTITUTIONAL CONV.
TREAS. OF PRINCETON

LOUISA ANNA HOUSTON
B. 1782   D. 1827

COL. WM. HENRY SMITH
D. 1705
GOVERNOR OF MOROCCO 1675
CAME TO AMERICA 1686
MARTHA TURNSTALL

MAJ. WM. HENRY SMITH

HANNAH SEARS

CALEB SMITH
B. 1723   D. 1762
Y.C. 1743

JANE SMITH
B. 1755   D. 1796

HEZEKIAH DICKINSON
D. 1688

ABIGAIL BLAKEMAN

JACOB MELYEN

REV. JONATHON DICKINSON
B. 1688   D. 1747
Y.C. 1706
FIRST PRES. COL. OF N.J.
PHYSICIAN

JOANNA MELYEN
D. 1745

MARTHA DICKINSON
B. 1726   D. 1757

APPENDIX II

*Gibbs' First Paper**

THE PROPER MAGNITUDE OF THE UNITS OF LENGTH, *& of other quantities used in Mechanics.*

Read before the Conn. Acad. Mch. 21. 1866.

A uniform system of weights & measures, adapted alike to the wants of practical life and to those of Science, is an acknowledged desideratum. I suppose that we all hope & expect, that the world will not long consent to do without so great a convenience. The problem of the formation of such a system is not a new one. France is entitled to the credit of having taken the first step toward its solution. And such is the excellence of her Metrical System, that it has already gained a foothold in most of the countries of the globe, & seems to promise to fulfil the design of its authors, that it should become cosmopolitan. And yet perhaps it may even now be not too late, to discuss on general principles the conditions, which the units of the several kinds of quantity should fulfil. For most purposes, the magnitude of the unit, which is chosen to measure any particular kind of quantity, is, within limits, quite immaterial. Yet in other cases the use of a particular unit may greatly simplify the relations of the numerical representatives of the quantities, & expedite the calculation. Thus in the Metrical System the adoption of the cubic centimetre of water as the unit of weight has greatly simplified the calculation of the weight of any body, of which the bulk or volume & the spec. grav. is known. The process is simply to multiply together the numbers which express these two quantities. Had not the units of volume & of weight been connected on some such principle, it would have been necessary to introduce a third factor, viz. the constant number expressing the weight of a unit of volume of water. I allude to a point so familiar, only because it is precisely in an analogous way, viz. in causing a constant factor (or divisor) to disappear, that the solution of Mechanical problems is simplified by the choice of appropriate units.

The most important & fundamental kinds of quantities which enter into mechanical problems are four,—*time, length, force,* & *mass.* For each of these a unit must be chosen. Many other kinds of quantities might be added, not

* As the manuscript of this paper was not prepared for publication but only for reading before the Connecticut Academy, many abbreviations are to be found in it. Some of these are given in a variety of forms, and as this variety might confuse the reader, the manuscript has been altered to make them consistent. Certain of the abbreviations whose meaning cannot be mistaken are left as written, and obvious misspellings corrected, but otherwise the manuscript is unaltered.

less important, but perhaps less fundamental, for which the appropriate units will naturally be suggested by the units of the quantities already mentioned. Thus: no one will doubt, that the most natural simple & appropriate unit of area is the area of the square of which the side is the unit of length; that the natural unit of volume is the volume of the cube of which the edge is the unit of length; that the natural unit of velocity is the velocity of a body moving at the rate of one unit of length in one unit of time; or that the natural unit of acceleration is the acceleration of a body which is gaining velocity at the rate of one unit of velocity in one unit of time. And so on, with other kinds of quantities too numerous to mention.

I shall first speak briefly of the nature of these quantities, which I have called fundamental, & of the units by which they are commonly measured; next I shall show why these units have not been convenient for the purposes of Mechanical Science, & what different units have therefore been introduced by writers on this subject; lastly, I shall seek those conditions which it is most necessary for these units to fulfil for the convenience both of men of science & of the multitude, & propose a set of units which shall satisfy these conditions. For the measurement of time we have natural units in the year & the day, upon the latter of which are founded the hour, minute & second. As a small unit of time is generally convenient for mechanical calculations, the *second* is made the principal unit in almost all treatises on Mechanics. It would indeed have been better in many respects if the day had been divided into 10 or 100 hours, the hour in 100 min. & the min. into 100 sec. Whether a change in this respect is now either desirable or practicable, I leave to others to discuss.

I need not dwell upon the great diversity of linear measures. It is enough to say that the *foot* is adopted as the principal unit by most Eng. & Am. writers, & to a great extent by the German, while the French & others who use the metrical system adopt of course the *metre*.

As the word force is applied to quantities of entirely different kinds & which are therefore measured by different units, I would say, that I have used the word in the sense in which it is used in Statics, & more definitely (for there are two kinds of force conceived of in Statics) I refer to continued not impulsive forces. In a word I mean such forces of which the magnitude or intensity can be expressed in pounds, ounces, tons, kilograms, or other units of wgt. Units of *weight* we call them, units of *force* we might say as well, for *weight* is but an example of *force,* a force, namely, arising from a certain cause, but as *force* differing in no respect from any other force (of the kinds of forces now under consideration) & measurable of course by the same units. Mechanical writers usually adopt either the pound or the kilogram as their principal unit.

Many writers define *Mass* as 'quantity of matter' or use the phrase 'quantity of matter' as synonymous with *Mass*. They go on to say, that all matter has to an equal degree two properties, which are accordingly possessed by all bodies with an intensity proportioned to the quantity of matter which they contain. One of these is the property of attracting other bodies and being attracted by them, in accordance with the law of Universal gravitation. The other is the property of resisting in virtue of its inertia, any change of velocity, so that an amount of force is required to change its velocity, greater or less indeed according to the rate at which its velocity is to be changed. The different intensities, then, with which either of these properties manifests itself in different bodies, may be taken as a measure of their quantities of matter. Thus: if one body is attracted toward the earth twice as powerfully as another under the same circumstances, the quantity of matter of the one is twice that of the other. Or if two bodies acted upon by different forces change their velocities at the same rate, while the force acting upon the one is twice that acting upon the other, then also we may say, that the quantity of matter in the one is twice that in the other.

Now this is certainly a very convenient way to state the case, and will answer for all practical purposes. Yet it is evident, that when the matter of the bodies compared is different in kind, we cannot strictly speaking say that the quantity of matter of one is equal, greater, or less than that of the other. All that we have a right to say, except when the matter is the same in kind, is that the gravity is proportioned to the inertia. To say *that,* is to express a great law of nature,—a law by the way of that class which we learn by experience and not by a priori reasoning. It might have been otherwise, but its truth is abundantly attested by experience. But to say, that the intensities of these two properties are both proportioned to the quantity of matter, is to bring in an element of which we know *nothing.* And yet something may be said in apology for such a statement. Not only is the intensity of either of these properties always proportioned to the quantity of matter, when the matter is of the same kind & under the same form, but the same is true for matter of the same kind under however different forms it may appear. Thus if we compare different bodies of ice, of water, & of steam, the quantity of matter in the bodies will be proportioned to the degree of these properties. The same might also be shown in the case of chemical composition. The rule is true then in all cases in which it can be put to the test, as results from two experimental truths or laws of nature; 1st the law already mentioned, that the properties of gravity & inertia exist in different bodies with intensities proportioned to each other; 2^d that changes of whatever kind in the form or state of matter do not in any degree alter these two properties. And if we were to assume that all matter is the same in kind, that all bodies can be resolved back into one primitive element, so that in the progress of science we will become able intelligently to compare the quantities of matter of bodies which now seem entirely different e.g. of gold & of lead, there is no doubt that we would find, that what are now called by the writers in question equal quantities of gold & of lead, would be found to be actually so. Yet as this assumption is a rather frail basis upon which to found the Science of Mechanics, it would seem better to suppose that such writers in using the term quantity of matter, mean quantity of matter, when only one kind of matter is in question, but when more than one kind is in question, mean that quantities (of different elements) shall be considered equivalent, which exhibit the properties above mentioned in equal intensity. As then this phrase *'quantity of matter'* requires an explanation of the sense in which it is to be used which explanation somewhat modifies the natural sense of the words, it is better to express the idea by a word, which does not present the fallacious appearance of defining itself. The word chosen by Mec[h]anicians is Mass. The *'Mass'* then of a body expresses the measure of its capability to manifest the phenomena either of inertia or of gravitation. It makes no practical difference, which of these properties we take. The first is generally made the basis of the definition of the term Mass, while the second is always used as the practical criterion of the equality or of the relative magnitude of the masses of two bodies. We measure the mass of a body by comparing it with some body of known mass, as the bodies which we call pounds, ounces, or kilograms, & express the Mass numerically in the number of pounds, ounces, or kilograms.

We see then that the units of mass or quantity of matter as it is loosely called, have the same names as the units of force. A pound & a kilogram alike express sometimes a certain amount of force, sometimes a certain amount of mass. This double meaning not of one word alone, but of a whole class of words without exception I think in all languages, has been the source of much confusion in the minds of learners, a confusion pardonable perhaps, as the writers have not always been free from the same. To avoid the possibility of being misunderstood in the course of my remarks, when I speak of a pound or a kilogram as a measure or unit of mass, I shall sometimes say mass-pound, mass-kilogram,—when I speak of a pound or kilogram as a unit of force, I shall sometimes say force-pound, force-kilogram. I may even use the terms mass-weight, force-weight, to denote weight in the sense of mass, & weight in the sense of force.

To distinguish these two meanings of the word weight, the terms relative weight & absolute weight have been used. rel. wgt $=$ mass-wgt; abs. wgt $=$ force-wgt. It would seem however a peculiarly unfortunate nomenclature, to call an attribute of a body which never varies *relative,* and one which changes with the position of the body absolute. For this reason, and because the terms have also been used in an entirely different sense, it does not seem worth while to adopt them here.

The reason why the same names are given to the units which measure two entirely different kinds of quantity, is of course, that in every body the quantities in question are seen to be sensibly proportional to one another. This proportionality, however, is not exact, & we may even imagine cases, impossible indeed to try in practice, when the disagreement would be as great as we choose. It is not an exact definition of a force-pound to say that it is the weight (force-weight of course) of a mass-pound; nor is it an exact definition of a mass-pound to say that it is the mass of a body which weighs one force-pound. In each of these cases it is necessary to give an additional limitation, and give the place where such a relation holds good. Thus, if we should say "a mass-pound weighs (i.e. gravitates) one force-pound at New York at the level of the sea," we would give an exact means of determining either of these quantities from the other, or, such a statement would define either of them, the other being supposed known. At different places, however, the same body, consisting of course of the same number of mass-pounds, weighs a different number of force-pounds. The number of force-pounds which a body will weigh is about ½ per cent greater at the Pole than at the Equator. The force-wgt. (measured in force-pounds) of a body is about ⁄₂₀₀₀ less at the height of one mile than at the level of the sea. The mass-wgt of the body is the same. At the elevation of 4000 miles one mass-pound would weigh about ¼ force-pound.

It may not be out of place, to observe that the instruments for measuring *mass-wgt* & *force-wgt* are theoretically at least entirely different. To measure *mass-wgt*, the common balance is the appropriate instrument. Then an unknown mass is placed in one scale, and known masses in the other. If there is equilibrium, the masses in the two scales are equal, (for equal masses at the same latitude & elevation gravitate equally) & the value of the unknown mass becomes known. I need not stop to show that the case is essentially the same with the steelyard. Yet this perhaps should be said that in both these cases the real measure of wgt is the piece of metal called a weight, that is a body of known mass-wgt. The balance & the steelyard are really only convenient means for ascertaining the equality between the known & the unknown masses. I think the same may be said of the bent-lever balance, at least it is theoretically a perfect instrument for measuring mass-wgt.

The most accurate method of measuring force-wgt at any place is doubtless a body of which the force-wgt at that place is known. But this measure is not portable, so to speak. If we take it to another place, its force-wgt is altered. If a spring-balance could be made, of which the elasticity would be affected neither by age, use, or temperature, & properly graduated it would be a perfect measure of force-wgt, or dynamometer.

It deserves notice that the wgt concerned in commercial transactions is what I have called mass-wgt;—so that instead of the terms, mass-weight, mass-pound, mass-kilogram, etc., the terms commercial wgt, com. pound, com. kil. &c might have been appropriately used. In the science of chemistry also the ordinary units of wgt are mass-wgt units. The importance of commercial interests has made most States adopt standards of commercial or mass wgt., I do not know that a unit of force has ever been established by Governmental Authority. The force wgt however of the units of mass wgt established by government are used as units of force. As the force wgt of any mass wgt is different in different places these units of force are inexact until defined by some place, where the mass-wgt is to be weighed.

Thus the French Academy with the sanction of the government established a unit of mass-wgt and called it a kilogram, (which for clearness I shall call a mass-kilogram) saying nothing about force-wgt, yet all French writers on mechanics speak of a unit of force which they call a kilogram. Unfortunately however they do not mention where the mass-kilogram of the Acad. is to be weighed, to give this new unit the force-kilogram. Perhaps they meant that it should be weighed at Paris.

We see then the common units of Time, Length, Mass, & force, viz the sec; foot, metre; mass-pound, mass-kil.; force-pound, force-kil. &c &c &c. Writers on Mechanics who have written especially for practical men, have of course generally felt compelled to use these familiar units. The majority of Mechanical writers have not done so. Let us see why they have not been satisfied with them, & by what changes they have endeavored to improve them.

One of the fundamental theorems of mechanics, a theorem already hinted at in the definition of Mass, is that if a force act upon a body for any time, the quantity of motion produced is proportioned to the product of the force & the time of its action, when the quantity of motion is taken to mean the product of the mass & the velocity. This may be expressed algebraically thus:—

$$MV: mv :: FT: ft \qquad \text{or}$$

$$\frac{MV}{FT} = \frac{mv}{ft} \qquad \text{or}$$

$$\frac{MV}{FT} = c \qquad \text{or } MV = c\ FT.$$

A general equation of this kind will hold good whatever may be the units which we choose to adopt for these four quantities. The value of the fraction will be the same for every experiment or case when the same units are employed. It will vary however when the units are changed. If we use sec. ft, mass-pound, force-pound, the value of c will be $32\frac{1}{6}$. If we use sec. met. mass-kilogram, force-kilogram c = 9.8088. These values of c are readily obtained. We have only to find the value of c in our experiment for each set of units. Thus for the sec. ft. mass-pound, force-pound, let the force represented by 1 act for the time 1 upon a Mass 1 (i.e. let a pound wgt fall for a sec.) and note the veloc. gained. It will be $32\frac{1}{6}$. $\therefore c = 32\frac{1}{6}$. Or for sec. met. mass-kilogram, force-kilogram, try a similar experiment and the value of c will be 9.8088.

Almost all writers, however, on Mech. are accustomed to simplify the above theorem by so choosing the units as to make $c = 1$; so that we have simply

$$MV = FT.$$

By this means in all formulae, which express the relations between forces & the velocities produced, we may dispense with one factor,—in all calculations where we deduce one of these quantities from the other we may avoid one multiplication or division.

It has been customary to effect this result by one of two ways.

1st Many writers adopt the usual units of time, length & mass, & choose that force as the unit of force, which will give one unit of veloc. to one unit of mass in one unit of time. This will mak[e] $c = 1$. Thus they adopt as units the sec. ft, mass-pound, and choose that force as the unit, which will give to one mass-pound in one sec. a veloc. of one ft. per sec. This makes the unit of force about $\frac{1}{32\frac{1}{6}}$ of one force-pound (a little less than ½ oz). I may place here the few Eng. & Amer. writers who have thought the mass of the cub. ft. of water more convenient than the pound as a unit of mass, & who have therefore adopted it as such, & chosen that force as unit, which can give in one sec. a unit of veloc. to this mass-unit. This makes the unit of mass = 62½ mass-pound, and the unit of force about 1.94 force-pound. Or one might also adopt as units the sec. met. & mass-kilogram, & choose that force as the unit, which in one sec. will give to one mass-kilogram a veloc. of 1 met. per sec. This would make the unit of force about $\frac{1}{9.8}$ of a force kilogram.

2dly It is more common to adopt the usual units of Time, Length, & Force, & choose that mass as the unit, which will receive in one sec. from the unit of force the unit of velocity. This, I say, is the 2^d method of making $c = 1$. Thus many adopt the sec. ft. & force-pound, & choose as the unit of mass one which will take a veloc. of 1 ft per sec, when acted upon for one sec. by one force-pound. This makes the unit of mass 32⅙ mass-pound. Or adopting the sec. met. & force-kilogram, they choose the mass as unit, which will receive from one force-kilogram in one sec. a veloc. of 1 met. per sec. This makes the unit of mass about 9.8088 mass-kilogram.

Such are the two methods by which Mechanicians have sought to dispense with the constant c in the above formulae, that is to reduce its value to unity. Perhaps I ought to illustrate more fully the advantages thus gained.

In regard to the equation above given, it should be understood that V refers to the veloc. given to the body in the time T by the force F, which velocity is to be compounded with the previous veloc. of the body, & any other velocities which may be imparted to it during the same time by any other forces. Moreover the velocity V is of course in the direction of the force F. When thus understood this equation may be said to contain within itself the whole science of theoretical Mechanics. It is easy therefore, to appreciate the advantages derived from simplifying its expression. And yet perhaps such general considerations may seem less forcible than a few examples, which I will take from widely different branches of the Science.

It is unnecessary to delay over the simpler examples which the equation will naturally suggest;—I will take for my first example centrifugal force.

$$\text{Centrif. force} = \frac{MV^2}{Rc}$$

My 2^d example will be the reduction of vis viva to work.

$$\text{Work} = \frac{MV^2}{2c}$$

My 3^d example will be the time of vibration of a musical string.

$$\text{Time} = L\left(\frac{m}{ct}\right)^{\frac{1}{2}}$$

where $L =$ length of string, $m =$ mass of string per unit of length, $t =$ tension of string.

My 4th example will be the veloc. of sound in any gas.

$$\text{Veloc.} = \left(\frac{ctk}{m}\right)^{\frac{1}{2}}$$

where t denotes the tension of the gas, i.e. the pressure upon unit of area. m denotes the density, i.e. the mass of unit of volume & k denotes the quotient of the spec. heat of the gas under constant pressure divided by its spec. heat under constant volume.

These examples are perhaps sufficient to illustrate the advantages of such a set of units as to cause the constant factor c to disappear. The fact however that Mechanicians have so generally departed from the ordinary units, to invent new ones, which will satisfy the above condition, is the strongest evidence of the high importance which they have attributed to it. And this evidence will be the more forcible, when we see the disadvantages to which they have submitted to gain their end.

The most evident objection to the two methods in use of reducing c to unity, is that they are at variance with the usage of common life, a usage too, not accidental or arbitrary, but founded upon what is little less than an absolute necessity. To the world at large the units of force must always be, as they always have been, the force-weights of the units of mass. The weights of commerce are essentially units of mass. They will always be familiar to all persons, and the forceweight also of these massweights will always be familiar to all, & will constitute the natural measures of force. To ask men to give up such measures of force is as useless as to ask them to cease to measure time by days. Now in the systems of units under discussion the unit of force is different from the force-weight of the unit of mass, so that even supposing that one of these systems should be adopted by physicists to the exclusion of all others, it could never be adopted by the world at large. Now the very chief aim, which we have in view, is to have a system of measurement, which shall be universal not confined to any nation or to any class of men. The practical working of such a diversity of units is as follows:—The theoretical investigation of many subjects is simplified as c disappears, but practical problems as they ordinarily occur, must often have their quantities reduced from the ordinary units to those of Mechanical Science before the formulae can be applied to them, & the results must often be reduced from the Scientific units to the ordinary in order to give the answer to the problem in a form intelligible to ordinary men. [Example Centrifugal Force] Now it is just the necessity for these reductions, which often renders a treatise on mechanics a sealed book to practical men. And the embarrassment of learners and readers is usually much increased by the fact that the Mechanicians themselves usually vacillate between their own Scientific units and the units of ordinary life. [Example]

But there is an inconvenience in the units just mentioned entirely independent of this,—an inconvenience which would not be lessened if all the world were to adopt them. It would continually become necessary to calculate from the known mass of a body, the force with which it gravitates toward the earth, & vice-versâ, which involves a multiplication or division. [Ex. RR train] This operation would be continually recurring in regard to any-thing which takes place upon the earth.

These two objections apply to both the methods adopted by Mechanical writers to dispense with the constant c. I will add two more objections, one of which applies to the 1st & the other to the 2nd of these methods. They are in truth simply consequences of the objections already mentioned, but they might not occur at first sight & therefore deserve to be developed here.

If we adopt the first method & change the unit of force, the unit of $Work$ must also be changed. Instead of the footpound we must adopt a unit $\dfrac{1}{32\frac{1}{6}}$ as great. Or applying this method to the metrical system, & making $\frac{1}{9.8}$ of a kilogram our unit of force, we must change the unit of work from a kilogrammetre to a unit $\frac{1}{9.8}$ as great. The undesirableness of this is evident.

The other objection is best illustrated in the works of the French Physicists who all adopt the 2^d method of eliminating the constant c. By rejecting the kil. as the unit of mass, and taking another 9.8 as great, they have made it necessary to distinguish between the specific gravity and the density of a body, which would otherwise under the metrical cystem [sic] be the same. (Under the Met. Sys. the Sp. grav. of any substance is the wgt of a unit of volume of that substance. The density is the mass of a unit of volume.) I have said that most writers on Mechanics make the constant $c = 1$. by their choice of units. Perhaps this statement & its exceptions should be made more definite by particular mention of different classes of writers.

In the 1st place, the most elementary writers do not generally adopt any particular units, or say anything about them.

2dly The most profound theoretical writers say little about units desiring apparently to treat the subject with the greatest possible generality. Yet this fact is significant, that they all expressly or impliedly require, that the set of units which their readers shall apply to their formulae, shall be such as to make the constant $c = 1$. Though they may require nothing else in regard to the units, & though they may allow the broadest liberty in the choice of them in every other respect, they uniformly insist upon this point.

Those writers who hold an intermediate position between rudimentary vagueness & the highest generality, make up the 3^d & 4th classes which I shall mention, & they are assigned to one or the other of these classes accordingly as their aim is practical or scientific.

3^d. As I have already said, those who have written for practical men use the common units, so that they are obliged to introduce the constant c into their formulae. This is true at least of Eng. & Amer. Writers.

4th But those whose treatises are of a more scientific character almost always adopt one of the methods mentioned to reduce c to 1.

Both of these methods are used by Eng. & Amer. Writers & the threefold diversity thus introduced (some *not* making $c = 1$, & others making it so by two different ways) united with other points of difference (some substituting the cub. ft. of water for the pound—some again rejecting both the foot & the pound for the met. & kil.) has produced a degree of diversity truly formidable to the student. I have no doubt, that this is in a large measure the cause of the great reluctance of Eng. & Amer. writers, compared with the French, to introduce units into their works at all. Diversity is indeed too mild a word—there is often confusion. Not only does one writer differ from another, but it too often happens that the same writer is at variance with himself.

It is only among the French Writers that we find any uniformity in the units adopted. They all so far as I have seen, adopt the second for time, the met. fôr length, the kil. for force, & 9.8088 kil for the unit of mass. I am the more surprised at this as the kilogram was made by its authors the unit of wgt, *not* in the sense of *force* but in the sense of *mass*. Yet the French Mechanicians have used the kilogram as the unit of a kind of quantity, for which the Academy did not establish any unit, & for that kind of quantity, for which the Acad. established the kil. as the unit, they have, for many kinds of problems, rejected the unit of the Acad. & chosen for themselves a new unit. Now with the *first* of these processes, I have no fault to find. When the French Acad. established a unit of *masswgt*, it was natural that the forcewgt of this unit of masswgt should be taken as the unit of force, & not unnatural that it should be called by the same name 'kilogram.' And for the 2^d process, we find a sufficient motive in the elimination of the constant c. In *this* only do they lay themselves open to criticism, that they disguise the fact that they deviate from the system of the Acad. They define the word wgt (poids) differently from the Acad, & then assume that the word kilo denotes a unit of wgt, in the sense in which *they* define wgt. While for wgt in the sense in which the Acad. used & defined the term, they choose a new unit, & disguise the change by calling this kind of quantity by a new name, viz. Mass. And yet ½ of them define Mass by the same words which the Acad. use to define wgt.

[Mem. Inst. Nat. Sci. (1799), II, 25, 55, 57.]

Let us now seek to find a system of units for the quantities; Time, Length, Mass, & Force, which shall answer the requirements both of Science & of common Life. The unknown quantities to be determined in this problem are four, viz. the magnitude of the four units. We can therefore satisfy four conditions. The question reduces itself to this: "What are the four most important conditions for these units to satisfy?" I think that they are the following, which I have already taken occasion to discuss in the preceding pages, & which therefore only need to be here brought into connexion.

1st The unit of time must be a small and simple fraction of the day. Unless a worldwide usage can be changed, it must be a second. I will assume that it must be a second.

2^d The unit of Mass must be the mass of a cube of water of which the edge is a unit of length. For definiteness we may add, "at its maximum density."

3^d The unit of force must be the forcewgt of the unit of mass. For definiteness we may add "at the level of the sea in lat. 45"

4th The unit of force must give a unit of velocity to the unit of mass in a unit of time. (A unit of velocity being the velocity of a body moving a unit of length in a unit of time)

To derive from these conditions the magnitude of the unit of length, we have only to imagine a unit of mass to fall from rest in a vacuum at lat 45 for one sec. It is acted on by a unit of force, (its own wgt) for the unit of time, hence it must receive a unit of velocity:—imagine it to move on for another sec. the action of gravity being suspended, & its veloc. therefore remaining constant,—it would move a unit of length. But we know from the theory of falling bodies, that the distance it would move in the 2^d sec under such a supposition would be twice the dist. through which it would fall in the first sec. $2 \times 16\frac{1}{12} = 32\frac{1}{6}$ ft. This then is the unit of length.

The 2^d condition gives us the unit of Mass. As the cube of water, of which the edge is the principal unit of length, would be inconveniently large, we may take a cube of which the edge is $\frac{1}{100}$ part of the principal length-unit. This then is the unit of *mass* or *Commercial weight*.

The 4th or the 3^d condition gives us the unit of force, viz. the force-wgt of this mass-wgt at lat 45' at the level of the sea.

We have not altered the usual divisions of time. If it should be thought practicable & desirable to divide the day into decimal parts, so as to make a sec. of the $\frac{1}{1,000,000}$ or $\frac{1}{100,000}$ of a day we would have results somewhat different, although in all respects analogous.

But preserving the usual units of time, we have found the principal units of Length, Mass, & Force. We may make as many subordinate units as we choose, by multiplying or dividing the units already found by 10 or 100.

Perhaps a word should be said upon the means of determining the primary unit of length with exactness. This unit of length is, as we have said, the distance through which a body would move in one second if, after falling freely for one second, it should continue to move uniformly with the velocity acquired by that fall. Or, as this is too clumsy a definition, we may say instead what may easily be proved to be equivalent: The unit of length is twice the distance through which a body falls in one second, (falling from rest, in a vacuum.) We will denote this length as usual by the letter g. Of course this cannot be measured directly with sufficient exactness. Yet it may be determined with great accuracy by means of the pendulum. If we denote by L the length of a seconds pendulum and by π the ratio of the circumference of a circle to its diametre, we have the following eq. the proof of which depends upon the theory of the pendulum.

$$g = \pi^2 L.$$

the value of π has already been ascertained with an exactness, which is almost inconceivable, the problem therefore reduces to the determination of the seconds pendulum.

There is much that is curious & interesting in the theory of the pendulum, and in the means used in practice to determine the length of the seconds pendulum. Yet it does not fall within the scope of this article to discuss these points. Let it suffice to quote a high authority in regard to the exactness with which this length can be determined.

[*Histoire Acad. Roy. Sci.* (1788), pp. 8, 14.
Mem. Inst. Nat. Sci. (1799), II, 98.]

Yet the consideration of the suitableness of this distance *g.* as a standard is only a secondary matter, for there is no necessity, that the unit of length should be also the standard of length. If there is anything in nature or in art more immutable than this distance *g,* or the seconds pendulum, let that be the standard of reference. The magnitude of the unit may still be derived from the double of the distance through which a body falls from rest in one second.

APPENDIX III

Catalogue of the "Scientific Correspondence"

These letters are arranged in the volume prepared by Addison Van Name, Gibbs' brother-in-law, alphabetically by name in each of the nationalities of the correspondents—American, English, German, Dutch and French—and numbered consecutively from the first American, Cleveland Abbe, to the last Frenchman, Henri Poincaré.

It has seemed best to me however, for the purposes of this catalogue, to arrange them chronologically. Thus under each year will be found the names of the correspondents, the numbers for the letters in the volume, the dates of the letters, and a brief statement of the content of the communication. The letters from which quotations have been made in the text, or those specifically referred to there, will be designated by an asterisk after the date. A draft reply by Gibbs will be indicated by its number in the collection immediately following the letter answered, with an asterisk if it has been used in the text. "On the Equilibrium of Heterogeneous Substances" is abbreviated E.H.S., the pamphlet *Vector Analysis* V.A., and the book *Statistical Mechanics* S.M.

1875

Correspondent: A. Freeman. The first two of eight letters.
Dates: #86, Feb. 18*; #87, Apr. 23.
Contents: #86 is a request for reprints of Gibbs' first two papers and tells of Maxwell's making the model of the thermodynamic surface. #87 acknowledges the reprints and comments on various matters.

1876

Correspondent: John Aitken. The first of two letters.
Date: #70, Dec. 15.
Contents: Is a request for reprints of Gibbs' first two papers and mentions that Maxwell had called his attention to them.

1877

Correspondent: John Aitken. The second of two letters.
Date: #71, Jan. 24.
Contents: Acknowledges reprints.

1878

Correspondent: G. Pirie. Two letters.

Dates: #113, Jan. 16*; #114, Apr. 10*.

Contents: #113 requests a reprint of E.H.S. and mentions that Maxwell had called his attention to it: #114 acknowledges the receipt of a letter telling how he could find the paper, and congratulates Gibbs on the introduction of the notion of the potential.

Correspondent: F. Massieu.

Date: #198, Oct. 9*.

Contents: Acknowledges receipt of E.H.S. and expresses his gratification in Gibbs' development of his (Massieu's) "characteristic functions."

Correspondent: A. Freeman. The third of eight letters.

Date: #88, Dec. 31.

Contents: Acknowledges reprint of the abstract of E.H.S. and comments on various technical matters.

1879

Correspondent: Robert E. Baynes.

Date: #73, Jan. 27.

Contents: Acknowledges reprints of thermodynamic papers.

Correspondent: H. A. Rowland. First two of three letters.

Dates: #54, Mar. 3*; #55, May 28.

Contents: #54 acknowledges reprints and comments on the state of mathematical physics in this country. #55 is concerned with Gibbs' forthcoming visit to Baltimore and gives details of the courses scheduled for the following year.

Correspondent: I. Todhunter.

Date: #128, July 7.

Contents: Acknowledges receipt of reprint of the paper, "Fundamental Formulae of Dynamics," and expresses interest in it.

1880

Correspondent: Charles Chambers.

Date: #83, Jan. 31.

Contents: Acknowledges receipt of the reprint of "Fundamental Formulae of Dynamics" and comments on E.H.S.

Correspondent: M. M. Pattison Muir.

Date: #112, Feb. 14*.

Contents: Expresses appreciation of the value of E.H.S. to chemists.

Correspondent: A. Freeman. Fourth letter of eight.

Date: #89, July 9*.

Contents: Acknowledges receipt of Gibbs' contribution of five guineas to the Maxwell Memorial Fund.

Correspondent: Joseph Lovering.

Date: #38, Dec. 31*.

Contents: As President of the American Academy invites Gibbs to be present in person to receive the Rumford Medal.

Draft of reply to #38.

Date: #39, Jan. 7, 1881.

Contents: Regrets his inability to appear and expresses his appreciation of the honor conferred on him.

1881

Correspondent: John Trowbridge. Three letters.

Dates: #66, Jan. 5; #67*, Jan. 9; #68*, Jan. 13*.

Contents: These three have to do with J.T.'s acting as proxy for Gibbs at the conferring of the Rumford Medal and with its transmittal to Gibbs.

Correspondent: C. S. Peirce.

Date: #50, Nov. 2*.

Contents: Acknowledges V.A. and criticizes Gibbs' notation.

Draft of reply to #50.

Date: #51, Dec. 1*.

Contents: Explains why V.A. was printed but not published, and tells of his vacillation in the matter of notations.

Correspondent: W. E. Birely.

Date: #14, Nov. 26.

Contents: Acknowledges V.A. and tells of having heard of Gibbs' course on the subject from a former student.

Correspondent: Wolcott Gibbs. First of three letters.

Date: #23, Dec. 4*.

Contents: Acknowledges V.A., makes queries about several thermodynamic points, and suggests a thermoelectric experiment to test Gibbs' formulas.

Correspondent: A. Freeman. Fifth letter of eight.

Date: #90, Dec. 20.

Contents: Acknowledges V.A. and has comments and queries on it.

1882

Correspondent: Thomas Craig. First of three letters.

Date: #18, May 24.

Contents: Acknowledges V.A. and comments favorably on it. Offers to send Gibbs photos of Cayley and Sylvester if he desires them.

1883

Correspondent: James Dewar.

Date: #85, Mar. 23.

Contents: Introduces a former student (a Mr. Finch) visiting in America who wishes to see in New Haven principally "the Maxwell of America."

Correspondent: J. J. Sylvester. First of two letters.

Date: #121, Apr. 12.

Contents: Acknowledges reprints from *Am. Journ. Sci.* and urges Gibbs to publish in the *Am. Journ. Math.*

Correspondent: Thomas Craig. Second of three letters.

Date: #19, Apr. 26.

Contents: Acknowledges reprints of optics papers and as editor invites a contribution from Gibbs to the *Am. Journ. Math.*

1884

Correspondent: William Ramsay. First of three letters.

Date: #115, undated but probably of this year*.

Contents: Tells of his experimental determination of the adiabatics of ether at temperatures near the critical.

Correspondent: J. M. Peirce.

Date: #52, Mar. 10.

Contents: Acknowledges V.A. with appreciation, especially of the linear vector function, and asks for more copies for use in his class.

Correspondent: A. Freeman. Sixth of eight letters.

Date: #91, Mar. 11.

Contents: Acknowledges the second part of V.A. and retails some scientific gossip.

Correspondent: C. A. Young.

Date: #69, Mar. 20.

Contents: Acknowledges V.A.

Correspondent: J. J. Thomson. First two of five letters.

Dates: #123, Apr. 2*; #124, July 13*.

Contents: #123 acknowledges V.A. and inquires about reprints of electromagnetic theory. #124 acknowledges E.H.S. and compares some of his own results with those of Gibbs.

Correspondent: H. A. Lorentz. First of two letters.

Date: #18₄, Apr. 8. (Postcard.)

Contents: Acknowledges V.A.

Letter from Wm. H. Taft to H. A. Newton.

Date: #58, July 18.

Contents: Requests Professor Newton to ask Gibbs to furnish his friend Judge J. B. Stallo with a copy of V.A.

Correspondent: J. B. Stallo.

Date: #57, July 30.

Contents: Acknowledges V.A. and apologizes for troubling Gibbs to send it.

Correspondent: H. A. Rowland. Third of three letters.

Date: #56, July 29*.

Contents: Urges Gibbs to accept appointment to National Conference of Electricians at Philadelphia.

Correspondent: A. A. Michelson. First of six letters.

Date: #42, Dec. 15*.

Contents: Acknowledges reprints, describes and asks Gibbs' advice on a proposed experiment since known as that of "Michelson-Morley."

1885

Correspondent: William Ramsay. Second of three letters.
Date: #116, Mar. 5*.
Contents: Gives further experimental verification of Gibbs' formulas for gas mixtures with convertible components, and recalls meeting Gibbs at Montreal.
Correspondent: W. H. Besant.
Date: #74, Aug. 8.
Contents: Acknowledges V.A. through kindness of Mr. Finch (see letter of James Dewar of Mar. 23, 1883).
Correspondent: Cleveland Abbe. First letter of four.
Date: #1, Sept. 28*.
Contents: Discusses and asks advice on problems connected with the wet and dry bulb psychrometer.
Correspondent: A. A. Michelson. Second and third of six letters.
Dates: #43, Nov. 30*; #44, Dec. 13*.
Contents: Both letters discuss points in Michelson's repetition of the Fizeau experiment and replies to Gibbs' queries as to his numerical results.

1886

Correspondent: A. A. Michelson. Fourth and fifth of six letters.
Dates: #45, Mar ?*; #47, May 21*.
Contents: Are further discussions with regard to the Fizeau experiment.
Correspondent: S. P. Langley. First of four letters.
Date: #33, June 9*.
Contents: Discusses his infrared measurements and refers to a previous communication from Gibbs (not included in this collection).
Correspondent: G. F. Becker.
Date: #9, Aug. 18*.
Contents: Submits two manuscripts on thermodynamics for criticism.
Draft of reply to #9.
Date: #10, Sept. 13*.
Contents: Gives a rather destructive criticism of the manuscripts.
Correspondent: Asaph Hall.
Date: #30, Sept. 2*.
Contents: Comments on the Buffalo address and in reply to a previous letter from Gibbs (not included in this collection) remarks on the habits and methods of computers.
Correspondent: J. J. Sylvester. Second of two letters.
Date: #122, Nov. 18*.
Contents: Acknowledges reprint of the Buffalo address and comments on the origin of the "matrix."

1887

Correspondent: P. Duhem. First two of four letters.

Dates: #191, Jan. 10*; #193, Feb. 16*.

Contents: #191 requests reprints of Gibbs' thermodynamic papers. #193 acknowledges Gibbs' reply (see #192) and proposes an exchange in the future of all the publications of each.

Draft of reply to #191.

Date: #192, Feb. 2.

Contents: Gives a list of the institutions in France where E.H.S. could be found, and sends such reprints as were at hand.

Correspondent: Oliver Lodge.

Date: #103, Jan. 20*.

Contents: Acknowledges reprints and letter with Gibbs' contribution to B.A.A.S. report.

Draft of letter to H. Grassmann.

Date: #139, Feb. 2*.

Contents: Urges Grassmann to publish his father's work on tides.

Correspondent: W. Ostwald. First of twelve letters.

Date: #151, Apr. 26*.

Contents: Tells of the starting of the *Zeits. für phys. Chem.*, asks Gibbs for a contribution to it, and suggests a German edition of E.H.S.

Draft of reply to #151.

Date: #152, Aug. 3.

Contents: Congratulates Ostwald on the new journal and regrets that he has nothing to contribute.

1888

Correspondent: V. Schlegel. First of two letters.

Date: #169, June 15*.

Contents: Acknowledges reprints of optics papers and comments on V.A. and the Buffalo address.

Draft of reply to #169.

Date: #170, Aug. 1*.

Contents: Outlines the origin and growth of Gibbs' interest in the field of multiple algebra.

Correspondent: H. Grassmann. First letter of five.

Date: #140, June 21.

Contents: Tells of the steps taken to publish a new edition of his father's works and difficulties encountered.

Correspondent: Oliver Heaviside. First of two letters.

Date: #96, July 3.

Contents: Acknowledges reprints of V.A. and optics papers.

Draft of letter to Thomas Craig.

Date: #20, July 13*.

Contents: Tells of the difficulties in the way of the publication of Grassmann's thesis on the tides in Germany, and asks if Craig would publish it in the *Am. Journ. Math.* if it proves to be impossible in Germany.

Correspondent: Thomas Craig. Third of three letters.

Date: #21, Aug. 6*.

Contents: Agrees to the publication of Grassmann's work as suggested by Gibbs in #20.

Draft of letter to Thomas Craig.

Date: #22, Aug. 14.

Contents: More on the publication of Grassmann's thesis.

Correspondent: W. Ostwald. Second and third of twelve letters.

Dates: #153 Nov. 14*; #155, Dec. 25*. (Postcard.)

Contents: #153 offers to translate E.H.S. into German. #155 proposes the publication as one of Ostwald's series, *Classiker der exacten Wissenschaften.*

Draft of reply to #153.

Date: #154, Dec. 7*.

Contents: Assents to Ostwald's proposition under certain conditions.

Correspondent: Veit & Co. First of two letters.

Date: #173, Dec. 30*.

Contents: Is a proposal for an edition of all of Gibbs' thermodynamic papers in either English or German, with supervision of the translation (if published in Germany) by Professor Felix Klein.

Draft of reply to #173.

Date: #174, Jan. 17*.

Contents: Regrets that he cannot accept the offer because of his commitment to Ostwald. On the same sheet containing this draft are two other drafts (not numbered), one informing Ostwald of the Veit offer and asking to hear more of his plans, and the other to Professor Klein thanking him for his interest in the matter.

1889

Correspondent: W. Ostwald. Fourth and fifth of twelve letters.

Dates: #156, Jan. 30*; #160, Mar. 31.

Contents: #156 renews the proposal of publishing the E.H.S. as one of the *Classiker* series. #160 apologizes for publishing a translation of Gibbs' B.A.A.S. communications on electrolysis in the *Zeits. für phys. Chem.* without specific permission.

Draft of reply to #156.

Date: #157, Feb. 16*.

Contents: Expresses Gibbs' preference for Veit & Co.'s proposal to publish *all* of the thermodynamic papers. On the same sheet is a draft of a letter (to which no number is assigned) to Veit & Co. authorizing them to go ahead with their proposal.

Correspondent: H. Hertz.

Date: #145, Mar. 3*.

Contents: Acknowledges reprints of optics papers and comments on E.H.S.
Correspondent: Veit & Co. Second of two letters.
Date: #175, Mar. 5*.
Contents: Discusses various phases of the translation and suggests that Gibbs
supply a commentary to accompany the work.
Draft of reply to #175.
Date: #176*.
Contents: Refuses to write a commentary and suggests that it would come
more appropriately from the translator.
Correspondent: H. Grassmann. Second of five letters.
Date: #141, Mar. 22. (Postcard.)
Contents: Gives news as to the progress being made toward the publication of
a new edition of his father's works. Acknowledges optics reprints.
Correspondent: J. P. Cooke. Two letters.
Dates: #15, June 5; #17, June 13*.
Contents: #15 asks Gibbs to write an obituary of Clausius for the American
Academy. #17 thanks Gibbs for acceding to the request of #15 and asks
his advice on the selection of new members for the academy.
Draft of reply to #15.
Date: #16, June 10*.
Contents: Accedes to the request of #15.
Correspondent: E. Study.
Date: #172, July 30.
Contents: Acknowledges various reprints.
Correspondent: B. A. Gould.
Date: #26, Oct. 16*.
Contents: Replies affirmatively to Gibbs' inquiry (in a letter not preserved)
as to whether Gould would accept for publication in the *Astronom. Journ.*
an article on orbit calculation.

1890

Correspondent: Thomas Hill. Two letters.
Dates: #31, Jan. 7; #32, Feb. 7.
Contents: Acknowledge reprints.
Correspondent: A. Freeman. Last two of eight letters.
Dates: #92, Jan. 20; #93, July 5.
Contents: #92 acknowledges reprints of Clausius memoir and the Buffalo
address and asks a question about a point in optical theory. #93 acknowl-
edges a reply to #92.
Correspondent: E. H. Moore. First of two letters.
Date: #40, Jan. 27.
Contents: Discusses points in multiple algebra.
Correspondent: A. A. Michelson. Last of six letters.
Date: #46, Apr. 24.
Contents: Asks Gibbs to review work of a Major Livermore on the law of

gravitation at molecular distances, and refers to a paper of his own on the application of interferometer methods for the determination of stellar magnitudes.

1891

Correspondent: W. Ostwald. Sixth to tenth of twelve letters.
Dates: #158, Mar. 3; #161, Apr. 12*; #162, undated*; #163, Aug. 9*; #164, Nov. 23*.
Contents: #158 tells of Veit's failure to find an acceptable translator, and offers to include a translation of the second paper with that of E.H.S. #161–164 are concerned with details regarding the translation and the decision to include translations of all Gibbs' thermodynamic papers.
Drafts of reply to #158 and #164.
Date: #159, Mar. 27*; #165, Dec. 11.
Contents: #159 accepts Ostwald's offer. #165 supplies biographical data requested by Ostwald.
Correspondent: H. P. Bowditch. Two letters.
Dates: #11, May 3*; #12, May 9*.
Contents: Both letters refer to a project for raising a fund for a Helmholtz memorial.
Draft of reply to #11.
Date: #13, May 6*.
Contents: Discusses ways and means for raising funds for the memorial.
Correspondent: L. Kronecker.
Date: #149, June 2.
Contents: Asks Gibbs' help in finding an American university position for a former student.
Correspondent: H. Grassmann. Third of five letters.
Date: #142, Aug 5. (Postcard.)
Contents: Acknowledges reprints from *Nature* and expresses admiration of Gibbs' part in the V.A. *vs.* Quaternions controversy.
Correspondent: V. Schlegel. Second of two letters.
Date: #171, Aug. 16*.
Contents: Discusses V.A. and Grassmann's *Ausdehnungslehre*.

1892

Correspondent: Wilhelm Englemann. First of two letters.
Date: #136, Mar. 10*.
Contents: Announces publication of "Thermodynamische Studien" and transmits complimentary copies.
Correspondent: Ludwig Boltzmann.
Date: #131, May 12*.
Contents: Asks for loan of the model of the thermodynamic surface to exhibit at the Nürnberg Mathematical Exhibition (Sept., 1892) and for a notice of it to go in the catalogue.

Correspondent: Lord Rayleigh. First of three letters.

Date: #118, June 5*.

Contents: Discusses discrepancies in the theory of reflection, comments on Gibbs' paper on Kelvin's quasi-labile ether, and urges Gibbs to write a book on thermodynamics.

Correspondent: H. Grassmann. Fourth of five letters.

Date: #143, Sept. 6. (Postcard.)

Contents: A further report on the progress made toward publication of his father's work on the tides.

Correspondent: Felix Klein. First of three letters.

Date: #146, Sept. 22*.

Contents: Has to do with the publication of Grassmann's works.

1893

Correspondent: Frederich Engel.

Date: #135, Jan. 8*.

Contents: Tells of completion of the new edition of Grassmann's works including the thesis on the tides.

Correspondent: J. G. Hagen, S.J. Two letters.

Dates: #28, Mar. 16; #29, June 20.

Contents: Discusses V.A., Hamilton, and Grassmann.

Correspondent: C. G. Knott.

Date: #102, Apr. 26*.

Contents: Discusses points in the V.A. *vs.* Quaternions controversy.

Correspondent: Cleveland Abbe. Second of four letters.

Date: #2, May 6.

Contents: Queries about supersaturation of water vapor in the atmosphere.

Correspondent: R. T. Glazebrook.

Date: #94, June 5*.

Contents: Is an invitation to attend the Nottingham meeting of the B.A.A.S.

Correspondent: Wilhelm Meyerhoffer.

Date: #150, June 23*.

Contents: Comments on the rapid spread of Gibbs' ideas in Europe and sends reprints of his own work on the phase rule.

Correspondent: Felix Klein. Second of three letters.

Date: #147, Sept. 17*.

Contents: Suggests arrangements for a visit to New Haven on his way home from Evanston, Illinois.

Correspondent: H. Grassmann. Last of five letters.

Date: #144, Sept. 23*.

Contents: Thanks Gibbs for himself and family for the part Gibbs had played in securing the new edition of Grassmann's father's works.

Correspondent: O. N. Rood.

Date: #53, Oct. 8*.

Contents: Tells of Helmholtz's regret at not meeting Gibbs while in New York.

1894

Draft of a letter to A. McAulay.
Date: #105, Jan. 21*.
Contents: Discusses points in the V.A. *vs.* Quaternions controversy.
Letter from A. McAulay to O. Heaviside. (Presumably sent to Gibbs by O.H.)
Date: #104, Feb. 18.
Contents: More on the V.A. *vs.* Quaternions controversy.
Correspondent: Oliver Heaviside. Second of two letters.
Date: #97, Apr. 6*.
Contents: Comments on the advance made by Gibbs with the linear vector function and the shortcomings of the quaternionists.
Correspondent: S. P. Langley. Second and third of four letters.
Dates: #34, Apr. 13*; #36, June 9*.
Contents: #34 submits the problem of the soaring of an unpowered plane. #36 thanks Gibbs for his solution and asks if he may publish it.
Draft of reply to #34.
Date: #35, May 30*.
Contents: Gives a solution for Langley's problem.

1895

Correspondent: S. P. Langley. Fourth of four letters.
Date: #37, Jan. 25.
Contents: Discusses aerodynamic topics; repeats request for permission to publish #35.
Correspondent: W. Ostwald. Last two of twelve letters.
Dates: #166, Apr. 13; #167, Nov. 14.
Contents: Requests a portrait for the *Zeits. für phys. Chem.* in #166, and acknowledges its receipt in #167.
Correspondent: Felix Klein. Third of three letters.
Date: #148, June 27*.
Contents: Introduces a former student, an American returning to the U.S.
Correspondent: J. E. Trevor. First three of six letters.
Dates: #59, Oct. 27*; #60, Nov. 1*; #61, Nov. 16*.
Contents: Discusses various points in the E.H.S. which were not clear to him.
Correspondent: F. Wald. First of two letters.
Date: #178, Dec. 7.
Contents: Discusses applications of the phase rule.
Correspondent: E. H. Griffiths.
Date: #95, Dec. 18*.
Contents: Asks Gibbs to comment on the proper choice of a thermal unit.
Correspondent: Wilhelm Engelmann. Second of two letters.

Date: #137, Dec. 23*.
Contents: Transmits copies of the photoengraving used in the *Zeits. für phys. Chem.*

1896

Correspondent: J. Trevor. Fourth of six letters.
Date: #62, Jan. 18.
Contents: Thanks Gibbs for clearing up his difficulties with the E.H.S. and apologizes for having troubled him with them.
Correspondent: F. Wald. Second of two letters.
Date. #179, Jan. 18.
Contents: Thanks Gibbs for his reply to #178 (not preserved) and raises further questions on thermochemical equilibrium.

1897

Correspondent: Alice Bache Gould.
Date: #27, May 15*.
Contents: Consults Gibbs about a medal in memory of her father to accompany grants from a fund to be administered by the National Academy.
Correspondent: Wolcott Gibbs. Second of three letters.
Date: #24, June 15.
Contents: Acknowledges memoir on H. A. Newton and transmits a book of Lorentz's sent to him by mistake.
Correspondent: W. Ramsay. Third of three letters.
Date: #117, June 17.
Contents: Acknowledges memoir on H. A. Newton, comments on rare gases in meteorites, and congratulates Gibbs on his election as foreign associate of the Royal Society.
Correspondent: R. Meldola.
Date: #110, Aug. 23*.
Contents: Requests Gibbs to serve on a committee for the Sylvester Medal. The word "Assented" in Gibbs' handwriting is penciled on the back of this letter.
Correspondent: J. Trevor. Fifth of six letters.
Date: #63, Dec. 11.
Contents: Explains the position of the editors on the publication in the *Journ. Phys. Chem.* of an article by P. Duhem which they felt was not quite fair to Gibbs.

1898

Correspondent: W. D. Bancroft. First of five letters.
Date: #5, Jan. 13.
Contents: Discusses critical states with miscible fluids.
Correspondent: Hugo Buchholz. Two letters.
Dates: #133, Sept. 16; #134*, Aug. 1.

Contents: Both letters concern Gibbs' vector method of computing orbits. Gibbs' reply was published in *The Scientific Papers,* Vol. II, item 6.

1899

Correspondent: J. E. Trevor. Last of six letters.
Date: #64, Feb. 4*.
Contents: Discusses thermochemical matters and transmits Le Chatelier's proposal for a French translation of E.H.S.
Draft of reply to #64.
Date: #65, Mar. 6.
Contents: Approves of a French translation by Le Chatelier.
Correspondent: A. Macfarlane. First of three letters.
Date: #106, Feb. 22.
Contents: Is an invitation to join the "International Association for the Promotion of Quaternions," and includes (item #107) a copy of its rules and regulations.
Correspondent: J. J. Thomson. Third of five letters.
Date: #125, Mar. 5*.
Contents: Asks for a contribution to the Stokes Jubilee Volume of the Cambridge Philosophical Society.
Correspondent: W. D. Bancroft. Second, third, fourth, and fifth of five letters.
Dates: #6, Mar. 18*; #6_2, May 20; #7, July 4; #8, June 4.
Contents: Submits MSS of an electrochemical article for criticism in #6. #6_2 acknowledges Gibbs' reply and requests that it be expanded into an article for the *Journ. Phys. Chem.* Asks for biographical data for Le Chatelier and returns Gibbs' reply. #7 submits a biographical sketch for approval and discusses the relation between μ and reaction velocity. #8 regrets that Gibbs does not feel like writing up the e.m.f. matter and stresses the importance of educating chemists on the significance of the chemical potential.
Draft of letter to H. Le Chatelier.
Date: #197, Oct. 28.
Contents: Acknowledges receipt of the French translation of the E.H.S.
Correspondent: M. Abraham.
Date: #129, Nov. 30.
Contents: Asks Gibbs to contribute an article on V.A. to the *Encyl. der math. Wiss.*
Correspondent: Louis Couterat.
Date: #190, Nov. 30*.
Contents: Invites Gibbs to take part in the International Congress on Philosophy to be held in Paris in 1900.

1900

Correspondent: H. Kammerlingh Omnes. Two letters.
Dates: #182, May 8*; #183, June 19*.

Contents: #182 invites a contribution to a twenty-five-year presentation volume for H. A. Lorentz. #183 asks for a contribution to the seventieth anniversary celebration for J. Bosscha.
Correspondent: P. Duhem. Third of four letters.
Date: #194, May 29.
Contents: Congratulates Gibbs on his election as foreign member of the Academy of Science.
Correspondent: J. D. van der Waals.
Date: #186, June 20. (Year not given but probably 1900.)
Contents: Asks Gibbs to transmit to the signatories his thanks for a letter of "congratulations and good wishes" from American scientists.

1901

Correspondent: Henri Poincaré.
Date: #199, Apr. 29*.
Contents: Regrets his inability to come to New Haven for Yale degree.
Correspondent: Lord Rayleigh. Second of three letters.
Date: #119, undated*, but presumably sent in the spring of this year.
Contents: Regrets his inability to come to New Haven for Yale degree.
Correspondent: A. Macfarlane. Last two of three letters.
Dates: #108, June 18; #109, July 12.
Contents: #108 thanks Gibbs for aid on a bibliography and inquires about obtaining copies of V.A. #109 thanks for information about the forthcoming Wilson-Gibbs V.A. and reminisces about Tait (recently deceased).
Correspondent: Lord Kelvin. First of three letters.
Dated: #98, July 29*.
Contents: Accepts invitation to come to New Haven for Yale degree.
Correspondent: Simon Newcomb. First of two letters.
Date: #48, Nov. 22.
Contents: Congratulates Gibbs on the award of the Copley Medal.
Correspondent: J. J. Thomson. Fourth of five letters.
Date: #126, Nov. 22.
Contents: Congratulates Gibbs on the award of the Copley Medal.

1902

Correspondent: A. Föppl.
Date: #138, Jan. 6.
Contents: Congratulations on the Wilson-Gibbs V.A.
Correspondent: A. H. Bucherer.
Date: #132, Jan. 30.
Contents: Inquires about obtaining a copy of V.A.
Correspondent: Simon Newcomb. Second of two letters.
Date: #49, Mar. 15.
Contents: Acknowledges S.M. and remarks on its importance.
Correspondent: Robert S. Ball.

Date: #72, Mar. 29.
Contents: Acknowledges S.M.
Correspondent: Max Planck.
Date: #168, Mar. 29.
Contents: Acknowledges and praises S.M.
Correspondent: Lord Rayleigh. Third of three letters.
Date: #120, Mar. 31.
Contents: Acknowledges S.M.
Correspondent: H. A. Lorentz. Second of two letters.
Date: #185, Apr. 1.
Contents: Acknowledges S.M.
Correspondent: H. W. Bakhuis Roozeboom.
Date: #180, Apr 3. (Postcard.)
Contents: Acknowledges S.M.
Correspondent: J. Bossche.
Date: #181, Apr. 3.
Contents: Acknowledges S.M.
Correspondent: P. Duhem. Fourth of four letters.
Date: #195, Apr. 9.
Contents: Acknowledges S.M.
Correspondent: Cleveland Abbe. Third and fourth of four letters.
Dates: #3, Apr. 10*; #4, Apr. 14*.
Contents: Both letters have to do with the effect on the vapor tension of sur-
face films on the walls of an enclosure.
Correspondent: Lord Kelvin. Last two of three letters.
Dates: #99, Apr. 11; #101, Oct. 14*.
Contents: #99 acknowledges S.M., with an expression of interest in it. #101
is a reply to Gibbs' letter #100, with comments on the advantages of
lottery trials.
Draft of reply to #99.
Date: #100, Sept. 26*.
Contents: Gives the theory of Kelvin's caged atom problem.
Correspondent: G. H. Darwin.
Date: #84, Apr. 18.
Contents: Acknowledges S.M.
Correspondent: Wolcott Gibbs. Third of three letters.
Date: #25, Apr. 19.
Contents: Acknowledges S.M. and expresses opinion that Gibbs is "our lead-
ing scientist."
Correspondent: H. Le Chatelier.
Date: #196, Apr. 29.
Contents: Acknowledges S.M.
Correspondent: S. H. Burbury. First five of eight letters.
Dates: #75, May 8*; #76, June 4*; #77, July 10*; #78, Oct. 7*;
#79, Nov. 12*.

Contents: Acknowledges S.M. and argues points in it, especially with regard to the proof of the equipartition of energy.

Correspondent: J. J. Thomson. Fifth of five letters.

Date: #127, May 15.

Contents: Acknowledges and praises S.M.

Correspondent: E. H. Moore. Second of two letters.

Date: #41, June 21*.

Contents: Asks Gibbs to supply a proof of a theorem in multiple algebra which he had stated in a letter to E.H.M. (not preserved) in 1887.

Letter from F. Vieweg und Sohn to Scribner's and sent by them to Gibbs.

Date: #177, July 7*.

Contents: A proposal to publish a German edition of S.M.

Letter from J. A. Barth to Scribner's and sent by them to Gibbs.

Date: #130, July 10*.

Contents: Requests permission to translate the S.M. into German.

Correspondent: J. W. Mellor.

Date: #111, Sept. 17.

Contents: Suggests a reprint of E.H.S.

Correspondent: Bernard Brunhes. Two letters.

Dates: #187, Oct. 26*; #188, Nov. 24*.

Contents: #187 requests permission to publish a French translation of the first two of Gibbs' thermodynamic papers. #188 acknowledges receipt of permission.

Draft of reply to #187.

Date: #189, Nov. 8.

Contents: Gives permission to B. Brunhes for the translation as requested.

1903

Correspondent: S. H. Burbury. Last three of eight letters.

Dates: #80, Jan. 1*; #81, Feb. 25*; #82, Apr. 4*.

Contents: Are further discussions of the equipartition matter.

APPENDIX IV

Gibbs' Mailing Lists for Reprints

There have been found four lists of names of those to whom Gibbs sent copies of his publications. They are all in his own handwriting. The first is a brief notation which reads as follows:

> Jan. 31, 1876. (C.A.) Vol. III, forms 14–23 (pp. 108–184)
> sent to Maxwell, W. Thomson, Clausius, Rühlmann.
> July 12, 1877 Vol. III, forms 44–51 (pp. 343–406) to the same.
> Jan. 20, 1878   "   "   52–60 (pp. 407–478) " " " .

These references are obviously to the galley proofs of the memoir "On the Equilibrium of Heterogeneous Substances" in the *Transactions of the Connecticut Academy*.

The second list is a long one containing the names and addresses of those to whom Gibbs sent reprints of the papers published up to 1893. It is reproduced below exactly as found among Gibbs' papers, except that in order to obviate the necessity for memorizing the key designations of the various papers which he set down opposite each name the abbreviated title of each paper (with a check mark for the one sent to each individual) is given on each page of the list. In the manuscript Gibbs inserted a dagger (in pencil) when the person had died. As reproduced here an asterisk is employed. This list is headed "Address List for Reprints."

The third list is headed (both in the manuscript and as reproduced below) "List sent to Scribners for distribution of *Statistical Mechanics*" and is that of the journals to which the book was sent for review.

The fourth list bears no heading in the manuscript, but there is good reason to believe that it represents Gibbs' personal distribution of *Statistical Mechanics*. To certain of the names on this list there is prefixed a check mark, and it is possible though not probable that the book was sent only to those thus indicated. As reproduced below this list is titled "Personal Distribution of the *Statistical Mechanics*."

ADDRESS LIST FOR REPRINTS

1. Graphical Methods in the Thermo-dynamics of Fluids
2. A Method of Geometrical Representation
3. On the Equilibrium of Heterogeneous Substances, I
4. On the Equilibrium of Heterogeneous Substances, II
5. On the Equilibrium of Heterogeneous Substances, Resumé
6. On the General Equations of Dynamics
7. On the Vapor-Densities

8. Vector Analysis, pp. 1-36
N. Optics, I, II, III
9. Vector Analysis, pp. 37-83
V. Vector Analysis, whole
A. Multiple Algebra, Buffalo Address
C. Optics, V
Q. Optics, VI
O. Orbits
R. Rudolf Clausius
T. Quaternions and the Ausdehnungslehre
M. Quaternions and the Algebra of Vectors
K. Quaternions and Vector Analysis

Name	Location	1	2	3	4	5	6	7	8	N	9	V	A	C	Q	O	R	T	M	K
Societe Hollandaise des Sciences										x		x	x	x	x					
Yamagawa, Kenjiro	Imp. Univ. Tokio														x		x			
Oliver, J. E.	Ithaca									x	x	x	x							
Jones, G. W.	Ithaca							x	x	x		x	x	x	x	x				
Newcomb, Simon	Washington	x	x			x		x	x	x		x	x	x	x	x				x
Smith, Charles A.	Brunswick								x			x		x						
Johnson, W. W.	Annapolis							x	x	x		x	x	x	x	x				
Hardy, A. S.	Hanover								x			x	x	x	x					
Peirce, Jas. M.	Cambridge								x		x	x	x	x	x					
Craig, Thos.	Washington, Baltimore								x	x		x	x	x	x					
Story, W. E.	Baltimore								x			x		x			x			
Beman, W. W.	Ann Arbor								x			x		x			x			
Ferrill, Wm.	U. S. C. S. Wash.								x			x		x			x			
Elliott, E. B. *	Stat. Bur. Wash.								x			x								
Hyde, E. W.	Cincinnati								x			x		x			x			
Hendrikson, W. W.	Annapolis								x			x		x			x			
Van Vleck, Jno. M.	Middletown							x	x	x		x	x	x	x	x				
Harkness, Wm.	Nav. Obs. Washington							x	x	x		x	x	x			x			
Eastman, J. R.	" " "								x			x		x			x			
Warder, R. B. Esq.	North Bend Hamilton Co. O								x			x		x			x			
Young, Chas. A.	Princeton									x		x	x	x	x					
Pickering, E. C.	Cambridge									x		x	x	x	x	x				
Langley, Saml. P.	Washington									x		x	x	x	x		x			
Rice, Jno. M.	Annapolis									x				x	x					
Fletcher, Dr. Lawrence B.	Middletown ?									x		x	x							
Koyl, C. H.										x		x	x							
Nichols, Prof. E. L.	Ithaca									x		x	x	x	x	x	x	x		
Mitchell, Prof. O. H. * ?	Marietta O									x		x	x							
Hall, Dr. Edwin H.	Cambridge									x		x	x	x	x	x				
Halsted, Prof. Geo. B.	Austin, Tex.											x	x	x	x	x				
Prentiss, Robt. W.	Naut. Al. Office Wash.									x	x				x					
Stringham, Prof. W. I.	Berkeley Cal.									x		x	x	x	x	x				
Van Veltzer, Prof. Chas. A.	Madison Wis.											x	x	x	x	x				
Nelson, Prof. A. B.	Danville Ky.											x	x	x	x		x			

1. Graphical Methods in the Thermodynamics of Fluids
2. A Method of Geometrical Representation
3. On the Equilibrium of Heterogeneous Substances, I
4. On the Equilibrium of Heterogeneous Substances, II
5. On the Equilibrium of Heterogeneous Substances, Resumé
6. On the General Equations of Dynamics
7. On the Vapor-Densities
8. Vector Analysis, pp. 1-36
N. Optics, I, II, III
9. Vector Analysis, pp. 37-83
V. Vector Analysis, whole
A. Multiple Algebra, Buffalo Address
C. Optics, V
Q. Optics, VI
O. Orbits
R. Rudolf Clausius
T. Quaternions and the Ausdehnungslehre
M. Quaternions and the Algebra of Vectors
K. Quaternions and Vector Analysis

Name	Place	1	2	3	4	5	6	7	8	N	9	V	A	C	Q	O	R	T	M	K
Stallo, Hon. J. B.	Cincinnati									x		x	x	x						
Michaelis, Capt. O. E.	Frankford Arsenal Pa.											x	x							
Michelson, Albert A.										x		x	x	x	x		x			
Evans Asher B.	Lockport N. Y.											x	x			x				
Brackett, Prof. C. F.	Princeton											x	x	x		x				
Pratt, Julius H.	Ithaca											x	x							
Barus, Carl	U. S. Geol. S. Wash	x	x									x	x			x				
Hill, Rev. Thos.	Portland Me.											x				x	x			
Taber, Dr. Henry	Worcester Mass.											x		x						
Meyer, Lothar	Carlsruhe Tüb ?					x	x													
Fresenius, Remigius	Wiesbaden			x	x															
Mohr, Frederich	Bonn ?			x	x															
Wichelhaus, H.	red. Ber. deut. Chem. gesell. Berlin			x	x															
Städel, Wilhelm	Tubingen			x	x															
Unverzagt, K. W. ?	(Realgymn) Wiesbaden									x			x	x					x	x
Lüroth, J. Prof.	Freiburg Baden									x	x	x	x	x	x	x	x			x
Eisenlohr, Frederich	Heidelberg										x	x	x							
Siemens, Werner	Berlin										x	x	x							
Schlegel, Dr. Victor	Hagen Prussia											x	x	x	x	x	x		x	x
Voigt, W.	Göttingen										x	x	x	x	x	x				
Schell, Prof. Wm.	Carlsruhe											x	x	x	x		x			
Weyr, Prof. E.	Prag.											x		x						
Fuchs, Prof. L.	Berlin											x		x						
Klein, Prof. Felix	Göttingen										x	x	x	x	x	x	x			
Reye, Th	Strassburg											x		x			x			
Study, Dr. Edward	Leipsic											x		x	x	x				
Wiedemann, E. (oProf. Ph.)	(Beibl) Erlangen Bav.											x	x							
Grassmann, Hermann	Halle a. S.											x	x	x						
Koláček, F.	Brünn Austria						x					x	x							
Exner, F.	Wien											x	x							
Tumlirtz, Ottakar	Prag									x		x	x							
Lommel, Prof. Eugen	München									x		x	x							
Ostwald, Prof Wilhelm	Leipsic	x	x				x					x		x	x					
Hertz, Prof. H *	Bonn									x		x	x	x	x	x				
Planck, Prof. Max	Berlin																	x	x	
Engel, Frederich	Leipsic																			x
Houel, Jules (Fac Sci)	Bordeaux									x		x	x				x	x		x
Fizeau, A-H-L	Institut									x				x	x		x			
Cornu, M-A	"									x				x	x					
Jannsen, P-J-C	"									x				x	x					

1. Graphical Methods in the Thermodynamics of Fluids
2. A Method of Geometrical Representation
3. On the Equilibrium of Heterogeneous Substances, I
4. On the Equilibrium of Heterogeneous Substances, II
5. On the Equilibrium of Heterogeneous Substances, Resumé
6. On the General Equations of Dynamics
7. On the Vapor-Densities

8. Vector Analysis, pp. 1-36
N. Optics, I, II, III
9. Vector Analysis, pp. 37-83
V. Vector Analysis, whole
A. Multiple Algebra, Buffalo Address
C. Optics, V
Q. Optics, VI
O. Orbits
R. Rudolf Clausius
T. Quaternions and the Ausdehnungslehre
M. Quaternions and the Algebra of Vectors
K. Quaternions and Vector Analysis

		1	2	3	4	5	6	7	8	N	9	V	A	C	Q	O	R	T	M	K
Mascart, E	Prof. Coll. France								x			x	x	x		x				
Croullebois, Prof. Marcel	18 Rue Sorbonne Paris								x				x	x						
Lemoine, Georges	76 Av d'Arras Paris								x			x	x	x	x	x	x			
Lairant,	84 Av Victor Hugo Paris											x							x	
Hermite, Chas	Paris											x							x	
Duhem, P.	78 rue Caumartin Lille	x	x		x		x		x			x	x	x	x	x	x			
Poincaré	Institut Paris														x	x	x			
Maxwell, J. Clerk *		x	x	x	x	x	x	x												
Guthrie, Frederick ?				x	x	x		x					x							
Thomson, Wm.		x	x	x	x	x	x	x	x			x	x	x	x	x				
Thomson, James *		x	x	x	x		x	x				x	x	x	x		x			
Stokes, G. G.		x	x	x	x	x	x	x	x			x	x	x	x		x			
Andrews, Thos. *		x	x	x	x	x		x												
Tyndall, John *		x	x	x	x	x		x				x	x	x		x				
Tait, P. G. *		x	x	x	x	x	x	x	x			x	x	x	x	x				
Freeman, Rev. A.	Marston Rectory, Sittingbourne, Kent.			x	x	x	x	x	x	x	x	x			x	x				
Stewart, Balfour *		x	x	x	x		x	x				x				x	x			
Cayley, Arthur		x	x	x	x	x	x	x		x		x	x	x	x	x			x	
Rayleigh, (Lord)				x	x	x	x	x	x			x	x	x	x	x			x	x
Playfair, Lyon				x	x							x				x				
Hirst, T. Archer		x	x	x	x		x					x				x				
Earnshaw, Sam'l Rev.				x	x		x	x				x								
Joule, James Prescott *		x	x	x	x	x		x				x								
Grove, Sir William Robert		x	x	x	x	x		x									x			
Stevens, Rev. A. J.				x								x								
Aitken, John, FRSE	Darroch, Falkirk, Scotl'd	x	x		x	x		x		x		x	x	x		x				
"Nature"	29 Bedford St. Strand London	x	x	x	x	x	x	x				x								
Pirie, G.					x							x					x			
Baynes, Robert E. (M.A.)	Christ Church Oxford	x	x		x	x	x	x	x	x		x	x	x		x				
Reinold, A. W.					x							x								
Challis, James *		x	x		x	x	x													
Clifton, R. B. Prof.	Oxford	x	x		x	x			x			x	x	x						
Jenkin, H. C. F.		x	x																	
Adams, John C.	Observatory Camb. *				x	x			x			x	x	x	x	x				
Barrett, Prof. W. F.	Dublin	x			x							x				x				
Everett, Prof. J. D.	Belfast	x			x	x			x			x	x°			x				
Foster, Prof. G. C.	Lond.	x			x				x			x				x				
Airy, Sir G. B.	Greenwich *				x	x			x			x	x							
Kelland, Prof. Phillip	Edinb. *				x	x														
Grant, Prof. R.	Glasgow				x	x						x			x					

1. Graphical Methods in the Thermo-dynamics of Fluids
2. A Method of Geometrical Representation
3. On the Equilibrium of Heterogeneous Substances, I
4. On the Equilibrium of Heterogeneous Substances, II
5. On the Equilibrium of Heterogeneous Substances, Resumé
6. On the General Equations of Dynamics
7. On the Vapor-Densities
8. Vector Analysis, pp. 1-36
N. Optics, I, II, III
9. Vector Analysis, pp. 37-83
V. Vector Analysis, whole
A. Multiple Algebra, Buffalo Address
C. Optics, V
Q. Optics, VI
O. Orbits
R. Rudolf Clausius
T. Quaternions and the Ausdehnungslehre
M. Quaternions and the Algebra of Vectors
K. Quaternions and Vector Analysis

		1	2	3	4	5	6	7	8	N	9	V	A	C	Q	O	R	T	M	K
Williamson, Prof. A. W.	London						x	x									x			
Roscoe, Prof. H. E.	Manchester						x	x									x			
Price, Prof. B.	Oxford						x													
Smyth, Prof. C. P.	Edinb.						x	x				x								
Clausius, Rudolph *		x	x	x	x	x	x	x	x	x	x		x	x						
Kirchhoff, Gustav *		x	x	x	x	x	x	x	x	x	x		x							
Boltzmann, Ludwig	Prof. Wien.			x	x	x	x	x		x			x	x	x	x	x	x		
Kopp, Hermann *		x	x	x	x	x	x	x		x			x	x	x		x			
Zeuner, Gustav	Prof. K. S. Poly. Sch. Dresd.	x	x	x	x		x	x		x			x	x	x		x			
Poggendorf, *		x	x	x																
Neumann, Carl	Leipzig	x	x	x	x	x	x	x	x	x	x		x	x	x	x	x	x		x
Neumann, Franz	Königsberg			x	x	x	x	x	x	x	x		x	x	x		x			
Kronecker, Leopold *		x	x	x	x	x	x	x	x	x	x		x	x	x	x	x			
Helmholtz, Hermann v. *		x	x	x	x		x	x	x	x	x		x	x	x	x	x			
Kundt, August *	Berlin	x	x	x	x		x	x	x	x	x		x	x	x	x	x	x		
Quincke, G. H.	Heidelberg·	x	x	x	x	x	x	x	x	x	x		x	x		x	x			
Rühlmann, Richard	Chemnitz Saxony			x	x	x		x		x				x	x		x			
Wüllner, Adolph	Aachen Prussia			x	x	x		x		x				x	x		x			
Bunsen, (Heidelberg) R. W.				x	x			x						x	x		x			
Weber, Wilhelm *	Göttingen Prussia			x	x		x	x	x	x	x		x	x	x		x			
Weirstrass, Karl *	Akad. Berlin			x	x		x	x	x	x	x		x	x	x	x	x	x		x
von Land, Victor	Akad. Wien.			x	x	x	x	x	x		x		x	x	x	x	x		x	x
Naumann, Alexander	Giessen			x	x	x		x							x	x	x			
Grunert, J. A. *	Archiv der Math. & Phys.			x	x	x	x	x												
Herwig, Dr. Hermann	Aachen			x	x			x												
Stefan, Joseph	Vienna			x	x		x	x		x				x	x		x			
Schlömilch, O	Zeits. fur Math & Phys.			x	x	x	x	x	x											
Schwalbe, B.	Fort. der Phys.	x	x	x	x	x	x	x				x		x	x					
Loschmidt, Joseph				x	x			x												
Horstmann, August	Heidelberg	x	x	x	x			x					x	x	x		x			
Szily, C.	Prof. am Polytechnicum. Ofen. Aus.			x	x		x	x					x				x			
Rüdorf, Dr. Fr.	Berlin			x	x			x					x				x			
Winkelman, Dr. A.	Aachen			x	x			x					x				x			
Müller, Dr. W.	Perleberg (Erzback)			x				x					x				x			
Pfanneller, Leopold	Innsbruck			x	x			x									x			
Ohrtmann, C.	Berlin Fort. der Math.	x	x	x	x	x	x	x	x				x	x	x	x	x			
Wiedemann Gustav	Leipsig	x	x	x	x	x	x	x	x		x		x	x	x	x		x		x
Wangerin		x	x																	
Dühring, Dr. Eugen.	Docent Berlin						x	x												
Klein, Dr. Hermann	Dresden						x	x												

1. Graphical Methods in the Thermodynamics of Fluids
2. A Method of Geometrical Representation
3. On the Equilibrium of Heterogeneous
Substances, I
4. On the Equilibrium of Heterogeneous
Substances, II
5. On the Equilibrium of Heterogeneous
Substances, Resumé
6. On the General Equations of Dynamics
7. On the Vapor-Densities

8. Vector Analysis, pp. 1-36
N. Optics, I, II, III
9. Vector Analysis, pp. 37-83
V. Vector Analysis, whole
A. Multiple Algebra, Buffalo Address
C. Optics, V
Q. Optics, VI
O. Orbits
R. Rudolf Clausius
T. Quaternions and the Ausdehnungslehre
M. Quaternions and the Algebra of Vectors
K. Quaternions and Vector Analysis

		1	2	3	4	5	6	7	8	N	9	V	A	C	Q	O	R	T	M	K
Ritter, A.	Aachen	x	x		x	x	x											x			
Bertrand, J	Membre de l'Institut			x	x		x	x	x		x			x	x	x		x			
Berthelot, M-P-E.	"			x	x		x											x			
Jamin, J ?	"	x		x	x		x		x	x					x	x					
Regnauld, V. *	"			x																	
Sainte-Claire Deville, Henri *	"			x	x	x	x														
Wurtz, C. A. ? *	"			x	x		x														
Liouville, J. *	"			x	x		x														
Resal, H.	"			x	x		x	x	x	x		x	x	x	x	x					
Dumas, J.-B. ?	"			x	x		x														
Barré de Saint Venant *	"			x	x		x	x	x	x		x	x	x	x						
Favre, P-A.	Marseille			x	x		x														
Dupré, Athanau	Rennes			x	x		x														
Briot, Charles	Prof. fac. Sci. Paris			x	x	x		x		x					x	x					
Mathieu, Emile	Prof. fac. Sci. Besancon	x		x	x	x		x	x	x		x	x	x	x	x	x	x	x		x
Cahours, Auguste	Mem. Institut			x	x		x											x			
Cazín, Achille ?	"	x		x	x		x														
Hirn, Gustave-Adolph	Elsass Colmar *			x	x		x						x					x			
Darboux, redr.	Bull. Sci. Math. Astron. Paris			x	x	x		x					x								
Person, C.-C.	Prof. fac. Sci. Besancon			x	x		x														
Vicain, E.	Prof. Ecole des Mineurs Saint Etienne			x	x		x														
Duclaux, E.	Prof. fac. Sci. Clermont-Ferrand			x	x																
Philipps, Eduard	Membre de l'Institut	x	x	x	x	x	x	x					x					x			
Massieu, F.	Prof. fac. Sci. Rennes	x	x	x	x	x	x	x					x								
Troost, Louis,	Prof. fac. Sci. Paris			x	x	x		x										x			
Redaction du Journ. des Savants				x	x	x															
Morigno, l'abbé,	Bur. du Journ. des Mondes	x		x	x	x	x	x	x		x										
Levy, Maurice	Ecole Polytechnique, Paris	x	x			x	x	x		x		x	x	x	x	x	x	x	x	x	x
Lippmann, Gabriel	Institut Paris			x	x								x					x	x		
Arch. des Sci. Phys. & Nat.	Geneva			x	x	x		x													
Mousson, Albert Prof.	Polyt. Zurich	x	x		x																
Jannsen, J.		x																			
Saint Robert, Paul de	Turin			x	x	x		x					x								
Schneider, Th.	red. Bull. Soc. Chim. Paris					x		x					x								
Collignon, Eduard						x							x								
Laurent, H.	Polytech.					x							x			x					
Serret, J-A *						x							x	x							
Gould, B. A.													x	x	x	x	x				
Barker, Geo. F.				x	x		x	x	x	x		x	x	x	x	x		x			
Gibbs, Wolcott		x	x	x		x	x		x	x	x		x	x	x	x		x			

1. Graphical Methods in the Thermodynamics of Fluids
2. A Method of Geometrical Representation
3. On the Equilibrium of Heterogeneous
   Substances, I
4. On the Equilibrium of Heterogeneous
   Substances, II
5. On the Equilibrium of Heterogeneous
   Substances, Resumé
6. On the General Equations of Dynamics
7. On the Vapor-Densities

8. Vector Analysis, pp. 1-36
N. Optics, I, II, III
9. Vector Analysis, pp. 37-83
V. Vector Analysis, whole
A. Multiple Algebra, Buffalo Address
C. Optics, V
Q. Optics, VI
O. Orbits
R. Rudolf Clausius
T. Quaternions and the Ausdehnungslehre
M. Quaternions and the Algebra of Vectors
K. Quaternions and Vector Analysis

Name	Location	1	2	3	4	5	6	7	8	N	9	V	A	C	Q	O	R	T	M	K
Richards, C. B.			x	x								x	x			x	x			
Sylvester, J. J.			x	x			x	x	x			x	x	x	x	x	x		x	x
Gibbes, L. R.	Charleston Coll.	x	x	x	x	x	x		x												
Peirce, Benjamin *		x	x	x	x																
Cooke, J. P.		x	x	x	x			x					x	x	x						
Sampson, W. T. Commander			x	x			x					x									
Eddy, H. T.		x	x		x		x	x	x	x		x	x	x	x	x					
Rowland, H. A.			x	x			x	x	x			x	x	x	x		x				
Hart, Dr. David S. *	Stonnington			x	x		x					x									
Hastings, Ch. S.		x					x		x	x	x		x	x	x	x					
Hall, Asaph						x	x	x	x	x	x		x	x	x		x				
Merriman, Mansfield	Bethlehem					x	x	x	x		x		x								
Peirce, B. O.						x							x								
Trowbridge, John	Cambridge					x		x	x	x			x	x	x	x					
A. M. Mayer	Hoboken	x	x							x			x	x	x	x		x			
Henry, J. *		x	x																		
Barnard, F. A. P. *		x	x					x					x								
Rood, O. N.		x	x						x				x	x	x	x		x			
McCulloch, R. S.	Lexington, Va.	x	x			x		x					x								
Phillips, A. W.								x			x		x		x	x	x				
Remsen, Ira						x		x										x			
Peirce, Chas. S.							x	x	x			x	x	x	-x						
Draper, H.	New York						x														
Rogers, Wm. B.	Boston						x														
Thurston, R. H.		x	x			x							x	x	x		x				
Geo. W. Hill													x	x		x					
Yale Coll. Libr.		x	x	x	x	x							x								
Newton, H. A.		x	x	x	x	x		x		x			x	x	x		x	x			
Dana, J. D.		x		x					x				x	x							
Trowbridge, Wm. P.		x	x	x	x	x		x	x	x	x		x					x			
Smith, Thos. A.		x	x	x			x	x	x	x			x					x			
Twining, *					x				x				x								
Adams, Prof. W. G.	Lond.					x	x						x			x					
Ball, Prof. R. S.	Dunkirk					x	x						x	x		x	x				
Pritchard, Prof. Ch.	Oxf.					x															
Watson, Henry Wm., M.A.		x	x			x	x	x	x		x		x					x			
Spottiswoode, Wm.	London *					x			x												
Todhunter, I. *	Camb.					x		x						x							
Jellett, Rev. John H.	Dublin					x								x							
Purser, Prof. John	Belfast					x															

1. Graphical Methods in the Thermo-dynamics of Fluids
2. A Method of Geometrical Representation
3. On the Equilibrium of Heterogeneous Substances, I
4. On the Equilibrium of Heterogeneous Substances, II
5. On the Equilibrium of Heterogeneous Substances, Resumé
6. On the General Equations of Dynamics
7. On the Vapor-Densities

8. Vector Analysis, pp. 1-36
N. Optics, I, II, III
9. Vector Analysis, pp. 37-83
V. Vector Analysis, whole
A. Multiple Algebra, Buffalo Address
C. Optics, V
Q. Optics, VI
O. Orbits
R. Rudolf Clausius
T. Quaternions and the Ausdehnungslehre
M. Quaternions and the Algebra of Vectors
K. Quaternions and Vector Analysis

			1	2	3	4	5	6	7	8	N	9	V	A	C	Q	O	R	T	M	K
Routh, E. J.	Cambridge							x					x								
Chambers, Charles	Bombay Colaba Obs.						x	x	x				x								
Frankland, Prof. Ed.	London						x		x												
Watts, Henry							x		x												
Muir, M. M. Pattison-	Cambridge							x					x				x				
Hopkinson, Dr. John	Kensington London									x					x	x					
J. J. Thomson,	Trinity Cambridge				x	x	x		x	x		x	x	x	x	x	x	x			
Thompson, Prof. Sylvanus	Bristol									x				x	x	x		x			
Fitzgerald, Prof. Geo. F.	Dublin									x			x	x	x	x	x	x			
Haughton, Rev. Sam'l	"									x				x	x	x					
Lockyer, J. Norman F.R.S.	South Kensington									x			x	x	x	x	x	x			
Glazebrook, R. T.	Cambridge									x			x	x	x	x	x	x			x
Siemens, C. Wm. *	Westminster									x											
Chrystal, Prof. G.	Edinb.												x	x							
Cox, Homersham	Trinity Cambridge												x	x		x					
Darwin, Prof. Geo. H.	Cambridge												x	x				x	x		
Greenhill, A. G.													x	x	x	x	x	x	x		
Ramsay, Wm. Prof.	London		x	x			x		x				x	x	x		x			
Dewar, Prof. James	Cambridge		x	x			x		x				x	x	x		x			
Prof. Schuster, Arthur F.R.S.	Manchester									x				x	x	x		x			
Abney, Capt. WdeW.										x			x	x	x	x	x	x			
Finch, F. G.													x	x							
Glaisher, Prof. J. W. L.	Cambridge												x	x	x						
Meyer, Oscar E.	Breslau		x			x		x					x					x			
Meyer, E. S. C.	Leipsig		x			x		x					x								
Handl	Czernovitz		x			x	x	x													
Du Bois Reymond P.	Berlin		x			x	x	x						x	x	x					
Kohlrausch, Frederich	Würtzburg Bav.		x			x	x		x					x	x	x		x			
von der Mühle, Carl	Leipsig		x			x		x						x	x	x		x			
Lippich, Ferdinand	Prague		x			x		x		x			x	x	x	x		x			x
von Jolly, J. P. G.	Munich		x			x	x	x													
von Feilitsch	Giessen		x			x	x	x													
Forster	Bern					x															
Claus, Adolph	Freiberg					x															
Ötingen, Arthur v	Dorpat					x															
Braun	Marburg					x															
von Wroblewski *	Strassburg					x		x						x							
Frome	Göttingen					x															
Subic	Gratz					x															
Cornelius, Carl	Halle					x															

1. Graphical Methods in the Thermodynamics of Fluids
2. 'A Method of Geometrical Representation
3. On the Equilibrium of Heterogeneous
Substances, I
4. On the Equilibrium of Heterogeneous
Substances, II
5. On the Equilibrium of Heterogeneous
Substances, Resumé
6. On the General Equations of Dynamics
7. On the Vapor-Densities

8. Vector Analysis, pp. 1-36
N. Optics, I, II, III
9. Vector Analysis, pp. 37-83
V. Vector Analysis, whole
A. Multiple Algebra, Buffalo Address
C. Optics, V
Q. Optics, VI
O. Orbits
R. Rudolf Clausius
T. Quaternions and the Ausdehnungslehre
M. Quaternions and the Algebra of Vectors
K. Quaternions and Vector Analysis

		1	2	3	4	5	6	7	8	N	9	V	A	C	Q	O	R	T	M	K
Hagenbach-Bishoff, Edward	Basel Switz.		x			x		x					x	x	x	x	x				
Krebs, G.	Frankfurt am Main	x	x			x		x													
Mayer, Dr. A.	Leipzig							x				x	x	x	x	x	x				x
Grashof, Dr. F.	Carlsruhe							x					x				x				
Reuleaux, Dr. F.	Berlin							x													
Scheffler, Baurath Dr. Hermann	Braunschweig							x													
Hansen, Peter A.	Gotha							x													
Förster, Wilhelm	Berlin							x					x	x	x	x	x				
Kummer, E. E.	"							x													
Zöllner, Johann	Leipzig							x													
Borchardt, C. W.	Berlin							x													
Hoppe, Ernst Reginald	"							x	x												
Lipschitz	Bonn							x					x				x				
Heine, Heinrich E.	Halle							x													
Kolbe, Hermann	Leipzig						x		x												
Kekulé, August	Bonn							x	x								x				
Thomsen, Dr. Julius	Copenhagen				x	x	x		x								x				
van der Waals, Johannes D.	Amsterdam				x	x		x	x		x		x	x	x		x				
Rachmaninoff, Prof.	Kiew Russia						x	x	x				x								
Sornoff, Prof. J.	St. Petersburg												x			x		x			
Weber, H. F.	Zurich						x	x	x	x											
Culmann, C.	"						x														
Du Bois Reymond, E.	Berlin									x			x	x	x						
Ketteler, Ed.	Bonn									x				x	x		x				
Hesse, Otto	St. Goarshaussen a. Rh.									x				x	x						
Lie, Prof. Marius Sophus	Leipsic												x		x						
Mittag-Leffler, G.	Stockholm												x		x						
Zeuthen, Dr. Hieron. Georg	Copenhagen												x		x						
Cremona, Luigi	Rome							x		x	x	x	x	x	x	x	x	x	x	x	x
Brioschi, Francisco	Milan							x			x		x	x	x	x	x	x	x	x	x
Betti, Henrico *	Pisa								x	x	x	x	x	x	x	x	x	x			
Battaglini, G.	Rome												x					x			
Basso, G.	Turin									x			x	x							
Grinuis, C. H. C.	Utrecht Holland									x		x	x	x	x	x	x	x	x	x	x
Lorentz, H. H.	Arnheim Holland									x		x	x	x	x	x	x	x	x	x	x

1. Graphical Methods in the Thermodynamics of Fluids
2. A Method of Geometrical Representation
3. On the Equilibrium of Heterogeneous Substances, I
4. On the Equilibrium of Heterogeneous Substances, II
5. On the Equilibrium of Heterogeneous Substances, Resumé
6. On the General Equations of Dynamics
7. On the Vapor-Densities

8. Vector Analysis, pp. 1-36
N. Optics, I, II, III
9. Vector Analysis, pp. 37-83
V. Vector Analysis, whole
A. Multiple Algebra, Buffalo Address
C. Optics, V
Q. Optics, VI
O. Orbits
R. Rudolf Clausius
T. Quaternions and the Ausdehnungslehre
M. Quaternions and Algebra of Vectors
K. Quaternions and Vector Analysis

		1	2	3	4	5	6	7	8	N	9	V	A	C	Q	O	R	T	M	K
Joseph A-F. Plateau *	Gand, Belgium			x	x			x		x										
Lamarle, Ernest	"			x	x	x	x		x			x	x	x						
van der Mensbrugghe, G.	"			x	x	x	x		x			x	x	x						
van der Willigen, V.-S. M.	Harlem									x		x	x	x			x			
Bakhuis-Roozeboom, H. W.	Leiden																		x	x
Spencer, Thomas									x	x	x		x	x						
Bostwick, Arthur E.									x	x		x	x	x	x					
Moore, E. Hastings									x			x	x	x		x				
Porter, Pres. Noah									x			x								
Wolff, Alfred R.	New York								x	x	x						x	x		
Christian, Geo. H.	Minneapolis									x	x									
Brown, Robert										x	x	x	x							
Beebe, Wm.								x		x	x	x	x							
Willson, Robt. W.								x		x	x	x	x							
Sherman, O. T.								x		x	x									
Clark, John E.									x	x		x	x				x			
DeForest, E. L. *									x			x	x							
Walradt, Arthur E.									x											
Kerchner, J. E.	Lancaster Pa.								x		x		x				x	x		
Phillips, Smith F.	East Chatham N. Y.								x		x		x							
Hazen, Henry A.	Signal Off. Wash.								x		x		x	x	x					
Little, Chas. N.	Lincoln Nebr.								x		x		x	x	x	x	x			
Byerly, Wm. E.	Cambridge								x		x		x	x	x					
Van Name, John									x		x		x	x	x					
Hillhouse, Wm.									x				x	x						
Hildebrand, Chas.									x											
Thacher, Thos. A.									x			x								
Hadley, A. T.									x			x								
Richards, Eu. L.									x			x	x							
Sumner, Wm. G.									x			x								
DuBois, A. J.									x	x		x	x					x		
Klein, J. F.		x	x	x	x	x			x	x	x	x	x	x			x			
Wright		x							x		x	x	x	x	x		x			
Lyman *		x							x		x	x	x	x	x					
Loomis *		x							x	x		x	x	x						
Norton *		x							x											
Johnson								x												
Waldo, Leonard		x	x			x	x	x	x	x		x	x	x	x	x	x	x	x	
Waldo, Frank	Signal Office								x		x		x							x
Dana, E. S.									x			x	x						x	

1. Graphical Methods in the Thermodynamics of Fluids
2. A Method of Geometrical Representation
3. On the Equilibrium of Heterogeneous
   Substances, I
4. On the Equilibrium of Heterogeneous
   Substances, II
5. On the Equilibrium of Heterogeneous
   Substances, Resumé
6. On the General Equations of Dynamics
7. On the Vapor-Densities

8. Vector Analysis, pp. 1-36
N. Optics, I, II, III
9. Vector Analysis, pp. 37-83
V. Vector Analysis, whole
A. Multiple Algebra, Buffalo Address
C. Optics, V
Q. Optics, VI
O. Orbits
R. Rudolf Clausius
T. Quaternions and the Ausdehnungslehre
M. Quaternions and the Algebra of Vectors
K. Quaternions and Vector Analysis

Name	Location	1	2	3	4	5	6	7	8	N	9	V	A	C	Q	O	R	T	M	K
Curtis, Geo. E.	Topeka K.								x	x		x	x	x	x	x				
McAulay, A.	Cambridge (Eng.)											x			x					
Salmon, Rev. Geo.	Dublin									x		x	x	x	x					
Scott, Robt. F.	Cambridge											x			x					
Forsyth, Andrew R.	Cambridge											x			x					
Besant, Wm. H. F.R.S.	Cambridge											x	x			x				
Lodge, Prof. Oliver	Liverpool			x	x							x	x	x		x				
Forbes, George									x				x	x		x				
Heaviside, Oliver	Paignton, Devon, Eng.								x		x	x	x	x	x	x	x			
Atkinson, Prof. E.	Sandhurst Eng.								x				x	x						
Lehfelt, Robt.	Firth Coll. Sheffield											x		x						
Chandler, S. C. Jr.	Cambridge (U. S.)											x	x	x	x					
Daniels, A. L.	Burlington Vt.											x	x	x	x					
Carhart, H. S.	Ann Arbor											x	x	x	x		x			
Ely, Geo. S.	Patent Office											x	x	x						
Franklin, Fabian	Balto.											x	x	x	x					
Fine, Prof. H. B.	Princeton											x	x	x	x					
Macfarlane, Prof. A.	Austin Tex.											x	x	x			x			
Mendenhall, T. C.	Terre Haute, Ind.											x	x	x			x			
Rockwood, C. G.	Princeton											x	x	x			x			
Stone, Prof. Ormond	U. of Va.											x	x	x	x					
Stockwell, John N.	Cleveland											x	x	x	x					
Taylor, Prof. Jas. M.	Hamilton N. Y.											x			x					
Ward, De Valron	Hoboken											x	x	x						
Ziwet, Alex.	Ann Arbor											x			x					
Kimball, Arthur L.	Balto.											x	x	x	x	x	x			
Davis, Prof. E. W.												x	x							
Crew, Henry												x	x							
Goodrich, Henry												x	x							
Hobbs, Chas. A.	Wilkes Barre Pa.											x	x	x	x	x				
Nipher, Prof. Francis E.	St. Louis														x	x	x			

The following were sent only the Buffalo address

American Acad. of Arts & Sciences		Barnard, Prof. E. E.	
Gordan, Prof. P.	Erlangen	Königsberger, Prof. L	Heidelberg
Schuvener, Eu.	Colmar	Mallard, Er.	Prof. Ec. des Mines
Gerono	32 rue Hallé		Tours
	Paris	Plarr, Gustav	
Allman, Prof. Geo. J.		Buchheim Arthur *	
Frost, Rev. Percival	Cambridge (Eng.)	Hennessy, Henry G.	
Ferriss, Rev. Norman M.	" "	Faei, de Bruno	Turin
Burnside, Wm. S.	Dublin	Henrici, Prof. O.	London
Lamb, Professor Horace	Adelaide ?	Living, G. D.	Cambridge
Liveridge, Prof. Arch.	London	Minchin, Prof. Geo.	
Muir, Thos.		McMahon, Capt P. Q.	Woolwich
Russell, Jno. W.	Oxford	Ranyard, Arthur C.	London
Tucker, Robt.	London	Williamson, Prof. Benj.	Dublin
Young, Dr. Sidney	Bristol	Knott, Prof. Cargill G.	Edinburgh
Durfee, W. P.	Geneva N. Y.	Hathaway, A. S.	Ithaca
Glashan, J. C. Esq.	Ottawa Can.	Hanus, Prof. Paul H.	W. Denver Col.
Thornton, Wm. M.	U. of Va.	Graef, Dr. Frdr.	

The following were sent only the Clausius memoir

Weyrauch, Prof. Jacob J.	Stuttgart	Riecke, Prof. E.	Göttingen
Schering, Prof. E.	Göttingen	Armstrong, Prof. Henry E.	
Shaw, W. N.		Thorpe, Prof. T. E.	
Threlfall, Prof. Richard	Sidney N. S. W.	Pupin, Michael	Columbia Coll.
Paul, Prof. Henry M	Washington		

The following were sent only the paper on "Orbits"

Rockwell, Chas. H.	Tarrytown	Campbell, W. W.	Lick Obs.
Rogers, Prof. W. A.	Waterville Me.	Hough, Prof. G. W.	Dearborn Obs. Chicago
Todd, C.	Adelaide	Boss, Lewis	Albany
	Australia	Schaeberle, J. M.	Lick Obs.
Harrington, M. W.	Ann Arbor	Hartwig, E.	Banberg
Dreyer, J. L. E.	Armagh Ireland	Galle, J. G.	Breslau
Schönfeld, E.	Bonn	Graham, A.	Obs. Cambridge
Folie, F.	Dir. Obs. Roy.	Porter, J. S.	Cincinnati
	Brussels	Thome, J. M.	Cordoba
Geelmuyden	Christiana	Gautier, E.	Geneva
Thiele, T. N.	Copenhagen	Christie, W. H. M.	Greenwich
Copeland, Ralph	Edinburgh	Turner, H. H.	Greenwich
Schur, W.	Göttingen	Downing, A. M. W.	"
Burnham, S. W.	Lick Obs.	Mannder, E. W.	"
Tupman, Col. G. L.	Harrow Eng.	Krüger, A.	Kiel
Doverck, W.	Obs. Hong Kong	Lamp, E.	"
Doubjago, D.	Kazan	Schumacher, R.	"
Gill, D.	Cape Town	Common, A. A.	63 Eatonrise London
Bruns, H.	Leipsic	Duner, N. C.	Lund
van de Land		Holden, E. S.	Lick Obs.
Bakhuijsen, H. G.	Leiden	Keeler, J. E.	" "
Huggins, Wm.	Upper Tulse Hill	Glanser, J.	Fluntern bei Zurich
	London	Chas. L. Poor	Balto
Pogson, N. R.	Madras	Todd, D. P.	Amherst
Allé, Moritz	Prague	Marth, A.	Markree Ireland
Fabricius, W.	Kiew	Schiaparelli, J. V.	Milan
Hertz, DR. Norbert v	Kuffnersche	Celoria, J.	"
	Sternwarte, Wien	Barnard, E. E.	Lick Obs.
Byrd, Mary E.	Northhampton	Stone, E. J.	Oxford Eng.
Borrelly, A.	Marscilles	Plummer, W. E.	"
Denza, F.	Moncalieri Italy	Jedrzejewicz, J.	Plonsk Poland
Bredichin, T.	Moscow	Crüls, L.	Rio Janeiro
Payne, W. W.	Northfield, Minn.	Prichett, H. S.	St. Louis
Zona, T.	Palermo Sicily	Gyldén, J. A. Hugo	Stockholm

Wolf, R.	Zurich	Doolittle, C. L.	So. Bethlehem Penn.
Tisserand F. F.	Dir. Obs. Paris	Perry, Rev. S. J.	Stonyhurst Coll. Obs.
Auwers, A.	91 Lindenstrasse		Whalley Eng.
	Berlin	Flammarion, C.	40 ave de l'Obs. Paris
Dunkin, Edwin	Blackheath Eng.		France
Parkhurst, H. M.	25 Chambers St.	Klein H. J.	Cologne
	Brooklyn	Hind, J. R.	Twickenham Eng.
Mohr, H.	Christiania	Kleiber, Dr. J.	56 Grande Moskaia
Schulhof, L.	3 rue Mazarim		St. Petersburg
	Paris	Lehmann-Filhés,	Wichmannstrasse,
Loewy, Maurice	Institut Paris		Berlin
	France	von Niessl,	Brünn Moravia
Werebriussow,	Kharkow	Upton, W.	Providence
Backlund, O.	Pulkowa Russia	Callandrian,	Obs. Nat. Paris
Tacchini, P.	Rome	Puireux	" " "

To summarize this list; there were distributed the number of reprints of the papers listed below, first to individuals and second to journals and institutions, as shown in the two columns at the right:

Graphical Methods in the Thermodynamics of Fluids	67	6
A Method of Geometrical Representation of the Thermodynamic Properties of Substances by Means of Surfaces	72	4
On the Equilibrium of Heterogeneous Substances. Part I.	89	10
On the Equilibrium of Heterogeneous Substances. Part II.	92	10
Abstract of the "Equilibrium of Heterogeneous Substances."	116	11
On the Vapor-Densities of Peroxide of Nitrogen, Formic Acid, Acetic Acid, and Perchloride of Phosphorus.	132	9
On the Fundamental Formulae of Dynamics.	81	6
Elements of Vector Analysis. pp. 1-36.	81	0
Elements of Vector Analysis. pp. 37-83.	52	0
Elements of Vector Analysis. Complete.	84	3
On Multiple Algebra (the Buffalo Address).	270	6
On the Determination of Elliptic Orbits from three Complete Observations.	197	2
On Double Refraction and the Dispersion of Colors in Perfectly Transparent Media. ⟩ On Double Refraction in Perfectly Transparent Media which Exhibit the Phenomena of Circular Polarization. ⟩ On the General Equations of Monochromatic Light in Media of Every Degree of Transparency. ⟩	125	2
A Comparison of the Elastic and the Electrical Theories of Light with Respect to the Law of Double Refraction and the Dispersion of Colors.	170	4
A Comparison of the Electric Theory of Light and Sir William Thomson's Theory of a Quasi-labile Ether.	164	4
Rudolph Julius Emanuel Clausius.	153	0
Quaternions and the Ausdehnungslehre.	32	0
Quaternions and the Algebra of Vectors.	10	0
Quaternions and Vector Analysis.	21	0
Totals	2008	77

It should be remembered that this list does not include the distribution made by the Connecticut Academy through exchange with other academies and learned societies. The inclusion of that distribution increases the totals of the third and fourth items in the above summary by some 170, as reported in Chap. VI, p. 96. Thus the total distribution of the "Equilibrium" monograph was approximately 270 copies.

List sent to Scribners for distribution of Statistical Mechanics

Science, Macmillan Co. 66 Fifth Ave. N. Y.
American Journal of Science, New Haven   E. S. Dana.
Bulletin American Mathematical Society.   Cole.
Journal of Physical Chemistry, Ithaca.   W. D. Bancroft.
Physical Review, Ithaca.   Prof. E. L. Nichols.
Nature (Editor of) Macmillan & Co. St. Martin's Street, London, W. C.
Philosophical Magazine, Taylor & Francis. Red Lion Court, Fleet Street, Lond.
Fortschritte der Physik, Deutsche Phys. Geselschaft.
Jahrbuch uber die Fortschritte der Mathematik. Prof. Emil Lampe, Berlin W. 35 Kurfürstenstr.
             139.

Beiblatter zu den Annalen der Physik, Walter König Greifswald Prussia.
Zeitschrift für Physicalische Chemie, Prof. Wm. Ostwald Leipsic.
Zeitschrift für Math. & Physik, Stuttgart.   Prof. Mehmke Weisenburgstrasse 29
Monatshefte für Math. & Physik, Prof. G v Escherich Wien.
Physicalische Zeitschrift, Dr. Max Abraham. Gottingen.
Bulletin des Sciences Math. G. Darboux. Paris Gautier-Villars.
Il Nuovo Cimento, Prof Angelo Battelli Pisa.
L'Enseighnment Mathematique ? C-A Larant 162 rue Victor Hugo Paris.
Revue semestrielle des Publications Math. Dr. J. Korteweg Amsterdam
Jahresbericht der Deutschen Math. Vereinigung, Care Prof A. Gutzmer Schaferstr. 4 Jena.
for Vect. Anal.
Christophe Alassia, Tempio Italy.

Personal distribution of the Statistical Mechanics

x Simon Newcbmb
x Lord Rayleigh
  Felix Klein
x P. Duhem
  H. Poincaré
x G. H. Darwin
x H. A. Lorentz
x G. Mittag-Leffler
x S. Kimura
x V-J. Bousinesq
  W. Ostwald
  Am. Acad.
  Göttingen Roy. Soc.
x B. Roozeboom
x Max Planck
x Acad. des Sciences Paris
x J. Hadamard
x Lond. Math Soc.
  Phys. Soc. Lond.
x Cambridge Ph. Soc.
  Henry Wm. Watson
x S. H. Burbury
x Wolcott Gibbs
  August Horstmann
  Math. Club

x Lord Kelvin
  Ludwig Boltzmann
  James Dewar
x J. J. Thomson
  J. H. van't Hoff
x Sir Robert Ball
  H. K. Omnes
  J. D. van der Waals
x H. Le Chatelier
x W. F. Magie
x Amer. Phil. Soc.
  Manchester L. & Phil. Soc.
  F. Engel
  L. Cremona
x.Societe Hollandaise
x Kön. Acad. Berlin
x P. E. Appell
x Roy. Soc.
x Royal Acad. Amsterdam
x John B. Van Name
x Williams College
  Friedrich Kohlrausch
  Joseph Larmor
x Francis E. Loomis

APPENDIX V

Abstract for Königsberger's "Repertorium"

J. Willard Gibbs: On the Fundamental Formulae of Dynamics. (American Journal of Mathematics, II, pp. 49–64, 1879)

The point of departure in this paper is found by writing in the general indeterminate formula of motion, in place of the variation of the coordinates and of other quantities determined by the configuration of the system, the variations of the second differential coefficients of the same quantities with respect to the time. If the sum of the moments of the forces is represented by $\Sigma(\mathrm{P}dp)$, the formula may be written (with Newton's notation for differentiation with respect to time)

$$\Sigma(\mathrm{P}\delta\ddot{p}) - \Sigma\left\{m(\ddot{x}\delta\ddot{x} + \ddot{y}\delta\ddot{y} + \ddot{z}\delta\ddot{z})\right\} \leqq \mathrm{O},$$

where m denotes the mass of any point or element of the system, and x, y, z its rectangular coordinates. When the forces are expressed by their rectangular components, X, Y, Z, we have

$$\Sigma\left\{(\mathrm{X} - m\ddot{x})\delta\ddot{x} + (\mathrm{Y} - m\ddot{y})\delta\ddot{y} + (\mathrm{Z} - m\ddot{z})\delta\ddot{z} \leqq \mathrm{O}.\right.$$

The character δ relates to any variations in the accelerations of the system consistent with its configuration and velocities at the instant considered, and with the constraints to which it is subject. It may easily be shown that the necessary relations between the variations of the type $\delta\ddot{x}$, thus understood, are identical with those which subsist between the variations of the type δx, when the coordinates are regarded as variable and only the time as constant (with respect to δ), whenever these relations may be derived from finite equations between the coordinates and other quantities determined by the configuration, with or without the time. In all such cases, the formula proposed may be regarded as equivalent to the ordinary formula, in the sense that either may be derived directly from the other. But in other cases when the constraints are expressed by the characters $\geqq$ or $\leqq$, or when they respect the velocities, the necessary relations between the variations $\delta\ddot{x}$, etc. are not always entirely identical with those which subsist between the quantities represented by δx, etc., *as naturally interpreted*. In these cases, the formula proposed has a certain advantage in respect to precision & perspicuity.

The formula proposed has also a certain advantage in respect to the naturalness & simplicity of the conceptions on which it is based. In nature, the accelerations of a system are determined by its configuration and velocities. The fundamental formula of mechanics is that which shows how they are determined. It is therefore natural to regard the configuration and velocities as given, and the accelerations as quantities to be determined. In the formula proposed, the accelerations which satisfy the dynamical laws of the system are virtually selected out of all the accelerations which are consistent with the constraints of the system by a comparison of these among themselves, the comparison of different values $\ddot{x}$, $\ddot{y}$, etc. giving rise to the conception of the quantities $\delta\ddot{x}$, $\delta\ddot{y}$, etc. This process appears more natural than the introduction of the conception of a change in the configuration or in the velocities of the system. (The expressions δx, δy, etc. in the ordinary formula of motion are sometimes interpreted as relating to velocities, although the notation does not seem appropriate to express that idea.) Moreover, the conception of a variation of acceleration, as employed in the formula proposed, is more simple than that of a variation of velocity or of configuration in that it does not involve any variation in either of these, while a variation of velocity may necessitate a variation of acceleration, and a variation of configuration may necessitate a variation both of velocity & of acceleration.

The formula leads directly to important theorems.

The forces being determined by the configurations and velocities,

$$\delta X = O, \ \delta Y = O, \ \delta Z = O,$$

and the formula gives

$$\delta\Sigma\left\{ m[(\ddot{x} - \frac{X}{m})^2 + (\ddot{y} - \frac{Y}{m})^2 + (\ddot{z} - \frac{Z}{m})^2] \right\} \geqq O,$$

which may be regarded as Gauss's Principle of Least Constraint.

Still more readily the formula may be transformed into the following—

$$\delta\left\{ \Sigma(P\ddot{p}) - \Sigma[\tfrac{1}{2}m(\ddot{x}^2 + \ddot{y}^2 + \ddot{z}^2)] \right\} \leqq O.$$

The quantity affected by δ is easily shown to be a true minimum. We are thus able to express the laws of motion by means of the condition that a certain quantity shall have a minimum value, the conditions under which the minimum subsists being such as the case naturally affords. This principle, as well as the original formula, may be considered more general than Gauss's Principle of Least Constraint, since the latter is hardly applicable to cases in which finite forces are applied to surfaces or points.

When the forces are determined by the configuration alone, the following principle is easily established:—The accelerations in the system are always such that the acceleration of the rate of work done by the forces diminished by one-half the sum of the products of the masses of the particles by the squares of their accelerations has the greatest possible value.

J. W. Gibbs.

APPENDIX VI

Bibliography of Articles and Books about Gibbs

This bibliography contains only the more important items which have appeared concerning the life and works of Willard Gibbs. It makes no pretense to completeness but is believed to embrace all of the material—aside from that in manuscript form deposited in the Yale library—which would be of value to future historians.

The items are arranged in chronological order, and it may not be without interest to point out how the manner of their grouping in time illustrates the growth of Gibbs' stature in the minds of men. Following the notices and articles of the first four years after his death, which with the exception of the biographical sketches of Bumstead and Alasia were concerned with discussions of isolated portions of his achievement, there come a considerable number of articles stimulated by the publication of *The Scientific Papers* which attempt a more comprehensive evaluation of his whole work and of his position in scientific history. These articles in the period between 1907 and 1910 give evidence that realization of the fundamental importance of Gibbs' contributions was spreading in an ever widening circle.

There follows an interval of twelve years in which no notices appeared— at least none has come to my attention. This was the period dominated by the clash of ideologies centering around the First World War and a time when many scientists were preoccupied with the adaptation and application of scientific techniques to the purposes of war. The theoretical physics of that time was concerned principally with development of the newer ideas of atomic structure which had followed in the train of the discovery of the electron and the emergence of the "quantum" hypothesis. No one then dreamed that these speculations would culminate in the most powerful and dreadful of all the warlike weapons.

Except in the field of physical chemistry the interest in the problems of classical physics waned, but in that domain there was great activity; hence it is not surprising to find that after the removal of the wartime restrictions the tremendous implications of Gibbsian thermodynamics for that science began to find expression in appreciations of his achievement in that domain. The list of publications shown below for the years 1923 to 1933 illustrates forcibly how great was the preponderance of the appreciation for this side of Gibbs' work.

But with the appearance of the *Collected Works* in 1928, and especially with the coming of the *Commentary*, there becomes apparent a broader appreciation of Gibbs as one of the greatest of physical philosophers and of the significance of his viewpoint in statistical mechanics as forming a bridge between the older and the newer physics. And with this broader realization came a demand for a more intimate picture of the man himself, one which has given us the more substantial biographies of the last fifteen years.

"Award of Rumford Medal to Willard Gibbs," *Proc. Am. Acad.*, N.S., *16* (1881), 417–421. Contains an account of the presentation ceremony, the citation, and Gibbs' letter of acceptance.

Hyde, E. W. "Wilson's Gibbs's Vector Analysis," *Terres. Magn. and Atmos. Elect.*, *7* (1902), 115–124. A review of the Bicentennial Volume.

Knott, C. G. "Vector Analysis, Founded upon the Lectures of J. Willard Gibbs," by E. B. Wilson, *Phil. Mag.*, ser. 6, *4* (1902), 614–622. A review.

Bumstead, Henry A. "Josiah Willard Gibbs," *Am. Journ. Sci.*, ser. 4, *16* (1903), 187–202. A biographical sketch, accurate and dependable both as personal history and in its critical judgments. Reprinted with some additions in *The Scientific Papers of J. Willard Gibbs* (New York, Longmans, Green, 1906), I, xiii–xxviii, and in *The Collected Works of J. Willard Gibbs* (New York, Longmans, Green, 1928), I, xiii–xxviii.

Smith, Percey F. "Josiah Willard Gibbs, Ph.D., L.L.D., a Short Sketch and Appreciation of His Work in Pure Mathematics," *Bull. Am. Math. Soc.*, 2d ser., *10* (1903), 34–39.

"J. Willard Gibbs," *Obituary Record of Graduates of Yale University 1900–1910*, pp. 237–239. Unsigned.

Bumstead, H. A. "On the Variation of Entropy as Treated by Professor Willard Gibbs," *Phil. Mag.*, ser. 6, *7* (1904), 7–14. A reply to a critical paper by S. H. Burbury in the same journal.

Alasia, C. "Josiah Willard Gibbs in Memoriam," *Rivista di fisica, matematica e scienze naturali, 12* (Pavia, 1905), 21–30. An amazingly inaccurate account.

Wilson, E. B. "On Products in Additive Fields," *Verhandlungen des Dritten Internationalen Mathematiker Kongresses* (B. G. Teubner, 1905), pp. 202–215. An explanation of Gibbs' viewpoint in multiple algebra.

Barus, Carl. "Certain Suggestions by J. Willard Gibbs on Geophysical Research," *Am. Journ. Sci.* ser. 4, *21* (1906), 461–462. Contains the text of a letter from Gibbs to Barus.

Duhem, Pierre. "The Scientific Papers of J. Willard Gibbs," *Bulletin des Sciences mathématiques*, ser. 2, *31* (1907), 181–211. An extended review including a biography. The same text was published later (Paris, A. Hermann, 1908) over the author's name and under the title "Josiah Willard Gibbs, à propos de la publication de ses mémoires scientifiques."

"Josiah Willard Gibbs," *Indian Engineering, 41* (1907), 38–39. Unsigned.

Larmor, Sir Joseph. "The Historical Development of the Doctrine of Energy," *London Times Literary Supplement,* March 22, 1907. Unsigned.

Jeans, J. H. "The Scientific Papers of J. Willard Gibbs," *Am. Journ. Sci.,* ser. 4, *23* (1907), 144–145. A review.

Peirce, Charles S. "The Scientific Papers of J. Willard Gibbs," *The Nation, 84* (1907), 92. A review, unsigned.

Wilson, E. B. "The Scientific Papers of J. Willard Gibbs," *Bull. Am. Math. Soc.,* 2d ser., *13* (1907), 250–252. A review.

"The Scientific Papers of J. Willard Gibbs," *The Mathematical Gazette, 4* (1907), 87–88. A review signed E.T.W.

"The Scientific Work of Willard Gibbs," *Nature, 75* (1907), 361–362. A review of *The Scientific Papers* signed C.G.K.

Ewell, Arthur W. "Gibbs' Geometrical Presentation of the Phenomena of Reflection of Light," *Am. Journ. Sci.,* ser. 4, *24* (1907), 412–416. Based on his lecture notes as a student of Gibbs.

Bumstead, Henry A. "Josiah Willard Gibbs," *Yale Alumni Weekly, 16* (1907), 444–445.

Wilson, Edwin Bidwell. "On the Theory of Double Products and Strains in Hyperspace, Part I, On a Multiple Algebra as Set Forth by Gibbs," *Trans. Conn. Acad., 14* (1908), 1–57.

Hastings, Charles S. "Josiah Willard Gibbs," *Biographical Memoirs* (National Academy of Sciences, Washington, D.C., 1909), VI, 375–393. A principal source of biographical material by a student and colleague.

Garrison, Fielding H. "Josiah Willard Gibbs and His Relation to Modern Science," *Popular Science Monthly* (May, June, July, August, 1909).

———. "Physiology and the Second Law of Thermodynamics," *New York Medical Journal* (September 11, 15, 25, 1909). Contains much about Gibbs' thermodynamics.

"What Science Owes to Willard Gibbs." An unpublished pamphlet used in connection with a campaign to raise funds for a memorial professorship at Yale in 1910. Consists of a collection of quotations from statements by eminent scientists, with an introduction by Henry A. Bumstead.

Slosson, Edwin E. "Willard Gibbs," *Leading American Men of Science* (New York, Henry Holt, 1910), pp. 341–362.

Getman, Frederick H. "J. Willard Gibbs and His Contribution to Chemistry," *Science,* N.S., *58* (1923), 129–133.

Read, W. T. "Pioneer Yale Chemists," *Ind. and Eng. Chem., 15* (1923), 204–206. Contains a brief biography and appraisal of Gibbs.

Cantelo, R. C. "J. Willard Gibbs, a Brief Biography and a Summary of His Contributions to Chemistry," *Canadian Chemistry and Metallurgy, 8* (1924), 215–217.

Donnan, F. G. "The Influence of J. Willard Gibbs on the Science of Physical Chemistry" (Philadelphia, Franklin Institute, 1924). An address delivered at the centenary celebration of the founding of the Franklin Institute. An admirable summary of Gibbs' position in the science.

Miller, William Lash. "The Method of Willard Gibbs in Chemical Thermodynamics," *Chemical Reviews, 1* (1925), 293–344.

Haber, Fritz. "Practical Results of the Theoretical Development of Chemistry," *Journ. Franklin Inst., 199* (1925), 437–456. Contains considerable discussion of Gibbs' treatment of adsorption.

Verrill, A. E. "How the Works of Professor Willard Gibbs Were Published," *Science*, N.S., *61* (1925), 41–42.

Williams, Horatio B. "Mathematics and the Biological Sciences," *Bull. Am. Math. Soc.*, 2d ser., *33* (1927), 273–293. The Josiah Willard Gibbs Lecture for 1926.

Poore, C. G. "Today Fame Comes to Josiah W. Gibbs," *New York Times Magazine*, November 28, 1926, p. 6.

"A Half Century of the Phase Rule," *Chemisch Weekblad*, September 18, 1926. This anniversary number contains articles on Gibbs and his work by W. P. Jorrison, H. le Chatelier, Wilhelm Ostwald, J. D. van der Waals, Jr., W. Lash Miller, F. A. H. Schreinmakers, G. Tammann, J. H. L. Vogt, J. J. van Laar, J. W. Terwen, F. G. Donnan, F. A. Freeth, and W. C. de Baat. This is an important item.

Cohen, E. "The Semi-Centenary of Willard Gibbs' Phase Law," *Science*, N.S., *64* (1926), 621. A brief summary of the articles in the *Chemisch Weekblad* anniversary number.

Stevens, F. W. "Josiah Willard Gibbs and the Extension of the Principles of Thermodynamics," *Science*, N.S., *66* (1927), 159–163. This article was reprinted in the *Literary Digest* for September 24, 1927.

Pupin, Michael. "Josiah Willard Gibbs." An address before the Graduates Club. Printed by the club in 1927. A part of exercises in celebration of the fiftieth anniversary of the publication of Gibbs' work on heterogeneous substances.

Johnston, John. "Willard Gibbs, an Appreciation," *Scientific Monthly, 26* (1928), 128–139. This includes a few quotations from the "Scientific Correspondence," the first to appear in print.

————. "Willard Gibbs, an Appreciation," *Yale Scientific Magazine, 2* (1928), 17–20. Differs somewhat from the *Scientific Monthly* article above. A reprint of the Yale article appeared in the *Journal of Chemical Education, 5* (1928), 507–514.

Fisher, Irving. "The Application of Mathematics to the Social Sciences," *Bull. Am. Math. Soc.*, 2d ser., *36* (1930), 224–243. The seventh Josiah Willard Gibbs Lecture, given before a joint session of the American Mathematical Society and the A.A.A.S. on December 31, 1929, at Des Moines, Iowa.

Van Name, Ralph G. "The Willard Gibbs Memorial," *Yale Alumni Weekly, 39* (1930), 806–807.

Wilson, E. B. "Reminiscences of Gibbs by a Student and Colleague," *Scientific Monthly, 32* (1931), 210–227. A most valuable source for personal biography.

———. "Josiah Willard Gibbs," *Dictionary of American Biography* (1931), VII, 248–251.

Guggenheim, E. A. *Modern Thermodynamics by the Methods of Willard Gibbs* (London, Methuen, 1933), xvi, 206 pp. One of the well-known texts in the subject.

Arveson, M. H. "The Greatest Scientific Philosopher since Newton," *The Chemical Bulletin, 23* (1936), 127–130. Published by the Chicago section of the American Chemical Society.

Donnan, F. G. and Arthur Haas, eds. *A Commentary on the Scientific Writings of J. Willard Gibbs.* (New Haven, Yale University Press, 1936), 2 vols. Vol. I: *Thermodynamics,* ed. by F. G. Donnan, xxiii, 742 pp. Vol. II: *Theoretical Physics,* ed. by Arthur Haas, xx, 742 pp. Contributions by Donald H. Andrews, J. A. V. Butler, E. A. Guggenheim, H. S. Harned, F. G. Keyes, E. A. Milne, George W. Morey, James Rice, F. A. H. Schreinmakers, Edwin B. Wilson, Paul S. Epstein, and Leigh Page.

Whitney, Margaret D. "One of the Prophets." An unpublished paper read before the Saturday Morning Club, New Haven, April 3, 1937. A valuable source for personal biography. A typescript copy is deposited in the Yale library.

Crowther, J. G. "Josiah Willard Gibbs," *Famous American Men of Science* (New York, W. W. Norton, 1937), pp. 229–297.

MacInnes, D. A. "The Contribution of Josiah Willard Gibbs to Electrochemistry," *Trans. Am. Electrochem. Soc., 61* (1937), 65–72.

Langer, R. E. "Josiah Willard Gibbs," *Am. Math. Monthly, 46* (1939), 75–84.

Pereira Forjaz, António. "Gibbs e o génio norte-americano (1839–1939)" (Academia das Ciências de Lisboa, 1939). A pamphlet in honor of the centenary of Gibbs' birth.

Kraus, Charles A. "Josiah Willard Gibbs," *Science,* N.S., 89 (1939), 275–282.

Schoolcraft, John. "A Professor's Theory and Its Practical Uses" (Yale University Press, 1939). Pamphlet.

Rukeyser, Muriel. *Willard Gibbs* (Garden City, Doubleday, Doran, 1942), ii, 465 pp.

Jaffe, Bernard. "J. Willard Gibbs," *Men of Science in America* (New York, Simon and Schuster, 1944).

"A Letter from Lord Rayleigh to J. Willard Gibbs and His Reply," *Proc. Nat. Acad., 31* (1945), 34–38. With comments by E. B. Wilson. A letter written to S. P. Langley in 1894.

"Willard Gibbs on Soaring Flight," *Proc. Nat. Acad., 31* (1945), 233–235. With comments by E. B. Wilson.

Wheeler, L. P., E. O. Waters, and S. W. Dudley. *The Early Work of Willard Gibbs in Applied Mechanics* (New York, Henry Schuman, 1947), vii, 78 pp.

Jefferson, R. William, Jr. "Willard Gibbs. America's Greatest Scientist," *Northwestern Engineer, 6,* No. 3 (1947), 15, 46, 48. This is a student publication.

"Personal Recollections and Impressions of J. Willard Gibbs," by his niece, nephews, and certain of his pupils (Sterling Memorial Library, Yale University, 1947), vi, 108 pp. An unpublished typescript volume, valuable for the firsthand information it contains.

Rukeyser, Muriel. "Josiah Willard Gibbs," *Physics Today*, 2 (1949), 6–13, 27.

APPENDIX VII

Supplementary Sidelights Based on Newly Discovered Material

In the collection of family correspondence mentioned in the preface to the revised edition, which was loaned to me by Alfred Dasburg, there is to be found much material amplifying the picture of Willard Gibbs' background as described in the first two chapters of this biography. In this connection the most important series is that written by his mother, Mary Anna Van Cleve Gibbs. It is the longest series by one person in the collection, numbering some 130 items. The letters cover practically the whole period of Mary Anna's married life, and are addressed for the most part to her younger sister, Margaret Fox Van Cleve, who in 1842 married Professor Ebenezer A. Johnson of New York University and who was the great grandmother of the present owner of the collection, Mr. Dasburg. There are in addition a number written to her other sister and to her three brothers as well as some to her niece and nephew, the children of the Johnsons.

Mary Anna was the eldest child of the Van Cleve family and these letters reveal clearly the sense of responsibility she felt for the welfare of her brothers and sisters after the death of their mother, which occurred at a relatively early age—before Mary Anna's marriage to Professor Gibbs. Her letters contain the news of the advent of each of the five Gibbs children and record the building of and the removal to the High Street house, together with a host of minor events in the history of the family and of the town now long forgotten. There is also to be found in them much that reminds one of the inconveniences and limitations (from a modern standpoint) of life in those days—the inadequate sanitation, the 'dependence on the volunteer bucket brigade in fighting fires, the difficulties and slowness of travel, and the prevalence of epidemics of diseases whose terrors have since been so largely mitigated by the progress of medical and sanitary science.

But the most lasting impressions one gains from a reading of her letters are those of Mary Anna's unselfish devotion to the interests of all in the family connection, of the depth and sincerity of her religious convictions, and of the uncomplaining courage with which she bore the pains of her own failing health and surmounted the bereavements she suffered in the loss of a daughter (Eliza) and a sister (Mrs. Johnson) within a few months of each other. The picture of her which we gain from this correspondence is one of a strong character, a wise guide to her growing children, happy and beloved in the family life.

When Chapter I was written very little could be said about the role of the children in the Gibbs family life before the Civil War. Now however we have in this collection a wealth of evidence on this point; and it all definitely corroborates the conclusions drawn from collateral considerations on page 11. There are for instance a number of letters of the Gibbs children written in early childhood. None of these give any evidence of an unusual precocity except possibly those of Eliza, who died in 1849 and whose letters written in her early teens reveal an already well-developed and charming personality. But those of all the children bear ample witness to a happy and harmonious family life. The two early letters of Willard which have been preserved (written when he was five and eight years old) are typical of the "duty" letters of a small boy carefully supervised by his elders. Other letters, from aunts and uncles and (a little later) from the Johnson cousins, but emphasize the intimate friendly relations existing in the Gibbs household. Reverting to the question of Willard's precocity in this connection it is perhaps worth while to quote from a letter of Julia's written when she was thirteen years old:

Uncle Alfred & father and mother are seated by the register, talking, at present. Eliza is reading at the table where I am writing, Anna and Hannah [another cousin] are in the dining room, and Fannie [Johnson], Emilie and Willie, who have been sitting on the floor and rolling a ball to each other, are examining the thermometer, Willie explaining its properties.

Willard was then ten years old.

Of greater interest, as filling in the gaps in the previous record of Gibbs' maturer years (particularly those noted in Chapter III concerning the European sojourn), is the series of letters by his oldest sister, Anna Louisa Gibbs, written to the several members of the Johnson family. This is the second longest single series in the collection (more than 85 items), and they cover practically the whole of her life. The twelve letters written from abroad well describe details of sight-seeing trips in France, Belgium, Holland, Germany, Austria, and Switzerland as well as much of the day-to-day experiences of their life in the periods of residence in Paris, Berlin, and Heidelberg. In Paris and Berlin they roomed with private families with whom they enjoyed most friendly relations, and aside from the absence of housekeeping cares their daily routines were not greatly dissimilar from those to which they were accustomed at home. In Heidelberg on the other hand they stayed at a large pension having a cosmopolitan clientele and a less "homey" atmosphere.

In one of her letters from the German capital Anna gives an entertaining account of Julia's wedding, which took place in the Sacristy of the Jerusalem church and was graced by the presence of the American ambassador, George

Bancroft. Both the Prediger who performed the ceremony and the family with whom they were staying conspired to make the event a gala occasion. In other of the Berlin letters Anna writes at length of their enjoyment during the summer months of outdoor concerts and of walks in the Thier Garten and, in the winter, of skating there, which was particularly appreciated by Willard. In one letter she reveals that Willard's riding lessons were taken in Berlin and not in Heidelberg as I surmised in Chapter III. In this letter she quotes her brother's comments on the German "theory" of equestrianism. This apparently marks the beginning of Gibbs' interest in an art in which he became quite proficient and whose further theory he developed so amusingly before the Mathematical Club at Yale as related on page 188. From all of these letters it appears that both socially and from a student's standpoint they considered the time spent in Berlin as the most rewarding of the European experiences. In fact in one of them Willard is quoted to that effect.

The remainder of Anna's letters both before and after the trip abroad are concerned mostly with matters of domestic interest and contain little bearing on her brother's activities. The same is true of Julia's letters in this collection. They have to do for the most part with arrangements for visiting between the Gibbs and Johnson families, with news of sundry domestic crises and illnesses, and with comments on the current books and reading in which they were interested.

The letters of Willard Gibbs himself which are preserved in the Dasburg collection, and also those of his father, are concerned mostly with financial matters and are of interest principally as evidencing a business acumen and judgment not usually associated with professors of physics or philology. In Willard's case they foreshadow his later success as an officer of the Hopkins Grammar School, as related on page 144. There is however one sentence in a note of Willard's dated April 8, 1870, which reveals a matter previously unknown to me or, so far as I am able to ascertain, to anyone of my generation. In apologizing for a slight delay in replying to a communication from his uncle, E. A. Johnson, he says: "I have been quite busy for the last few days or I should have acknowledged it earlier. I have been teaching French this term at the Scientific School & have my examinations this week." This revelation obviously necessitates a modification of my statement on page 54 that during the interval between his return to New Haven and his appointment to a professorship "he had no routine appointments or duties outside of the family life." But I cannot feel that the general conclusions of the paragraph on that page are in any way invalidated. That he was again drawn into the teaching of language (as in his earlier tutorial appointment) does not contradict the assumption that this interval was a period marked by a maturing of those intellectual interests which had been broadened and strengthened by the years abroad.

Of the many letters in the collection written by members of the Johnson family, as in those of his sisters, there is little reference to the activities of Willard's maturer years. However there are two letters of Fanny Johnson which contain interesting and quotable comments on Gibbs' great "Equilibrium" monograph. In a letter to her brother Alfred dated New Haven, May 12, 1876, she says:

"Equilibrium of Heterogeneous Substances" is the title on the proof sheets before me, which is keeping Willard very busy just now. It looks full of hard words & signs & numbers, not very entertaining or understandable looking, & I wonder whether it will make people wiser or better. As Anna said yesterday he was writing something nobody could understand, but she immediately qualified that by saying she did not mean that exactly, but such as we.

That such a reaction was not unique even among Gibbs' faculty colleagues has been pointed out on page 84. The quotation illustrates the isolation necessarily incurred by one who breaks out a path on which his friends and loved ones are not equipped to travel.

In another letter, also to her brother, written after a short visit to New Haven and dated Feb. 17, 1878, she says:

Willard was amusing himself examining soap bubbles, not blowing them in a pipe but dipping an ivory ring in the soap suds & standing it up under a box lined with black, but a glass side to look through, & then examined the bubble which was between the sides of the ring. It was quite interesting to see how different the bubbles would be with more or less soap in the water or with glycerine added.

This naïve description is interesting as showing that there was an experimental background for the discussion of soap films which occurs in the second part of the equilibrium monograph. That the work was done at home and with home-made equipment is not surprising as at that time no laboratory facilities for physical research existed at Yale or, for that matter, elsewhere in American colleges. The fact here first revealed that he actually did experimental work in connection with his theoretical studies of capillarity and surface tension affords further support for Hasting's contention (page 189) that no one who knew him could doubt Gibbs' mental qualifications for experimental research.

The letters sent me by Fräulein Ostwald are concerned for the most part with details which arose in connection with Ostwald's translation of Gibbs' thermodynamic papers and the publication of the *Thermodynamische Studien*. They add little of importance on these matters to what has been said on pages 99–102, although it is interesting to observe the evidence shown in one of them of the meticulous pains Gibbs took as a proofreader of a mathematical text. This goes a long way to explain why all his published work is so free from errors in that regard.

In a like manner the newly discovered letters from Gibbs to President Gilman of the Johns Hopkins University require nothing to be added to the account of his call to that institution as described on pages 90–93. However, in this collection there is a letter written from London to President Gilman by Professor J. J. Sylvester which deserves quotation. It was this letter which was discovered by Mr. Murphey and led to the finding of the others. It is dated June 12, 1880, and the pertinent portions read as follows:

. . . I am glad to find that the negociation with Willard Gibbs is not closed. If we could secure him it would be more than a compensation for the loss of Lanman. His character here is such—I mean the estimation in which he is held as a mathematical physicist—that I am sure if you and the Trustees could be made fully aware of it, you would think no inducements held out to him could be too high to secure his coming among us. Profr Dewar of Cambridge told me that almost the last thing Clerk Maxwell did was within a fortnight of his death to show him with exultation a model of what he called "a Willard Gibbs surface." I am fully persuaded that were he in England you would not think a full professorship on a permanent tenure at $5000 per annum too high a price to pay for securing the benefit of his name and cooperation, and that considering what Lanman is to get and might (as he says) have obtained at the Johns Hopkins Gibbs would be "dirt cheap" at that price.

And in a postscript:

Dewar who besides his professorship of "Natural Experimental Philosophy" at Cambridge is Fullerian Profr at the Royal Institution introduced the name of "that Willard Gibbs" spontaneously, and on my saying that I supposed he was the best man in his line in America added "Aye—and in this country too": he does not know him personally, so that his eulogy was completely disinterested.

Although the "negociations" with Gibbs had actually terminated with his letter of declination of April 29 (pages 92–93), it is obvious that Gilman's letter to Sylvester, to which the above letter was a reply, must have been written prior to that date, and thus the matter was still one of importance to the writer, as was also that of Lanman's leaving the Johns Hopkins for Harvard. But in spite of the fact that Sylvester's letter was too late to influence the outcome of the call to Gibbs, it is nevertheless of interest in other respects. Thus its date, less than three years after the appearance of the second part of the "Equilibrium" monograph, as well as the testimony of Dewar, emphasizes and strengthens my thesis of Chapter VI that, contrary to a quite general impression, Gibbs' abilities and work received in reality a very prompt recognition.

A final point of interest in this letter is that in it may be found a possible explanation of the absence of any correspondence with Maxwell with regard to the model of the thermodynamic surface as discussed on page 85. Although a model of the surface was undoubtedly made by Maxwell before February 1875, as related in the Freeman letter (page 74), no record remains as to when it (or a copy) was received in New Haven. Now the fact, as related in this Sylvester letter, that within a fortnight of his death (November 5, 1879) Maxwell exhibited such a model to Dewar "with exultation" suggests that it may have been but recently created. Thus it becomes possible that it (or a copy) may have been sent to Gibbs after his death by a colleague or student, cognizant that such was Maxwell's intention. In this case of course one would not expect to find a covering letter from the donor.

This explanation is naturally highly speculative but seems to me, in view of the care which Gibbs took in the preservation of all his correspondence, to be more probable than that, as surmised on page 85, it was mislaid or lost.

Index